THE NEW NATURALIST

A SURVEY OF BRITISH NATURAL HISTORY

THE LAKE DISTRICT

EDITORS:

Margaret Davies, C.B.E., M.A., Ph.D.
John Gilmour, M.A., V.M.H.
Kenneth Mellanby, C.B.E., Sc.D.

PHOTOGRAPHIC EDITOR:

Eric Hosking, O.B.E., Hon. F.R.P.S., F.I.I.P.

The aim of this series is to interest the general reader in the wild life of Britain by recapturing the inquiring spirit of the old naturalists. The Editors believe that the natural pride of the British public in the native fauna and flora, to which must be added concern for their conservation, is best fostered by maintaining a high standard of accuracy combined with clarity of exposition in presenting the results of modern scientific research.

The text and line illustrations are here reproduced unaltered, but the process of manufacture used to achieve an economic price does not, unfortunately, do full justice to all the photographs; and those originally in colour appear in black and white.

THE NEW NATURALIST

THE LAKE DISTRICT

A Landscape History

W. H. PEARSALL D.Sc. F.R.S.

and

WINIFRED PENNINGTON

(Mrs T. G. Tutin) Ph.D.

Bloomsbury Books
London

To all those young people, from industry, universities and sixth forms, who, in 'the inquiring spirit of the old naturalists' have helped in so many ways with the field studies needed to complete this book – help which has included such efforts as carrying a boat up Rossett Gill and Sty Head, and camping on the High Street ridge through a full gale – and particularly to students of the Ullswater and Eskdale Outward Bound Mountain Schools, the Brathay Exploration Group, and the Cadet Wardens of the Lake District National Park.

First published 1973
Reprinted 1977

This edition published 1989 by
Bloomsbury Books an imprint of
Godfrey Cave Associates Limited
42 Bloomsbury Street, London WC1B 3QJ
under license from William Collins Son's & Co. Ltd.

ISBN 1 870630 58 0

CONTENTS

Chapters 4, 7, 8, 9, 10, 15 and 17, have been written by Winifred Pennington, with help from the contributors named, using notes left by Professor Pearsall. Chapter 1, 2, 3, 13 and 16 have been written by W. Pennington to complete his plan.

PLATES

TEXT FIGURES

EDITORS' PREFACE

This volume was first commissioned from Professor W. H. Pearsall, F.R.S., formerly Quain Professor of Botany at University College, London. It has been completed by his colleague, Dr Winifred Tutin, and by others who knew and respected Pearsall. Several of them, including Dr Tutin, are members of staff at Ferry House on the western shore of Windermere. Professor Pearsall was a founder member of the Freshwater Biological Association and Chairman of its Council from 1954; he wisely guided the development of research at Ferry House.

W. H. Pearsall was educated at Ulverston Grammar School. Dr Tutin, too, grew up in Low Furness and has known the Lake District from her childhood. In this volume she and her colleagues synthesise the results of many years of experimental and field work on lake waters, lake beds, land use and landscape.

Dr Tutin shows how basic geological factors are responsible for great diversity of scene, how the humped mountains, Skiddaw and Blencathra, in the relatively soft northern slates, contrast with the sharp Scafell Pikes at the focal point of the Borrowdale Volcanics and how Coniston Water and Windermere lie among gentler hills underlain by softer Silurian rocks. She depicts the glaciers gouging out hollows now filled by mountain tarns, and, in the main valleys, narrow lakes flanked by ice-scarred cliffs. She describes in detail the subsequent silting of many lake basins and the post-glacial changes in their vegetation.

The natural and human history of the Lake District, as depicted in this volume, reveals landscapes greatly modified by man and his grazing animals. Neolithic man approached it from the Irish Sea coast and Bronze Age man from the Yorkshire Dales and eastern limestone fringes. Only gradually, over the centuries, was the mountainous core occupied, and then, mainly, for use as summer pasture. The story told here is one of gradual destruction of forests, to clear grazing land, or later for charcoal for smelting, of quarrying of slate and building stone, and of a farming system based on valley meadows and extensive grazings on the open fells. The farmsteads and their large stone barns and outbuildings still dominate most valleys, but the towns and villages of the Lake District have long functioned as holiday as well as market centres, and many of their inns are old established as tourist facilities.

Daniel Defoe, describing Westmorland in 1726, said, 'nor were these hills high and formidable only, but they had a kind of inhospitable terror in them'. The fells lacked profitable pits and were 'all barren and wild, of no use or advantage either to man or beast'. Urban symmetry better pleased the Georgians, the wild mountains were 'horrid'. They had picturesque virtues, especially when viewed in a convex mirror. Many of today's car and coach-borne visitors view the Lake District only from its roads; some may even be repelled, as were the eighteenth-century visitors, by the stark grandeur of its mountains. The lakes themselves are the magnet for most visitors, and Derwentwater and Windermere, with their lovely shores and wooded islands, have more popular appeal than scree-bordered Wastwater.

The Lake District is a fairly small and compact area which was designated a national park in 1951. Tourist pressures existed before designation, but there has been an enormous increase in car-borne visitors since 1951 and motorways have brought the Lakes within three hours' drive of the Midlands. The book discusses the serious problems posed by visitor pressures on roads, settlements and landscapes for those who administer the national park. With the help of the National Trust, a major land-owner, the Lake District Planning Board has conserved the fells and lake margins with considerable success since designation; the results of strict control of development are apparent everywhere. Dr Tutin is a distinguished ecologist, with a profound knowledge of Lakeland, and her contribution to one of the controversial issues of landscape conservation, made here, deserves the attention of all thoughtful residents or visitors, though there may not be general agreement on the need to afforest over-grazed pastures.

There are many guides for Lake District climbers and fell walkers. This volume contains much that is of interest for them and for less active tourists who seek to understand the beautiful and unique landscape of the Lakes, the farming system which has left its imprint on it, and the need to conserve and care for this particularly treasured northern corner of England. Giving as it does both the scientific background and the detailed natural history of well-known scenery, it should inspire readers to look with informed eyes as they walk, sail or drive in this very beautiful countryside.

AUTHOR'S PREFACE

'There is another Britain, to many of us the better half, a land of mountains and moorlands and of sun and cloud, and it is with this upland Britain that these pages are concerned.' Professor Pearsall wrote this in the opening paragraph of his book in this series, *Mountains and Moorlands*. Into this book he put so much of his great store of knowledge of the natural history of his native Lake District, that when he came to write a regional book, he decided to make it essentially a history of the landscape, which would trace the development of the habitats found in the region through the ten thousand years of postglacial time, and especially through the last five thousand years of modification by man. He had spent several years collecting notes and material for this book when, in 1964, his last illness struck with tragic suddenness. In the early stages of his illness, dissatisfied with his own work, he destroyed all the completed prose in order to make a fresh start. So only his plan and notes remained. The Pearsall family and the New Naturalist Editors asked me if these could be reconstructed into a book. This was a task beyond the powers of any single author except Professor Pearsall. With the generous help of many other contributors I have tried to work out Professor Pearsall's plan, to stitch together the existing fragments of his writings which form part of the plan and to provide the five chapters required by his plan for which not even notes could be found.

Everyone who has contributed to the book is either a native of the Lake Counties or works within them or at the University of Lancaster. So much of Professor Pearsall's material for the book referred to the human history of the Lake District, and so much archaeological research has gone on since the publication in 1933 of R. G. Collingwood's review on which Professor Pearsall had based an earlier account of the ecological history of the Lake District, that it seemed essential that the early human history should be dealt with by a specialist. Miss Fell, one of the local archaeologists most involved in post-Collingwood research, and in 1964 President of the Cumberland and Westmorland Antiquarian and Archaeological Society, very kindly agreed to do this, and this was the first major step towards completion of the book. She has provided a summary of the present state of factual knowledge of the early human history of the Lake District from Mesolithic to Viking times. This makes a firm foundation for the discussion of its ecological and landscape history, a subject which interested Professor Pearsall more and more during his last years. Professor Manley, who must know more than anyone else about the climate of north-west England, kindly agreed to provide a chapter on climate. Colleagues at this laboratory who had known Professor Pearsall for many years in the Lake District, both in the laboratory and in the field – Dr and Mrs Lund, Dr Macan and Dr Frost – have provided contributions in their specialist fields along the lines they thought this book called for. Dr D. A. Ratcliffe has generously allowed me to make very full use of his published work on the mountain flora and mountain birds of the Lake District, and has contributed sections on two areas of which he has special knowledge. Professor Pigott has kindly found time to provide an authoritative account of the present state of Esthwaite Fen, describing the most recent survey by his students which continues the vegetation record begun by Professor Pearsall in 1914.

Apart from those who have contributed under their own names, many people have provided help without which the book could not have been completed. Dr G. H. Mitchell, author of many works on Lake District geology, read my manuscript of Chapter 2 and made a great many valuable suggestions. Mr J. S. R. Chard, Conservator (North-west), Forestry Commission, has very kindly allowed me to quote extensively from his published work. For the data on which is based the discussion of birds in Chapters 4, 8 and 10, I am greatly indebted to Miss M. Garnett, Miss K. M. Atkinson and Mr K. Shepherd, and for the data on Leighton Moss to the reserve warden, Mr J. Wilson; I am also grateful to the Carlisle Natural History Society for permission, through the late Mr E. Blezard, to make full use of their publications. Mr G. J. Thompson and Mr W. Askew at this laboratory have patiently answered many questions about their native Lake District, and the book owes much to them.

Many others have answered questions and provided specialist help. I am particularly grateful to the following: Mr C. H. D. Acland (National Trust), Miss J. I. Aitken (Skiddaw Forest), Mr G. V. Berry

(Friends of the Lake District, and for photographing many subjects specially for this book), Mr J. S. Corder (Burlington Slate Quarry), Mr J. Fletcher and Mr W. Grant (Forestry Commission), Mr M. Godfrey (Manchester Corporation Waterworks Forestry), Major E. Hasell, Mr D. L. Hawksworth (lichens), Mr F. L. Herdman and Mr J. T. Inman (sheep farmers), Dr E. M. Lind and Miss J. McCormack (Lake District Naturalists' Trust), Miss A. Palmer (records of the gunpowder industry), and the late Mr J. Wilson (swiller).

Thanks are due to the following for reading and giving useful criticism of chapters; all errors and inadequacies are the responsibility of the author. Dr R. B. McConnell (Chapter 3), Dr G. Halliday (Chapters 8, 9 and 10), Dr T. G. E. Powell (Chapter 11), Mr B. R. Hartley (Chapter 12), Prof. R. Cramp (Chapter 14) and Mr L. Hewkin (Chapter 17).

Chapter 11, written in 1967, uses Prof. Hawkes's A, B, C division of the Early or Pre-Roman Iron Age in Britain. This is no longer used but occurs in most literature on the subject published during the last forty years.

C.I.F.

Ferry House,
Windermere.   **Winifred Pennington**

THE LANDSCAPE OF THE LAKE DISTRICT

Fair seed-time had my soul, and I grew up
Fostered alike by beauty and by fear:
Much favoured in my birth-place . . .
William Wordsworth: *The Prelude* 1850

'Many years ago, W. G. Collingwood said, of one of the most beautiful parts of Britain, the English Lake District, that its beauty was the result of a thousand years of human occupation. Here is an idea to remember. These amenities, both for mind and for body, are as important as is material production, in marking the progress of mankind.'
W. H. Pearsall: 'Conservation as a world problem', *Oryx* IV, 1958

SINCE in this book reference will be made from time to time to W. G. Collingwood's book *The Lake Counties*, which Hugh Walpole considered included 'the grandest prose writing about the Lake District in existence', it is perhaps permissible to begin by quoting its opening paragraph.

'Through a gap, for a moment, as the train runs north from Lancaster, there is a peep of the sand, and – far away – the first sight of the mountains. In old times, when I was a schoolboy, what a moment that was! After months in town, after the rush through the Lancashire smoke, and the gradually lifting skyline, slowly rising foreground of hedges and fields, at last – "Behold – beyond!" Even now, though so many years might have deadened the excitement, there is almost more pleasure in that moment's foretaste than when I come out at Coniston station in full view of the crags and the cottages. At Hest Bank we cross our frontier: it is good-bye to the South, and "Home once again in the North Country". I will not promise that everyone feels the same who lives between the Morecambe and the Solway sands; but once in a beautiful place on the south coast, in a charming house by the forest and the sea, this was said to me: "Your poor children! It is hard on them to bring them up at the Lakes; they will never be happy anywhere else." '

Now, Coniston station is no more, and most visitors and returning exiles approach the Lake District by M6 and so miss the view from Hest Bank, but from certain points on the downward sweep of this road as it goes by Lancaster, it is still possible, on a clear day, to share in Collingwood's excitement of more than half a century ago. The foreground is of white limestone hills ringing the northern shores of Morecambe Bay;

Warton Crag, Arnside Knott, Whitbarrow and the far hills of Low
Furness. Behind rise the dark knobbly fells of ancient slaty sediments,
High Furness of the little rocky knolls and the great coppice oakwoods of
the old charcoal-burners, and eastwards by the fells round Kendal to the
bare moors of Longsleddale and Bannisdale. And behind again, the great
fells standing up like a wall, from the whaleback of Black Combe in the
west to the blue cone of Ill Bell in the east. It is there in the east that we
see the most indefinite frontier of the Lake District, where the fells of
Kentmere and Shap merge into those of Tebay and Ravenstonedale and
Mallerstang and on into the Pennines of the West Riding.

The motorists who follow the main road into the Lake District by
Kendal to Windermere travel in the footsteps of the young Wordsworth,
who came home for his first long vacation from Cambridge in 1788, but
the modern motorist on his way to Hawkshead often has a less ex-
hilarating approach to the Windermere ferry. The tourist traffic for
Ambleside and Rydal and Grasmere sweeps on by wide main roads, and
on over the great central pass of Dunmail Raise to Thirlmere under
Helvellyn side and Keswick, where the traffic ties itself in knots as the
tourists swing round into Borrowdale while the through lorries churn on
to Bassenthwaite or Carlisle. A branch stream turns off to the right
between Windermere village and Ambleside, and goes over the higher
pass of Kirkstone to Patterdale and the long lakeside panorama of
Ullswater, and then joins the traffic of Penrith and the motorways again.
Collingwood concluded an earlier book (*Lake District History*, 1928):
'Goodbye! old Lake District that we have loved' – his ghost would indeed
be miserable among the car-parks and caravan sites of the tourist belt.

Collingwood's 'Old Lake District', before the modern era of the internal
combustion engine, was the product largely of romantic interest, aroused
in the late eighteenth century and developed in the nineteenth, which
introduced an alien settlement of wealthy 'offcomers' to the old native
economy of subsistence farming, by small 'statesmen' farmers who had
grazing rights on the open fell commons. This landscape and its inhabitants, as seen through the eyes of an observant and highly articulate
native, are faithfully recorded in the Grasmere Journal of Dorothy
Wordsworth, 1800–3. In these pages the Wordsworths' statesman neighbour Thomas Ashburner and his family, and the Mackereths from whom
William and Dorothy hired horses when they needed them, rub shoulders
with the tea-drinking gentry whose residences were there in the Vales,
including the Lloyds of Old Brathay, the pleasant Georgian house at
Clappersgate. By about 1820 these residences were swallowing valuable
valley meadows in their amenity woods and landscaped gardens. Nearly
all the east side of Windermere, wooded and beautiful, is an artificial
landscape dating from this period, and the same influence can be seen all
along the Rothay valley to the foot of Dunmail Raise, appearing again

round Derwentwater, in parts of lower Borrowdale, and along Ullswater. By contrast, to the west of Windermere, much pre-Romantic landscape has been preserved intact, partly by the continued ownership of the ancient family of Sandys, who still continue to protect Esthwaite Water from the speed-boat and the water-skier. And in the far western dales the old landscape of farms and fells is still there, though modified in parts by the activities of the Forestry Commission.

But many of those who now pour northwards to the Lake District every fine weekend come for yet another landscape, that of the high open fells above the farms and the southern foothills and the tourist valleys. Most of the central mountainous heart is common land with free access, rough grazing for fell sheep, high montane grasslands, scree and crag. In recent years it has been magnificently described for the walker in the seven volumes of Wainwright's Guides; the mountain Youth Hostels have their shelves of well-worn copies. 'And in the darkest hours of urban depression, I will sometimes take out that dog's-eared map, and dream awhile of more spacious days; and perhaps a dried blade of grass will fall out of it, to remind me that I was once a free man on the hills.' This quotation from A. H. Sedgwick was seen hanging in Cockley Beck farmhouse, near the head of the Duddon, in the nineteen-twenties. The view of the high fells as a source of spiritual refreshment for the townsman is, of course, still strange to the true native of the fells, who even now generally climbs the mountains only by way of business when gathering sheep, or sport when following the foot packs of foxhounds.

The sheer crags of hard volcanic rock on Scafell and Great Gable, Gimmer, Pillar Rock and Dow Crag, attracted the rock climbers of the nineteenth century, usually comparatively leisured professional men who in holidays at Wasdale Head and Dungeon Ghyll kept in practice between their annual visits to Zermatt and Chamonix. Collingwood records that the earliest known rock-climber was Coleridge, who descended Broad Stand on Scafell, the thirty foot rock step which is the only major interruption to the walker on any Lake District ridge walk, and then went on to write his 'Hymn before sunrise in the Vale of Chamonix'. Now the crags are the playground and gymnasium of countless young people from the towns of northern England, who come every weekend, have taken over high abandoned farms and quarry-huts as their club-houses, pitch their little tents at the very foot of the crags, and dot the landscape with the cheerful and practical colours of their anoraks.

There is yet another Lake District landscape, which can be seen by those not too impatient to travel by the coast line of the old Furness Railway, resigned to the inevitability of stopping at 'all stations to Workington' on leaving Carnforth. From this viewpoint the Lake District is seen, not as a beautiful jewel to be preserved and polished and admired, but as an enthrallingly interesting piece of country which has earned its living by a succession of technologies, from the polished stone axes of between four and five thousand years ago which were traded all over England, through two and a half thousand years of the Iron Age to the nuclear power of Calder Hall.

Crossing the estuaries of Kent and Leven, the train potters on, through stations like Cark-and-Cartmel which have changed little since the beginning of the railway age, between the little limestone hills, the dark peat mosses and the salt marshes, to the haematite country of Low Furness, where the beck runs red through the soaring sandstone ruins of Furness Abbey. Once the iron carts came down through red lanes to small anchorages where the ore ships put in, one of which was Barrow, where now the docks and cranes and nuclear submarines still keep a town at work, though the haematite mines are all closed and the great iron and steel works shut down. One of the best of all views of the Lakeland mountains is from the splendid sand-dunes on either side of the glittering Walney Channel, which comes into view as the train leaves Barrow. From the dunes of the North End of Walney or from Roanhead, places where the larks sing on summer evenings as nowhere else, the great panorama swings round the Duddon estuary, from the long ridge of Black Combe, the rugged skyline of Pillar and Steeple, the triple giant of Scafell, its Pike and Great End, round to the bulk of the Coniston Fells which hide Bowfell from the southern side of the estuary, though the poet Norman Nicholson can see it from the edge of Millom.

At Foxfield there is the beginning of the dead Coniston branch, where Collingwood used to change trains, closed after just a hundred years of useful life carrying slates and copper ore and green building stone, as well as mails and provisions and passengers, up and down the narrow valley from Kirkby Pool by Woodland to Torver and Coniston. From Foxfield the coast line goes on and round the 'corner' of Black Combe to the fresh sea wind of the unspoiled Cumberland coast. Presently Eskdale opens up on the right of the railway line, with its grand circle of mountains, from Scafell round to Crinkle Crags and Harter Fell, now quite close. Crossing the combined estuaries of the Irt, flowing from Wastwater, the Mite and the Esk, the railway passenger can see the beginning, at Ravenglass, of the miniature railway, 'Laal Ratty', which was built to carry ore from the mines at Boot, but survives as one of the main local tourist attractions and the only public transport in the remote valleys of Eskdale and Miterdale. From the Roman port of Ravenglass, now asleep on its shingle bank by the three-pronged estuary, and the famous gullery on the sand-dunes across the water, where black-headed gulls and four species of tern nest, the train goes on through Drigg and Seascale, with Great Gable's pyramid now the dominating mountain inland, to Sellafield with the tall towers of Windscale, and Britain's first nuclear power station across the river Calder.

The line still thrusts northward, to the headland of St Bees, and the now desolate industrial area of West Cumberland inland, where the old iron villages make sad rusty blots up to the very gates of Ennerdale, and on to Whitehaven, where the miners who used to go out under the sea down Haig Pit and William Pit speak with harsher accents than their cousins in the dales, and the waves once came breaking black with coal dust into the harbour, where Lowther and Curwen fortunes were made. And so again 'round the corner' and Solway sands come into view, with Criffel across the water in Scotland. Here we have reached the northern limit of the Lake District, for from here its boundary coincides with the geological border between the old rocks of the mountains and the newer sandstones and limestones of lowland Cumberland.

Why does the landscape look as it does? Can we look at it not only as it now appears, but going back through time until we understand the reason for what we see?

Nowadays, from both the scenic and the scientific point of view, the character of the Lake District is largely determined by the balance between the high grasslands of the hills and the patches of woodland remaining on the lower slopes. This balance is largely the result of the human occupations which have made their mark on the vegetation of the district, but also important has been the romantic interest it has attracted in the last two hundred years, for this has helped to preserve elements that had amenity value.

The occupations in the Lake District in historic times which have mainly determined the existing pattern of vegetation and animal life were of two main types – those appertaining to sheep breeding (and to a lesser extent dairy farming) and those associated with growing and harvesting small timber, originally used either for charcoal for smelting metallic ores and for the manufacture of gunpowder, or for making cotton-bobbins, oak baskets (swills) and other products of woodland industries. Sheep-breeding led to the development and extension of the mountain sheep-walk at the expense of the upper woodlands, but charcoal-burning was responsible for the maintenance of considerable areas as enclosed coppice woodlands, frequently cut for small timber but preserving parts of the woodland fauna and flora. Under modern conditions the industries which utilised small timber have largely disappeared, and there is now no longer much local economic reason for woodlands of this type. Thus their conservation is becoming more and more neglected. To some extent the decline of the native timber industries has run parallel with the growth of amenity interest. The scenic value of many of the best-known areas round Windermere and Derwentwater has been due very largely to land-owners who redeveloped vanished woodlands along natural lines, often no doubt from the remnants of coppice, and generally so successfully that it is now difficult to distinguish the second-growth woodlands from fragments of original or semi-natural oak forest which may still remain. The 'amenity' woodlands formerly differed from the economic ones in being well-grown timber. The impact of two wars has, however, altogether destroyed many of the best amenity woodlands, and they have either disappeared or been replaced by conifer plantations, in either case with loss to the native flora and fauna, and with a change in the scenic balance.

The Lake District as it was at the beginning of the 'amenity' planting is preserved for ever in the lucid prose of Wordsworth's *Guide through the District of the Lakes* which is, in the opinion of that authority on the history of the English landscape, Professor W. G. Hoskins, 'one of the best guide books ever written, for poets make the best topographers'. The reader is accordingly referred to Wordsworth for a full and unrivalled account of the topography of the district. In the century and a half since he wrote, the rise of scientific disciplines, which was foreshadowed in the publication of letters from Professor Adam Sedgwick to Wordsworth on the geology of the Lake District in the 1853 edition of the *Guide*, has provided us with ever-increasing knowledge of how the landscape was indeed shaped by 'the great impersonal forces of Nature' and of the steps by which the human inhabitants have modified the primeval woods, through five thousand years of human history, into the comely landscape of today. Professor Sedgwick, a native of Dent, has left us a vivid and charming picture of early field studies in the district, when in his own old age he wrote of Wordsworth: 'he was ready for any good occasion that carried him among his well-loved mountains. Hence it was that he joined me in many a lusty excursion, and delighted me (amidst the dry and sometimes almost sterile details of my own study) with the outpourings of his manly sense, and with the beauteous and healthy images which were ever starting up within his mind during his communion with Nature.' We can only regret that there is no surviving portrait of these two benign old men on one of their lusty excursions in the mountains.

Field studies are the basis of any consideration of the development and history of the landscape. A landscape is the product of geology and history. Geology tells us about the bones of the landscape, and explains among other things why the crags and skylines of our own mountains, Bowfell and Scafell and Helvellyn and Skiddaw, are different from the Horns and Spitzes of the younger skylines of the Alps. The poet observed and contrasted the stability of his native hills with the intensely erosive processes which are everywhere so conspicuous in the Alps, where, he said 'it is difficult, notwithstanding the naked loftiness of the *pikes*, and the snow-capped summits of the *mounts*, to escape from the depressing sensation that the whole are in a rapid process of dissolution; and, were it not that the destructive agency must abate as the heights diminish, would, in time to come, be levelled with the plains.' Wordsworth's observations are so perceptive and so much in accord with modern ideas that it comes as a shock to realise that the concept of recent glaciation of the Lake District was unfamiliar to him.

The latest and shortest of geological periods, so recent that it scarcely counts as geology at all, was the Pleistocene or Quaternary, with its successive glaciations of Britain. Since the final retreat of the ice, a mere ten thousand years ago, post-glacial deposits in the form of lake sediments and peats have accumulated, and have preserved the records of stages in the evolution of the landscape. For the first five thousand years of the post-glacial period, men in northern Europe were still hunters, dependent on wild animals, birds and fish for their food, and affecting the landscape little more than did the animals they hunted. Then, a little before 3000 B.C., men with new knowledge spread widely over north-west Europe, the knowledge of how to domesticate animals and so ensure a continuous food supply, and of how to cultivate certain plants which provided palatable seeds, fruits, leaves and so on. So agriculture began, but because in north-west Europe the primeval forest covered all the land except the mountain tops, it must have begun with certain rather specialised techniques. History takes over from geology at this point, but in Britain, three thousand years of unwritten history separate the first impact of man on the primeval landscape from the point at which Roman historians began the written record of the countryside. The story of these three thousand years has been primarily deciphered by archaeologists; the others who have assisted have been climatologists, ecologists, geographers, soil scientists, and physicists concerned with dating methods. 'Earth sciences' is sometimes used as a comprehensive description of their activities.

In the study of landscape history, the earth scientist comes between the geologist and the local historian; the geologist reads history in the rocks, the local historian in manuscripts and documents and buildings, but archaeologists and earth scientists must decipher the record in soils, in organic remains preserved from decay in sediments and peats, and in human monuments so ancient that their structure and purpose must be investigated by the patient disciplines of scientific research. Often, in the Lake District, we must learn as much about the numbers and way of life of the earliest human inhabitants from the remaining traces of their effects on vegetation and soils, as from direct study of human monuments or artefacts. Such studies provide the background for all contemporary field studies of the plants and animals of the district today.

In these considerations about the Lake District, past and present, it becomes necessary at some stage to define the region we are thinking about. Each person who knows the Lake District well has his own definition of these boundaries, which would probably differ slightly from that of anyone else. In some ways one can only think of it in terms of the larger unit of 'The Lake Counties' – Cumberland, Westmorland and Lancashire-north-of-the-sands, a natural region with its regional capital and cathedral in the dark red sandstone streets of Carlisle. When coming back from Scotland and the Debatable Land of the Borders, the native knows he is at home as soon as he crosses Eden Bridge, though he may yet have a long way to travel to the slaty recesses of Borrowdale or Langdale, the sheltered limestone of Kendal or Cartmel, or the windy fields and fells of Furness. On the other hand, the most limited definition of the Lake District, as the country lying within a circle, centred on Easedale Tarn, and passing through the foot of most of the major lakes, is too exclusive; this is a purely artificial boundary, based on an aesthetic definition of a particular type of scenery. A rational definition of the Lake District, for the purposes of this book, would certainly fall somewhere between these two extremes.

The boundary of the National Park, shown in Fig. 20, p. 285, is one place to draw such a limit, and quite a reasonable one. It includes some of the ring-frame of newer rocks around the hard old mountain core, but none of the industrial fringe, and it excludes all the lowlands of the Vale of Eden and North Cumberland, with their deeper soils and richer farmlands. Nevertheless in the south it is a highly unsatisfactory boundary, which even cuts out the lowest stretch of Wordsworth's Duddon and all its lovely estuary. No native of Furness could regard as real a boundary which runs up the Crake and across Gawthwaite Moor (excluding even a classic exposure of the Borrowdale Volcanic Series at Greenscoe above the Duddon) and yet includes in the Lake District the limestone of Whitbarrow and Yewbarrow. Again, the criterion would seem to be aesthetic rather than based on a real difference in essential nature.

So it has been admitted that it is impossible to set formal limits to the Lake District. As each aspect of its being and the history of its landscape is considered, the natural boundaries of the region under discussion may fall inside or outside the line on the map which delimits the National Park, and sometimes we shall be talking about 'The Lake Counties'. Perhaps the best way to think of the problem is to equate 'The Lake District' with the National Park, a human conception which includes that part which contemporary man considers to be of very great natural beauty. 'Cumbria' is the region, an entity shaped by geology and climate and five thousand years of modification by native men who have not been so very much concerned with aesthetics. Within the natural region of Cumbria, the drift-covered lowland north and east of Cockermouth and Maryport, and the Vale of Eden, are geographically separate and will not be considered in any detail, but there is no natural boundary on the west and south between the Lake District and the sea, so from the mouth of the Derwent to the estuary of the Kent, the boundary of the National Park will be ignored.

This book is about the ecology of the Lake District. A distinguished

American ecologist has written: 'That the land is a community, is the basic concept of ecology; but that land is to be loved and respected is an extension of ethics. We abuse the land because we regard it as a commodity belonging to us. When we see the land as a community to which we belong, we may begin to use it with love and respect.' (Aldo Leopold.) This is what conservation is all about.

Everyone who knows and loves the Lake District has an interest in its conservation. Naturalists are anxious to preserve the habitats and characteristic plants and animals of the mountains, woodlands and wetlands; holidaymakers whose enthusiasm is for wild places wish to protect the wilderness of the high fells from mining and commercial forestry, and those who love the wooded watery dales want to keep them secure from the irreversible changes of development, and their lakes and clear mountain streams free from twentieth-century pollution. At the same time it must be remembered that, as W. G. Collingwood reminds us, the Lake District owes much of its beauty to a thousand years of human occupation and trimming of the landscape by man, and it cannot be preserved without agreement and co-operation from the native men and women who must earn their living in the modern world. This book will try to put on record, as the senior author wished, the story of how man has indeed formed part of the community of the land of the Lake District for at least five thousand years, in the hope that a contribution to the understanding of our past may help to suggest a way to a future in which all may take pleasure, in this beautiful corner of Britain which Wordsworth thought should become 'a sort of national property'.

CHAPTER 2

GEOLOGY – THE BASIS OF THE LANDSCAPE

He knew beneath the mutation of year and season
Flood and drought, frost and fire and thunder,
The frothy blossom on the rowan and the reddening of the berries,
The silt, the sand, the slagbanks and the shingle,
And the wild catastrophes of the breaking mountains,
There stands the base and root of the living rock, `
Thirty thousand feet of solid Cumberland.

Norman Nicholson: *Duddon*

THE earliest recorded account of Lake District geology appeared in the Lonsdale Magazine for 1820 – a letter by Jonathan Otley, the Keswick guide, entitled 'The threefold division of the rocks of the Lake District'. In the 1853 edition of Wordsworth's *Guide through the District of the Lakes* Professor Sedgwick wrote five letters on Lake District geology. These convey a fascinating picture of the field work by which the Lakeland rocks were first described, and their age and structure worked out, developing the conception, first put forward by Jonathan Otley, of the 'two great slaty sedimentary groups of Pre-Carboniferous strata, separated by volcanic rocks, and traceable in upward succession southward from the Skiddaw area' (Hollingworth 1955). With more than a hundred years of subsequent work to describe, the writer of today finds the same problem as Professor Sedgwick: '. . . in commencing my task I meet with a great difficulty. I wish to convey some general notion of the structure of the Lake District, and it would be an easy task, even within the compass of one letter, to enumerate the successive great rock formations, to explain their order, and to give a short description of them. But in this way my narrative would inevitably be so dry and repulsive, that no one but a professed geologist would ever think of reading it, and even such a person would do so with very little profit. I wish to address more general readers – any intelligent traveller whose senses are open to the beauties of the country around him, and who is ready to speculate on such matters of interest as it offers to him.'

To such an intelligent traveller one can do no better than to recommend Professor J. E. Marr's entirely delightful classic which appeared in 1916 – *The Geology of the Lake District and the Scenery as influenced by Geological Structure*. This has long been out of print but has recently been reprinted, and should be read by all who love the Lake District landscape. In the fifty years since 1916, much more work has been done on the nature and relative ages of the rocks, on the structures imposed upon them by up-heavals of the earth's crust, and on the shaping of them by millions of years of exposure to all the agents of erosion. Dr G. H. Mitchell and the late Professor Hollingworth have both been major contributors to this research and have written recent reviews (see references).

Basically, the Lake District is a region of old hard rocks, repeatedly uplifted by movements of the earth's crust and then worn down again by the normal processes of erosion and weathering. The 'two great slaty groups of Pre-Carboniferous strata' are the Skiddaw Slates of Ordovician age and the great thickness of Stockdale Shales, Coniston Flags and Grits, Bannisdale Slates and Kirkby Moor Flags of Silurian, that is younger, age. The volcanic rocks which separate the two slaty groups, the Borrowdale Volcanic Series, were poured and shot out from volcanic vents, above the Skiddaw Slates, in Ordovician times, about 400 million years ago, and then the Silurian slaty beds were laid down on top of them. The central mountain dome of the Lake District proper, made up of these three groups of rock, shows by its structure, and its relationships with the newer limestones and sandstones which surround it, some of the details of its long and complex history since the ancient rocks were formed. The Ordovician and Silurian rocks were first submerged in the ancient Carboniferous sea, about 280 million years ago, and were then uplifted into the desert environment of the Triassic period. Within the shallow Carboniferous sea, the calcium carbonate of shells and skeletons of myriads of marine animals accumulated to build the lovely rock we call the Mountain (Carboniferous) Limestone. This once covered the whole of the Lake District, but now appears only as the ring of limestone country, incomplete on the west, which frames the mountains in a ring of lower hills but rises to the east of the Lake District in the mountains of the northern Pennines, from the fierce scarp of Cross Fell to the high Craven plateau. Together with the Permian and Triassic (New Red) sandstones which formed also at one time a cap over the Lake District, the Carboniferous rocks have been stripped off by wind and weather and water from the mountain heart.

The Skiddaw Slates and Borrowdale Volcanics, with later rocks in-truded into them, make all the mountains, all the peaks described in Wainwright's Guides, with the exception of Great and Little Mell Fells, which are of a later conglomerate. But Coniston, Ambleside, Hawkshead and Windermere most certainly belong to the Lake District, though it is clear to the most casual observer that they lie in a very different sort of country, and Esthwaite Water is scenically a very different picture from Wastwater or Ennerdale Water. The wall of the Borrowdale rocks, forming the ridges of the Coniston Fells, from Walna Scar, the Old Man and Swirl How to Yewdale Crags and Wetherlam, stands above the

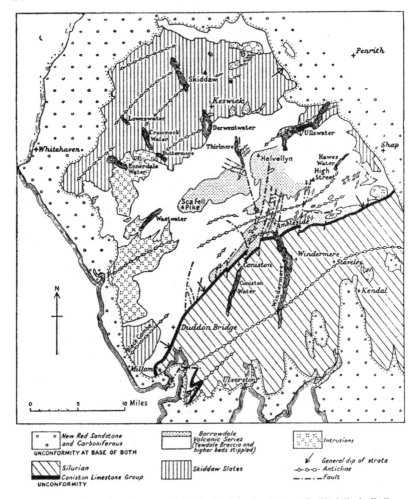

FIG I. Geological sketch-map of the Lake District. From G. H. Mitchell, Proc. Yorks. Geol. Soc. 1956 *30*.

Silurian lowlands as one of the most dramatic contrasts in the British countryside. The harder Borrowdale rocks have weathered slowly, and form crags and precipices above the softer, soil-covered sediments to the south and east. These Silurian rocks roll as moorland ridges from the head of Coniston Water through High Furness and the moorlands north of Kendal to Longsleddale, Bannisdale and the Howgill Fells, which look like sleeping elephants across the great gorge of the Lune. In discussing the type of scenery characteristic of each of the three major rocks, Marr points out the importance both of the alternation of harder and softer bands and of the 'jointing' of the volcanic rocks – a system of joints or planes of weakness dividing the rock into bold blocks. 'The present difference in the scenic characters of the tracts occupied by the rocks of the three great divisions is in fact probably not so much due to difference of hardness between the three types of rocks, as to the difference between the uniform characters of the Skiddaw Slates, and to some extent of the Silurian rocks, and the very varied characters of the volcanic rocks, and also in very considerable degree to the greater regularity and larger scale of many of the divisional planes in these volcanic rocks as compared with those of the Skiddaw Slates and Silurian strata.' (Marr 1916, p. 130.)

THE SKIDDAW SLATES

These, the oldest rocks of the Lake District, were formed mainly as muds in an ancient sea and subsequently hardened and cleaved into slates, but the cleavage is generally poorly developed so there has been comparatively little use of these rocks as roofing slates. Accompanying the mudstones there were sands, and in places gritty beds; there is no lime in them, and their colour is rather dark, greyish, blue or black. Estimates have been made of the probable limits and coastline of this ancient sea in which these rocks were formed, but there is no factual evidence as to the geography of Skiddaw Slate times. The shallow sea contained primitive marine animals, and the remains of these can be found as a rather inconspicuous fossil fauna in the Skiddaw Slates, mainly of graptolites and trilobites, two invertebrate groups now extinct. Evolutionary changes took place in these animals within the time-span represented by these rocks.

The main outcrop of the Skiddaw Slates forms the northern Lake District, from Ennerdale foot in the west, by Loweswater and Crummock Fells to the east side of Derwentwater and the classic locality of Skiddaw and Saddleback (Blencathra). It makes such well-known and graceful peaks as Grisedale Pike and Causey Pike, as well as the massive bulk of Mellbreak and Grasmoor and the familiar whale-backs and ridges of Skiddaw and Saddleback. An isolated Skiddaw Slate mountain is the smooth swell of Black Combe above the Duddon estuary, formed by an outcrop of these rocks in the south-west. Marr says: 'The Skiddaw Slates consist very largely of argillaceous rocks. There is, it is true, much grit, but the grits, with local exceptions, are fine-grained. Grit and shale alike are generally jointed with innumerable minute joints, and accordingly break into small pieces as the result of weathering action. The clay-rocks become separated into their component particles as the result of the mechanical effects of weathering, and by solution of the binding material between the grit grains, the gritty rocks are also marked by separation of their component grains. Thus slates and grits alike become reduced at the surface into a mass of fine incoherent material which masks the solid rock beneath on the flatter ground, and by being carried down as rain-wash, and by the general downward creep of the material, tends in time to cover up such cliffs as may have been formed previously. This loose material furnishes a soil favourable for the growth of moorland vegetation, as grass and heather; hence the generally smoothed outlines of the Skid-daw Slate district at the present time.' (Plates 2, p. 33, 3, p. 48, 4, p. 49, and 11b, p. 112.)

Late in Skiddaw Slate times, volcanic activity set in around the margins of the sea, heralding the great outpouring of lavas and ashes which was to follow. The solidified volcanic ashes (tuffs) and lavas which are inter-bedded with the highest mudstones of the Skiddaw Slates came from submarine volcanic vents, and can now be seen at the junction between the Skiddaw Slates and the overlying Borrowdale Volcanic rocks, at some places, e.g. Clough Head, east of the Vale of St John.

THE BORROWDALE VOLCANIC SERIES

These rocks, the Green Slates and Porphyries of Professor Sedgwick, form the mountainous heart of the Lake District and consist, in Marr's words, of 'ejectamenta shot or poured out from volcanoes'. Ashes were shot out and solidified into tuffs, fine-grained rocks which were often converted by subsequent pressure into slates; showers of coarser fragments fell and became cemented into breccias and agglomerates; while lava flows, the origin of the porphyries, included both dark free-flowing types and paler, more viscous varieties, and some cooled as they flowed so that the flow broke up the solid surface and produced a 'flow-breccia'. A narrow strip of these rocks appears east and north of Skiddaw, and a small but interest-ing outcrop on the east side of the Duddon estuary, but otherwise the area of the volcanic rocks corresponds with the mountain core. 'The Roof of England' as A. H. Griffin calls it, owes its being to the hardness of the volcanic ejectamenta and to the bold jointing developed within the rocks, so that their response to the subsequent weathering of frost and sun and the sculpturing of ice was to shatter into the crags and chasms of Scafell and Gable, and the glorious rugged profiles of Great End and Bowfell, Fairfield and Pillar. Together, the various members of the Borrowdale Volcanic Series reach a total thickness of about eight to twelve thousand feet. Neither fossils, apart from some tracks, nor any material derived from the erosion of a land surface have been found within them, so there is no conclusive evidence as to whether the volcanoes which formed them were terrestrial or marine. The series is now considered to follow con-formably upon the Skiddaw Slates, though Marr and others describe places where the junction is faulted, and other authors record local unconformities. This generally conformable junction shows, however, that no severe crustal movements occurred at the time. 'The interbedding of the lowest tuffs and flows with the Skiddaw Slates suggests that the earliest beds were submarine. Deposition in water seems certain in the case of the delicately bedded fine tuffs which, when later cleaved, have been transformed into slates. . . . The bulk of the flows and tuffs, however, seem to have been of subaerial origin.' (Mitchell 1956.) (Plates 6, p. 65, 7, p. 80, 8, p. 81, 9, p. 96, 10, p. 97 and 12, p. 113.)

In the rocks of the Borrowdale Volcanic Series, the sequences of tuffs and lavas (andesites which are more basic in composition and rhyolites which are more acid) which have been described at various sites, can be correlated into a series, from the base which is in contact with the Skiddaw Slates to the uppermost rhyolites of the Kentmere district. A contribution to an understanding of this sequence of the Borrowdale rocks was made by a study of the succession of rocks exposed in the walls of the tunnel driven to carry the Haweswater aqueduct. In summarising the available evidence Dr Mitchell makes the point that 'it becomes increasingly apparent that closely similar lavas and tuffs were repeatedly erupted at different times during the history of the volcanic pile, and consequently appear at widely different (time) horizons. . . . The time available for the formation of this thick group of volcanic rocks suggests violent eruptions and rapid accumulation.' The sites of the old 'volcanoes' from which the Borrowdale Volcanic rocks were erupted are not conspicuous, but a number of old vents are marked by volcanic breccias. The crag of Castle Head, Keswick, may well be a 'plug' which solidified inside a vent.

In many of the rocks of this series, alteration of the minerals has produced secondary minerals, including calcite, chlorite, sericite and epidote. Garnets are characteristic of both lavas and ashes, either microscopically small or up to the size of peas; the garnet may have been present within the original magma, or may be due to secondary alteration. Much of the mineral wealth of the rocks is made up of the results of later changes – the intrusion into the Borrowdale rocks of later masses of igneous rock, with consequent secondary alteration by the heat of the intrusion, and the development of other secondary minerals within veins usually associated with faults or fractures.

THE CONISTON LIMESTONE SERIES

At the end of the great outburst of volcanic activity which formed the Borrowdale Series, that vast pile of solidified lavas and tuffs was submerged beneath a shallow sea. There is no evidence as to whether the highest existing Borrowdale rocks – the Upper Rhyolites of Kentmere – were the final products of the volcanic episode, or whether later eruptions produced other rocks which were soon eroded away. There is a great unconformity between the Borrowdale rocks and the marine sediments of the Coniston Limestone Series which overlie them. During the time represented by this unconformity, gentle folding of the rocks took place, the axes of the folds running north-north-east to south-south-west, and there was much denudation of the folded Borrowdale rocks, which in places must have been completely worn away, for near the Duddon estuary rocks of the Coniston Limestone Series rest directly on Skiddaw Slates. The general lie of the basal beds of the Coniston Limestone Series is across the somewhat folded and tilted Borrowdales.

The oldest beds of the Coniston Limestone Series are coarse conglomerates and grits, made up of material eroded from the old land surface of the volcanic rocks, which accumulated as beach deposits round the spreading Coniston Limestone sea. The fossiliferous deposits of this sea are represented by the limestones and shales of the Coniston series and by the Ashgill Shales, which are blue fossiliferous slates. Volcanic activity did not entirely cease until the end of Coniston Limestone times, for ashes and rhyolites are interbedded with the lower sediments of the series, as can be seen in some of the stream sections.

The outcrop of the Coniston Limestone Series forms a narrow band running north-east from the head of the Duddon estuary to Shap, and broken by subsequent faulting; patches also occur on both sides of the Duddon estuary. The narrowness of the outcrop and its not very calcareous nature minimise the effect on the scenery of the Coniston limestone, but the characteristic limestone weathering is distinctive; one of the best places to see it is on the Yewdale road out of Coniston, beside an old lime-kiln. The fossiliferous beds contain a fauna of trilobites and brachiopods which has been described in detail by Marr and others, particularly from the old quarry at Ashgill below Torver High Common, the type locality for the Ashgillian. This fauna is made up of animals of comparatively shallow water.

THE SILURIAN SLATES, GRITS AND FLAGS

This great thickness of marine sediments, the upper of the 'two great slaty sedimentary groups' of Jonathan Otley, follows conformably on the Ashgill Shales, from which the basal beds are distinguished by their fossil fauna, which includes many graptolites, and represents accumulation, in deeper water, of the corpses of these planktonic animals. These basal beds are the Skelgill Beds of the Stockdale Shales, and crop out parallel to the Coniston Limestone Series, though the outcrop is very narrow. Above them follows a tremendous thickness of sediments, laid down in a sea of fluctuating depth but without any major interruption in deposition. Above the Stockdale Shales were formed successively the Lower Coniston

PLATE I   *Above,* Honister Pass: the view down the Pass to Buttermere, showing the northern boundary of the Borrowdale Volcanic rocks on the left, with Skiddaw Slates on the right.   *Below,* Coniston fells, Brown Pike and Dow Crag: the southern boundary of the volcanic rocks – the mountain wall of Borrowdale Volcanics rising behind Silurian moorlands.   The old quarry at Ash Gill (type locality of the Ashgillian) is in the middle distance.

PLATE 2 *Above*, Bowscale Fell from Carrock Fell: the walls in the foreground are of comparatively recent date, built from stones of the Iron Age hill-fort. In the background is the cove containing Bowscale Tarn and its large moraine, incised into smooth fells of Skiddaw Slate. *Below*, Scales Tarn and Sharp Edge: unusually craggy scenery in Skiddaw Slates.

(Brathay) Flags, the Upper Coniston Flags or Coldwell Beds, the Coniston Grits, the Bannisdale Slates and the Kirkby Moor Flags, the whole series showing a general tendency towards shallower conditions as time went on, though with temporary periods of deeper water. The fluctuations in the depth of the sea are reflected in the types of marine animals preserved as fossils in the Silurian strata, and the fossils are sufficiently well-known to permit the recognition of a series of zones based on changes in the organisms.

The Stockdale Shales are deep-water deposits, divided into Skelgill Beds and Browgill Beds; the Skelgill Beds are dark, blue or black, with beautifully preserved graptolites; these are well exposed in Skelgill near Ambleside. In the Browgill Beds the graptolite shales are thin, grey rather than black, and there are mudstones, greenish grey and red near the top. The overlying Brathay Flags appear to have been formed in shallower water than the Stockdale Shales, as laminated silty fossiliferous muds. In the gritty Lower Coldwell Beds there are no fossils, but the Middle and Upper Coldwell Beds are fossiliferous silts, the Middle Beds being shelly with a shallower-water fauna and often comparatively calcareous, while the Upper Beds consist of laminated silts with both shells and graptolites. The Coniston Grits are almost entirely non-fossiliferous. The Bannisdale Slates, consisting of alternating beds of mudstone and gritty silts, usually leaden-grey in colour, contain few fossils but include some graptolites; together with the Coniston Grits these make up by far the greatest thickness of the Silurian sediments. The Kirkby Moor Flags, the highest members of the Silurian system, are fine-grained flaggy grits with abundant fossils, particularly in the soft calcareous bands which are included; the flags are in general grey-green in colour. In all, about 15,000 feet of these marine sediments of Silurian age remain; it is not known how much has been removed by later erosion.

Their composition, as prevailingly mineral sediments accumulated in generally muddy seas, is in general poorer in lime and other bases than that of the rocks of the Borrowdale Volcanic Series (though in the Browgill and Middle Coldwell Beds there are calcareous mudstones). However, from their lower altitude and greater depth of soil, consequent on their softer nature, the Silurian hills and valleys present a gentler aspect than the central mountains; this provides the contrast characteristic of many of the famous views of the Lake District, from the word-picture of Esthwaite Vale in Wordsworth's *Prelude* to the views of Coniston Water, Esthwaite and Windermere which are familiar from a million picture-postcards. (Plates 1b, p. 32, 14a, p. 149.) Variations in hardness between the successive strata and the effects of recent glaciation have produced between them a charmingly knobbly and characteristic landscape in all the little hills and valleys which run south between the Lickle and the Lune. Just how characteristic is the appearance of these Silurian rocks is brought home to those who come upon them unawares in the valley bottoms near Ingleborough, where they poke up through the white Mountain Limestone as outlying islands of Lake District scenery.

THE FIRST MOUNTAIN-BUILDING PHASE: THE DEVONIAN PERIOD

At the end of the period of deposition of the Silurian sediments, one of the great mountain-building episodes of the earth's history began. The rocks formed during Ordovician and Silurian times were uplifted by the convulsions of the 'Caledonian' upheaval. The folds into which they were buckled by this vast wrinkling of the earth's crust run approximately west-south-west to east-north-east. The Skiddaw Slates, being less resistant than the hard volcanic rock, were more severely folded and faulted. A broad upfold structure was developed through Skiddaw. The Borrowdales were thrown into major troughs (synclines) and arches (anticlines); a great syncline extends from Scafell to north of High Street along the general axis of folding. An anticlinal fold dating from this period has been shown by Hartley to coincide with the present course of Great Langdale; shattering along the line of weakness determined by the tension has been one of the factors determining the present course of this valley.

Variation in intensity and direction of the folding, partly related to the character of the different rocks of the Ordovician and Silurian systems, has produced a structural picture of enormous complexity. The principal structural elements of the Lake District rocks were established during these Caledonian earth movements. In many of the fine-grained sediments and volcanic tuffs, lateral pressure brought about a rearrangement of particles which produced a slaty cleavage, independent in direction of that of the bedding planes of the original rock. The local slates will be described in Chapter 16. The culmination of the earth movements of this period was to raise the great anticlinal arch trending east-north-east through Skiddaw; traces of the worn-down remnants of this structure are seen in the north–south section through the Lake District (Fig. 2, p. 35), in which the younger Borrowdale rocks appear on both the north and the south of the outcrop of the oldest rocks, the Skiddaw Slates, in the axis of the anticline. The folding of the rocks during earth movements was accompanied by fractures and by faulting; movements to and fro along the lines of these produced fault-zones and shatter-belts of weakened rock, some of which have been subsequently hollowed out by erosion and form cols followed by through passes, such as Dunmail Raise and Esk Hause, or deep gullies. A glance at the geological map shows how the Coniston Limestone and Stockdale Shales have been severely faulted with much lateral displacement. The comparatively soft Skiddaw Slates were

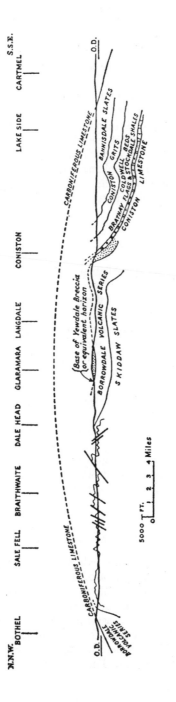

FIG. 2. Generalised section across the Lake District. From G. H. Mitchell, Proc. Yorks. Geol. Soc. 1956, *30*.

crumpled and severely faulted. The much more resistant Borrowdale Volcanic rocks are not so severely folded, in general, but one response to pressure was the formation of the series of joints or fracture lines which traverse these rocks.

Another major accompaniment of the great disturbance of the rocks was the intrusion into them of great masses of igneous rock, welling up from deep sources of magma into fractures and bedding planes, and metamorphosing (changing both chemically and physically) by heat and vapours the rocks into which they were intruded. The results of this have been a great contribution to the mineral wealth of the Lake District, a certain effect on the scenery from the major intrusions, and a small but interesting effect on plant distribution consequent on the secondary mineralisation (Chapter 9).

THE SHAP GRANITE

This famous rock is the only one of these intrusions which can be dated with certainty to the time of the Devonian mountain-building episode. Both Silurian sediments and rocks of the Borrowdale Volcanic Series have been metamorphosed by the heat of this intrusion, so it was later in time than the Silurian period, and also fragments of this granite including the well-known pink felspar crystals are conspicuous in the basal beds of the overlying Carboniferous Limestone. This, of course, places the time of intrusion of the Shap Granite in the Devonian period. Its outcrop, on the eastern margin of the Lake District, is a roughly circular area about three miles across, and has been extensively quarried. The granite was intruded into rocks of the Borrowdale Volcanic Series in the form of a laccolith, and heated vapours from it introduced new minerals, especially molybdenite, into the country rocks; in the later stages of the intrusion, a series of dykes injected into the surrounding rocks brought about metamorphosis both of Borrowdale Volcanics and of Silurian strata.

The age of the other large intrusions in the Lake District is much less certain.

THE ESKDALE GRANITE

This rock, a pleasant pinkish granite which is rough to sight and touch, forms the surface rock of a large area of country round the foot of Wastwater, most of Miterdale, and the valleys of the Esk and its large tributary the Whillan Beck as far as Hardknott Fort and Burnmoor Tarn respectively. It extends south along the coastal fell country as far as Bootle. The granite is probably of Devonian age, since its intrusion metamorphosed the Borrowdale rocks, and a pebble of it has been found in the Millstone Grit of the Carboniferous period. The pink colour, due to haematite, gives a special character to the scenery of mid-Eskdale, and the area of the outcrop can be identified by the stone walls which, built of the rounded cobbles into which the granite weathers, contrast very strongly with the angular slaty blocks of the drystone walls in both Borrowdale and Silurian country. The granite has responded to glaciation to produce characteristic knolls and hollows reminiscent of the glaciated gneiss of Sutherland, among the low moors which separate Eskdale and Miterdale. (Plate 9b, p. 96.)

THE ENNERDALE GRANOPHYRE

This, another hard and acid pinkish rock, which crops out on either side of Ennerdale Water and extends over to Buttermere, making up most of Buttermere Red Pike, has also metamorphosed the adjacent Skiddaw Slates and Borrowdale Volcanics, and has recently been shown to be older than the conglomerate below the Carboniferous limestone at Hodbarrow, near Millom. The intrusion seems to have had the form of a stout columnar stock. East of Floutern Tarn, the hardness of the Ennerdale Granophyre in comparison with the adjacent Skiddaw Slate has affected the scenery, producing the upstanding wall of the Red Pike to Starling Dodd ridge, and the waterfall of Scale Force where Scale Beck drops over the hard granophyre.

OTHER INTRUSIONS

Three intrusions round Skiddaw, the Carrock Fell complex, the Skiddaw Granite, and the Threlkeld Microgranite, are presumed to be of similar age. The hard gabbro and granophyre of the Carrock Fell complex form the striking bulk of that hill, which, crowned by its Iron Age hill-fort, stands high above the Skiddaw Slates of the Caldew valley and the limestone plateau of Greystoke and Hutton Roof, forming one of the most sharply defined boundaries of the Lake District. The complex of plutonic rocks includes, as well as gabbro and granophyre, diabase and felsite, all cropping out approximately parallel to the local strike of the Borrowdale Volcanics and Skiddaw Slates. The Skiddaw Granite appears to have replaced the country rock (the Skiddaw Slates) in the region of the main anticline of the Lake District; it has three separate outcrops in the Skiddaw Forest area, associated with considerable alteration of the slates by thermal metamorphism, and the Grainsgill outcrop includes quartz veins which contain the tungsten ores, wolfram and scheelite. The Threlkeld Microgranite, which has been intruded between the Skiddaw Slates and Borrowdale Volcanics with comparatively little thermal metamorphism, is a grey fine-grained rock extensively quarried for paving stones and roadmetal.

Numerous dykes – narrow sheets originating as molten rock – were intruded into the older rocks during this great episode of upheaval and contortion. Where the intruded rock was harder than the country rock they appear as resistant walls, but sometimes the heat-hardened country rock has proved more resistant to weathering than the intruded material of the dyke, so that the course of the latter is now marked by a gully. One of the largest and most familiar of these is Mickledore, the precipitous hollow between Scafell and its Pike. Many of the dykes consist of more basic rock than that into which they were intruded, and small gullies representing the weathering of these basic dykes provide specialised habitats where some of the most interesting plants can be found. (Plate 6a, p. 65.)

At some stage in the Caledonian mountain-building episode, the earth movements which folded and buckled the Skiddaw Slates, Borrowdale Volcanics, Coniston Limestone and the Silurian sediments, must have raised the upthrust rocks above the surface of the sea. Then through fifty million years of the subsequent Devonian and early Carboniferous times, these emergent mountains would be exposed to all the forces of subaerial denudation, just as the crests of the Alps and Himalayas, formed by Tertiary mountain-building movements, are being reduced today. The result of this would be to strip off the cover of Silurian sediments from the crest of the anticline through Skiddaw, and then to remove much of the great volcanic pile, exposing the oldest rocks (the Skiddaw Slates) along the crown of the anticline. Vast masses of eroded material must have been deposited in distant seas. In the Lake District the Devonian was a period of uplift and enormous erosion, and general deposition did not begin again until the early Carboniferous sea began to invade the country from the south.

THE CARBONIFEROUS LIMESTONE

The great worn-down Caledonian anticline of the Lake District then gradually sank beneath the shallow Carboniferous sea, full of corals and stone-lilies (crinoids). The conglomerates below the Carboniferous, which appear most strikingly as the two Mell Fells, poking up as the marginal mountains of the Lake District north-west of Ullswater, were formed as stony accumulations in the shallowest parts of this encroaching sea. The main Carboniferous Limestone was formed in this sea which encroached from the south and eventually submerged all of the worn-down Caledonian mountains. 'The sea was never deep; the limestones were often exposed at the surface, like those of the Barrier Reef to-day, and mud and silt from a not distant land were washed down and enclosed between the sheets of pure limestone.' (B. Smith, in Collingwood, 1932.) As the shallow sea, in which corals and crinoids and calcareous algae built up the lovely Mountain Limestone, became even more shallow, silts and massive grits were laid down, and marginal swamps became the sites of Coal Measure forests, where masses of vegetation accumulated in layers between river-borne clays, silts and sands.

At the end of Carboniferous times, the old Caledonian anticline must have been buried under a total of something approaching 3000 feet of Carboniferous sediments. Another uplift phase then began.

THE SECOND EPISODE OF MOUNTAIN-BUILDING

The Hercynian mountain-building movements, which became widespread towards the end of the Carboniferous period, raised the old rocks of the Lake District, beneath their covering of Carboniferous sediments, into a roughly dome-shaped uplift. The old rocks had, however, been fractured along many lines of weakness by the Caledonian movements, and the Hercynian upheaval renewed movement along these old fracture lines, so that the dome must have been much broken by faults and fractures. Many of the mineral riches of the district, including the copper of Coniston and the lead of Glenridding, originated at this time by introduction of material from below into these fault-fractures.

The Carboniferous sediments were then removed by erosion from the centre of the dome, after the mountain-building movements of this uplift had raised the Lake District once more above the sea. The layer of Carboniferous Limestone was left above the ancient rocks only round the margins, its bedded strata dipping outwards in all directions from the emerging core of ancient rocks. From study of the younger rocks round the margins, it can be deduced that the rising dome suffered this erosion under warm and arid conditions.

THE POST-CARBONIFEROUS HISTORY OF THE LAKE DISTRICT ROCKS

Under these desert conditions were formed the rocks known as Brockrams, coarse Permo-Triassic breccias now found in the Vale of Eden and West Cumberland. These consist of large angular fragments of the Carboniferous Limestone and the older rocks of the Lake District, which must have accumulated as cones of debris from shattered desert mountains, probably shot down gullies on to the margin of the upland, and there consolidated into breccias. The Brockrams pass laterally in places into Magnesian Limestone, formed in shallow and evaporating inland seas, and in other places into Triassic sandstones such as that of St Bees, formed by wind-blown sand and desert rivers.

In the west, red sandstones of this group still cover the Carboniferous sediments and overlap on to the ancient Skiddaw Slates and Borrowdale

Volcanics. It is thought probable that at one time the Trias covered over the Hercynian dome, and that in a period of submergence at the end of the Trias, Keuper Marl may have been laid down over the whole, but this is not certain.

There has been a great deal of discussion and disagreement about the origin of the mineral deposits of the district. Whereas the ores of copper and lead are generally agreed to be Hercynian, the origin of the haematite, which occurs both in the older rocks and in the Carboniferous Limestone is more controversial. Most of the deposits in the limestone are thought to be the result of metasomatic replacement in solution caverns in the limestone, as a result of the percolation of iron-bearing waters from the overlying Trias. Such is supposed to have been the origin of the great Hodbarrow deposit near Millom, and the worked-out deposits of Park mines and other places in Low Furness. However, there is more disagreement about the origin of the numerous haematite veins in the older rocks, particularly in the Borrowdale Volcanics and the Eskdale Granite – veins which have given rise to old iron workings such as Red Gill and Brant Rake in Eskdale and at Red Tarn above Wrynose. These haematite veins are probably of different origin and more ancient date. Ore Gap, between Allen Crags and Bowfell, and the Red Tarn hollow, between Cold Pike and Pike o'Blisco, follow haematised fracture lines in the ancient rocks.

There is no direct evidence as to the state of the Lake District during the deposition of Mesozoic rocks – marine strata of Jurassic and Cretaceous age – over Midland and Southern England. Marr thought that these rocks too could once have covered the Lake District, and other authors admit the possibility.

At some time during the late Mesozoic or in the Tertiary period, perhaps sixty million years ago or rather more, further dome-like uplift, this time with the centre somewhere near Scafell, must have taken place. The existing river pattern indicates superimposition of the generally radial drainage from a cover of more recent sediments, now removed. Hollingworth believed that first there was uplift of the present surface into a dome, and then a series of intermittent uplifts, without tilting, raised the domed surface to its present elevation. During these uplifts denudation continued to strip off the newer sediments from the ancient rocks, and the mountain forms were planed down to comparatively smooth relief. Hollingworth has pointed out that several old dissected platforms or shelves, cutting through rocks of all ages, and appearing at the same altitudes around the Lake District, can be recognised. These are interpreted as terraces formed during periods of stationary sea-level, as yet undated, and the fact that they have not been subsequently tilted is evidence as to the nature of the uplift which followed.

Broadly then we can suppose that during the Tertiary period, from perhaps sixty million years ago, while the great Miocene earth movements were raising the Alps, Himalayas, Andes and Rockies, the ancient rocks of the Lake District, having once more appeared at the surface, were being slowly and intermittently raised to something approaching their present altitude. The forerunners of Derwent and Greta, Cocker, Liza and Calder, Esk and Duddon, Brathay, Rothay and Kent, and a host of lesser becks, had impressed on to the dome a pattern of radiating valleys and were in process of carving them deeper and deeper into the rock. This radiating valley system bears in general little relation to the structure and disposition of the old rocks which were being progressively exposed; it is the classic example of a superimposed drainage pattern. But here and there it follows lines pre-determined by the nature and history of the ancient rocks. The subsequently glaciated trough of Great Langdale follows the line of tension at the crown of a Caledonian anticline; the great gash of Piers Gill on Lingmell follows a fault line, and along lines of ready erosion, determined by shatter-belts and softer strata, many streams have cut back and captured the head-waters of others.

At the end of the Tertiary period, perhaps a million, perhaps two million years ago, Scafell, Helvellyn and Skiddaw must have stood at something like their present height, and we can visualise the Late-Tertiary Lake District landscape from the rounded western profiles of Helvellyn and the High Street ridge, with V-shaped valleys like Mosedale above Swindale, and some of the becks of West Cumberland. But the final sculpture of the mountains and valleys was the result of world-wide climatic changes at the end of the Tertiary period; a cooling down so drastic that repeatedly during the last million years have the polar ice-caps expanded into latitudes as low as the plain of North Germany, and the mountain glaciers on the great Miocene mountain ranges have descended far into the lowlands. Even on the comparatively lowly British hills, snow and ice accumulated unmelted until the valley glaciers rose up over the intervening ridges and coalesced into great outwardly moving ice-sheets. The Lake District was so thoroughly ground and scraped bare by the latest of these glacial episodes – the Weichselian – which ended about 15,000 years ago, that no traces remain of previous glaciations, but it is important to remember that the sculpturing of the landscape has been the effect of at least three, and possibly five, repeated glacial episodes, separated by mild interglacials. Each glaciation would scour in the footsteps of its predecessor, carving the corries and troughs yet deeper and plucking at the crags.

Finally then, we have today 'the wild catastrophes of the breaking mountains' as seen perhaps from Birker Moor; the fierce and lovely skyline of the mountain heart, from Seatallan by Red Pike and Pillar, the stark fluting of Kirkfell, the helmet of Gable, the wave of Scafell breaking into the crags of Cam Spout, the high and buttressed pyramids of Esk Pike and Bowfell, the craggy back of the Crinkles – hard upstanding masses of solidified volcanic 'ejectamenta', shaped by the hardness of lavas and ashes, by the jointing imposed by long-past convulsions of the earth's crust, carved by the rivers and rived by the frosts of millions of years, and finally sculptured by ice.

THE GEOLOGICAL PERIODS

Period			Approximate age in millions of years since beginning of period	
			Zeuner (1958)	Holmes (1965)
Cenozoic	Quaternary (Pleistocene)		1	2–3
	Tertiary	Pliocene		12
		Miocene	28	25
		Oligocene		40
		Eocene	60	70
Mesozoic		Cretaceous	130	135
		Jurassic	155	180
		Triassic	185	225
Palaeozoic		Permian	210	270
		Carboniferous	265	350
		Devonian	320	400
		Silurian	360	440
		Ordovician	440	500
		Cambrian	520	600
		Pre-Cambrian	Unknown	Unknown

CHAPTER 3

GLACIATION – THE SHAPING OF THE LANDSCAPE

And so never ending, but always descending,
Sounds and motions for ever and ever are blending;
All at once and all o'er, with a mighty uproar,
And this way the water comes down at Lodore.

Robert Southey

WATERFALLS

THERE can have been few waterfalls in the Lake District as it was before the Pleistocene glaciations of the last million years. In the upper valley of Swindale, in the far east, is one of the most vivid pictures of the change in scenery brought about by ice-erosion. Mosedale Beck flows in a gently graded moorland valley, a broad V in cross section, with tributary becks entering the main stream at its own level; the hillslopes are smooth and rock outcrops rare. Suddenly it drops in waterfalls, Swindale Forces, over crags which form the eastern part of a semi-circle stretching across the Swindale valley. The beck Hobgrumble Gill, falling in longer and steeper falls from a high combe in the southern side of Selside Pike, drops in a force over this semi-circle and joins Swindale Beck at the foot of the crags – that is, Swindale Beck is formed by the union of Mosedale Beck and Hobgrumble Gill after both have descended to the lower valley (the one called Swindale) which has the flat floor and craggy sides characteristic of a glaciated valley. Accumulation of ice in this lower valley, from Selside Pike and other parts of the high ridge between it and Mardale, must have formed a glacier of sufficient weight and power to grind out the broad valley of Swindale and lower its floor; this now lies five hundred feet below the floor of Mosedale, but it is possible that ice erosion was not the only reason for the difference – some geomorphologists would consider that even before glaciation there was a break or 'knick-point' in the valley profile at this point, representing the stage then reached in a normal cycle of erosion. In Mosedale, which begins in the lower fells between the head of Longsleddale and Shap Fells, there can never have been such a great accumulation of ice, so its pre-glacial form was scarcely changed. Mosedale, and the combe of Hobgrumble Gill are therefore 'hanging valleys', entering the ice-gouged floor of the main valley by waterfalls.

Such high tributary valleys are very numerous in the Lake District, for nearly all the main valleys are excavated to a greater depth than the floors of their tributary valleys, so the tributaries now 'hang' above the main streams at the mouths of the branch valleys, and the tributary streams cascade into the main dales as waterfalls. All the numerous Sour Milk Gills have the same origin, and so do Taylor Gill Force above Seathwaite in Borrowdale, Measand Force above Haweswater, Stanley Gill and Birker Force in Eskdale, and the dropping threads of white which appear above Coniston village after rain. Some of the hanging valleys are rounded corries like that of Hobgrumble Gill, Stickle Tarn and the Coniston corries; others like Fordingdale, through which flows Measand Beck, and Mosedale above Swindale, are valleys in which the thickness of ice and consequently its erosive power must have been much less than in the main valley. At Southey's Lodore, Watendlath Beck from its long tributary valley hangs high above the floor of Borrowdale, which it therefore enters in waterfalls, but here the difference in height of the valley floors is accentuated by the junction between the harder Borrow-dale Volcanic rocks, which form the floor of the Watendlath valley, and the softer Skiddaw Slates in which the main dale is at this point excavated.

ROCK-TYPES AND GLACIAL FEATURES

The waterfalls are only one of the many elements in the landscape which result from the comparatively recent effects of glaciation. On the western sides of the High Street and Helvellyn ridges there are still to be seen the pre-glacial mountain shapes – smooth convex skylines, not broken by crags, but like Mosedale, showing very little outcrop of rock at all. On these smooth slopes there are few or no erratics (blocks which have been carried and dropped by ice) whereas on the intensely glaciated mountains erratics are abundant. There has been considerable discussion as to the reason for this difference in topography, but it is now generally agreed that the smooth ridges represent a surface which was only very slightly modified during the glaciations, and therefore represents the nearest surviving approach to pre-glacial topography. The slopes are character-istically mantled with a cover of weathered rock debris. The contrast between these and glacially modified topography is seen in the enormous difference between the smooth western slopes of Helvellyn and High Street and the rugged alternation of crag and scree on the eastern sides of both. To climb Helvellyn by Striding Edge, with the final scramble up the eastern cliffs, and then run down the grassy slopes to Wythburn, is to experience this contrast.

The interest and excitement of the Lakeland mountains and valleys is largely due to the intensity of glaciation and the effects of ice action on rocks of varying hardness. Over most of the district the most powerful agent in the history of the landscape has been sculpture of the rocks by the plucking and grinding of ice during the successive glaciations of the last million years. This sculpture has intensified the cragginess which originates from the contrast between hard upstanding bands of rock and intervening softer ones. In the country of the Borrowdale Volcanics this cragginess is everywhere present on a bold scale, and in the lower Silurian country to the south both rock faces and hollows are smaller, but the cragginess is there in miniature. This contrast between rock types adds interest to the views from such well-known beauty spots as Tarn Hows.

The plucking action of the ice, brought about by penetration of water (which then froze) into surface cracks and joints, and the quarrying action of the ice which levered great pieces of rock from exposed surfaces and removed them on the flowing ice of glaciers, resulted in the exposure of fresh surfaces to renewed plucking and cut deeply into slopes and valley sides. This process formed the great crags of Scafell, Great End, Gable, Pillar, Gimmer, Dow, and all the lesser-known precipitous valley sides. The cragsman's rocks are the hard and boldly jointed Volcanics, in which the precipitous plucked faces now stand as almost vertical walls of clean hard stone. But at every valley head the ice has bitten back into the rock to form a greater or lesser steep-sided hollow of an 'armchair' shape – what we know as the Welsh 'cwm', the Scots 'corrie', the French 'cirque' and locally in the Lake District by the Old English 'cove', from *cofa*, a hollow. Wordsworth described the head of the little-known Westmorland Deepdale as follows – 'It is terminated by a cove, a craggy and gloomy abyss with precipitous sides; a faithful receptacle of the snows that are driven into it, by the west wind, from the summit of Fairfield.' Traces of the last glacier which occupied this green cove of Deepdale, under the towering precipices of the back of Fairfield, can be seen very clearly in the high green moraines with the flat floors of former lakes between them. The driven snows of the glacial periods accumulated in these hollows on the mountain sides and formed glaciers, and rock fragments plucked from the eroding walls became frozen into the solid ice, so that the sole of the glacier worked like a giant nutmeg-grater in grinding out an ever-deepening hollow – a true rock basin – in scores of corries. Most of the high tarns lie in such rocky corries, like Red Tarn under Helvellyn and Angle Tarn under Bowfell, and, even more striking places, Small Water and Blea Water beneath the craggy eastern face of High Street. The depth of the basin and hence of the tarn is increased by the deposit of rock waste forming the moraine on the lip of the corrie, but in all four of these tarns the valley profile shows that solid rock crops out in the course of the outflow stream within a vertical distance of the outflow which is much less than the depth of the tarn, so these tarns are true rock basins, though deepened by moraine dams. Marr, in his classic account of the geology of the Lake District, did not know the depth of the tarns, and for a time he doubted whether true rock basins exist. He observed that in many of these tarns the present outflow is clearly not the original one, but repre-

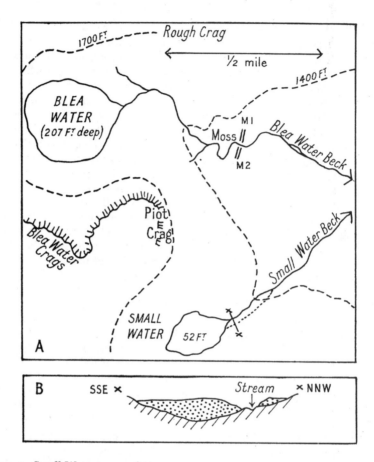

FIG. 3. Small Water – a corrie tarn

A. Plan of Small Water and the neighbouring Blea Water, showing the course of the former stream (broken line) (before the valley below Small Water was blocked with morainic material) and the position of the breached moraine (M1, M2) which once dammed a small lake at *c.* 1400 feet in the valley of Blea Water Beck.

B. Section across Small Water Beck, just below the tarn. Hatching represents solid rock, dotted represents morainic deposit. South of the present stream course is the old valley, now blocked.

(after Marr, J. E. Q.J.G.S. 1895)

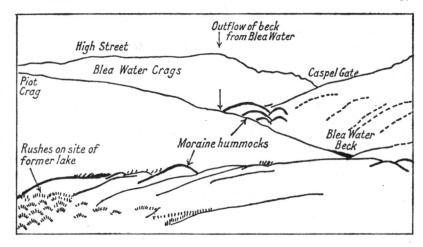

FIG 4. Fresh moraine in the valley of Blea Water Beck
Sketch looking upstream from point M1 in Fig. 3. In the foreground is the mass of hummocky moraine associated with the former lake, the bed of which (now a marsh) is defined by patches of rushes in the left foreground. Higher up the valley is more fresh moraine, between Blea Water and the highest tributary of Blea Water Beck, and traces of lateral moraine on the hillside, shown by dotted lines. At Caspel Gate on the ridge between Blea Water and Riggindale there is what appears to be older drift at nearly 1900 feet.

sents a diversion from the former outflow due to an infilling by morainic material, which has produced a new outflow over the present lowest point of the margin of the basin, here a rocky lip. This can be seen very readily at the outflows of Small Water (Fig. 3, p. 46) and Levers Water above Coniston. Marr expressed the view that the existing corrie tarns probably owe their continued existence to just this set of circumstances, for where the outflow poured over a moraine dam, it must have cut down very rapidly through the loose material and drained the tarn quite soon; an excellent example of this can be seen in the moss below Blea Water, which represents a former tarn only temporarily dammed by moraine (Fig. 4, above), and here the breach in the morainic ridge can be clearly seen. The diversion of the outflow of existing tarns to a rocky lip has in many examples preserved the morainic plug in the former outflow by removing the scouring action of an outflow stream; this has maintained the barrier and hence the existence of the tarn. A very fine example of a former tarn which was drained by downcutting of the outflow is the one below Wolf Crags on the northern edge of Matterdale Common; the old coach road from the Vale of St John to Dockwray runs along the crest of the breached moraine. Marr had no idea of the very great depth of some of the corrie tarns, and had he known that Blea Water is 207 feet deep, a fact which has been established by the efforts of a Brathay Exploration Group party, he could not have doubted the existence of true rock basins. (Plates 8b, p. 81, 11, p. 112, 26, p. 241.)

It is now well known that there were several glaciations during the two million years or so of the Pleistocene, and that these were separated by long interglacials. In each successive glacial epoch, the deposits of previous glaciations would be scoured away. The drift and moraines which remain, therefore, are those of the latest glaciation, but the shaping of the rocks has been the work of several successive glacial episodes. The plucking of the valley heads, through each successive glaciation, ate back into the ridges until between neighbouring corries there were sometimes only knife-edges (arêtes) remaining. In the Alps the pyramidal peaks called 'Horns' are the final remnants of such arêtes. In the comparatively subdued relief of the Lake District there are no Horns and no spectacular arêtes accessible only to the rock climber – not even the excitement of Crib Goch on Snowdon, but only Striding Edge between Red Tarn cove and Nethermost Cove on Helvellyn, and the Straits of Riggindale and Threshthwaite Mouth where opposed glacier heads scooped coves into the sides of the High Street ridge.

In each of the main glacial episodes, long-continued severity of climate must have piled up snow in the corries until the small glaciers spilled over their lips and descended to the main valleys below, joining up into great streams of ice in the major dales, where the thickness of the ice gouged out the deep troughs on the sides of which the minor valleys hang. The sole of the valley ice, grinding on its slow journey to the lowlands, encountered rocks of different hardness, and the effect of its erosion was to emphasise the difference, biting so much more quickly into the softer rocks as to leave hard bands, particularly in the Borrowdale Volcanic rocks, standing as barriers or rock-steps across the valleys. Some of these now give rise to major waterfalls, like Skelwith Force where the Brathay pours over the rock-step across the Langdale valley below Elterwater. Most of the valleys in the Borrowdale rocks show an 'alternation of broad flat and gorge' (Hollingworth, 1949), such as that part of the upper Esk where after the flat of Great Moss the river then plunges through the gorge of Green Crag Gill below, and in the course of Lincove Beck, Green Hole is succeeded by the Throstle Garth gorge below. The gorge section is, of course, that where the stream has cut deeply into the harder rock forming the step. Many upland areas of comparatively soft rock were scoured out to form hollows, now filled by shallow moorland tarns or peat bogs.

At the height of each glacial episode, the thickness of the ice must have become so great that its surface rose above the confining sides of many of

PLATE 3 *Above*, Buttermere and the Grasmoor massif: on the summit of Grasmoor, to the left, there is a particularly extensive development of *Rhacomitrium* heath. *Below*, Loweswater and the Buttermere fells: hay meadows round Loweswater, Mellbreak, and the distant skyline of Honister Crag.

PLATE 4 *Above*, the Newlands Valley: Skiddaw Slate fells and sheep-farming dales, with small remnant woodlands. *Below*, the Derwent Fells: Causey Pike, with a foreground of herb-rich upland grassland.

the valleys and coalesced into a great ice-cap like that of Greenland today, in which the general direction of movement was outwards towards the lowlands, but within which ice flowed across ridges from one valley to another, as can be seen from the direction of the striae, or rock scratches, in many places. Drift deposits on such high ridges as Caspel Gate at nearly 2,000 feet between Mardale and Riggindale (Fig. 4, p. 47), and ice scratches on rock up to 2,500 feet on Scafell, testify to the thickness of the ice. On High Stile above Buttermere there are erratics – boulders dropped by moving ice – at 2,600 feet.

The topography produced by the action of this over-riding ice is very different in the areas of different rock types, with a particularly striking contrast between the Skiddaw Slate country, which lies between the Buttermere–Crummock valley and the Skiddaw massif on the one hand, and the Borrowdale Volcanic country to the south of it. Between Butter-mere and Bassenthwaite there are neither mountain tarns nor corries. Professor Hollingworth has pointed out that these parts of the district were almost certainly very different even before the onset of the Quaternary glaciations. In the Skiddaw Slate country the valleys would be wider and cut back farther into the intervening hills than the narrow steep-sided valleys in the hard Borrowdale rocks. The long slopes produced by degradation of the upland in the less resistant Skiddaw Slates, before glaciation, are seen in the frequent conical shapes of the hills – for example, in Grisedale Pike and Whiteless Pike. The comparative uni-formity of the Skiddaw Slates – the absence of contrast between harder and softer rock types – is the reason for the absence of much of the craggi-ness which the ice produced, in both Borrowdale Volcanic rocks and in the Silurian country, because of the alternation of harder and softer beds. The Skiddaw Slate mountains, with their rather uniform slopes, appear somewhat dull to the young and energetic, but when in middle age the joints begin to creak and Rossett Gill becomes a source of major dis-comfort both in ascent and descent, then the long smooth uncraggy slopes of Skiddaw can be appreciated. The valley heads in Skiddaw Slate country are usually bounded by long slopes rather than by the crags of a cove; the only exceptions are the craggy corries on the back of Saddleback (in particularly hard Skiddaw Slates) which contain Bowscale Tarn and Scales Tarn. Other differences in the effects of glaciation on the various rock types are seen in the absence of steeply hanging tributary valleys, with a consequent scarcity of waterfalls, in Skiddaw Forest and the Loweswater and Buttermere fells. An even more striking illustration of the response of different rocks to the action of ice can be seen in the shape of Great and Little Mell Fells, built of the less resistant conglomerate; these are rounded-conical little hills, smoothed and abraded by the ice, in sharp contrast to the rugged ice-plucked outlines of Gowbarrow Fell and the Helvellyn ridge nearby.

L.D.—D

All over the district there are abundant examples of other features of a glaciated landscape. Smoothly rounded masses of solid rock, like vast recumbent sheep – 'roches moutonnées' – often with a steepened profile facing the direction from which the ice came, and huge 'perched' blocks of rock left behind by the ice-stream which carried them, like the Bowder Stone in Borrowdale and the Pudding Stone below Low Water on Coniston Old Man, are very common. In the central Lake District, within all three major rock types, the typical valley form is a straightened trough from which projecting spurs have been removed, or truncated, by the erosion of moving ice. The view of Saddleback across the skirts of Matterdale Common from the old coach road is a classic illustration of such truncated spurs. The absence of interlocking spurs in a severely glaciated valley can be readily appreciated from the shape of most of the lakes in the main valleys.

MORAINES

The Lake District landscape is one where the erosive effects of an intense glaciation predominate. The vast masses of rock debris which were carved, quarried and scraped off the mountains by the outwardly moving ice were mainly deposited on low country far outside the hills. Shap Granite boulders were dumped on the Cheshire plain, boulder-clay of Lake District origin covers much of Lancashire, and the plain of lowland Cumberland to the west, north and east of the mountains is thickly plastered with mounds and ridges of clay, sand and gravel sorted out of the debris of the ice-cap by running water, as well as by thick deposits of unsorted boulder clay which were dumped by the ice. Within the Lake District proper, in addition to the erratics already mentioned, there are thin deposits or sheets of stony or bouldery clay, generally termed 'drift', which as we have seen can be found in places up to about 2,000 feet, and also mounds and ridges made up of drift of various kinds. Conspicuous among these are the relatively enormous 'drumlins', mostly found outside the central Lake District, in the Lune valley and on the plain of lowland Cumberland, but seen within the Lake District proper in the Esthwaite valley. Here a branch stream of ice must have left the main Windermere valley near where Blelham Tarn lies today, and flowed through a side valley into the Esthwaite valley above Hawkshead, leaving the great smooth whalebacks nearly a hundred feet high which were deposited beneath the ice. These form characteristic projecting promontories called 'Ees' in Esthwaite Water. Others were formed in the main Windermere valley. The smaller ridges and mounds of glacial debris, usually called moraines, must have been greatly modified by weathering and stream erosion since the end of the glaciation, and the interpretation of the shape of these moraines has given rise to a good deal of controversy.

The mental picture of a glacier which most people have is derived from the great valley glaciers of the Alps; we all know pictures of the Great Aletsch Glacier, even if we have never seen it, with its stripes of lateral and medial moraines, and the idea of the terminal moraine of Alpine glaciers is familiar. These, it must be remembered, are glacial features produced by a long period of climatic equilibrium, with great permanent snowfields on the mountains, of more or less constant size and in balance with the moving streams of ice (the valley glaciers) nourished by them. On the balance of evidence, it does not seem likely that there was a long stage of this character during the final glaciation of the Lake District. It seems more likely that the main glaciation, during which conditions resembled more the present Greenland ice-cap, was followed by a rather rapid warming-up of the climate, so that the stage during which valley glaciers like those of Switzerland today flowed down Borrowdale, Langdale, Troutbeck, etc., would be comparatively short. The snow line would rise so rapidly that, on these comparatively lowly mountains, the snowfields would soon shrink to small remnants, incapable of nourishing strong streams of ice flowing down to the mouths of the main valleys.

A fascinating picture of the very early stages in the waning of the Lake District ice-cap was worked out in West Cumberland by field officers of the Geological Survey, including Professor Hollingworth; see Geol. Surv. Whitehaven Memoir 1931. At the height of the last main glaciation, the outflowing Lakeland ice met ice flowing south in enormous quantities from the higher and more extensive mountains of Scotland. This Scottish ice filled the present basin of the Irish Sea and overflowed on to the plain of north and west Cumberland, deflecting the outward flow of Lake District ice. As soon as the climate improved a little, so that the flow of ice became less vigorous, splits between the Lake District ice and the Irish Sea ice began to appear, and the gaps were immediately filled with melt-water forming 'glacier-lakes' – very temporary features. These glacier lakes eventually drained, either by the removal of an ice dam by further retreat or, as the retreat proceeded, by catastrophically vigorous erosion by water to produce a spill-way through a rock-cut channel. Some gorges which were cut during the successive stages of the marginal glacier-lakes of West Cumberland can still be seen; especially striking is the great Nannycatch gorge east of Flat Fell. Other evidence of a stage when the great Glacier-lake Ennerdale, impounded between the mass of ice in the Irish Sea basin and the waning ice from the fells round the head of Ennerdale, stood at a level about 800 feet above present sea level, can be seen on the fell-side north of the foot of the lake, above the farms Roughton and Beckfoot. Where the ancestor of the present beck coming down from Herdus entered Glacier-lake Ennerdale, it deposited a delta – a mound of alluvial debris whose underwater outlines, somewhat modified by subsequent subaerial erosion, can be seen. As the surface of the glacier-lake fell, successive levels can be traced by terraces cut in the highest delta, and by the subsequent deposition of deltas at lower levels; each successive level can be correlated with a gap in the fells at an equivalent height, through which drainage reduced the water surface to the next lowest stage. 'Marginal drainage channels' on a smaller scale than those of Glacier-lake Ennerdale can be seen at very many places round the central mountains; they are steep-sided rock-cut channels, now either dry or occupied by only a small stream, which were cut by water which had been temporarily held up by an ice barrier or by a great plug of ice occupying a main valley or by streams beneath the ice.

We have seen how the excavation of rock basins by the action of the nutmeg-grater in the sole of the glaciers went on, and each successive glaciation of the one or two million years of the Quaternary period would tend to deepen each rock basin. Nearly all existing lakes are the result of a combination of rock basin and a block or dam formed by moraine; the moraine must, of course, date only from the waning of the latest of these glaciations. Windermere, for instance, consists of two rock basins, a North Basin and a South Basin, each excavated to a depth well below present sea level, but the existing level of the lake is held up by a mass of glacial drift, including a ridge which may be a terminal moraine of one stage in the glacial retreat, which blocks the valley at its lower end. All the large valley lakes have been formed by this same process – a combination of a rock basin gouged out of the valley's rock floor with a plug of glacial drift deposited beyond this rock basin. Windermere's relatively complex morphology, with the island-studded ridge sticking up from its rock floor and separating the northern rock basin from the southern one, is thought to have arisen from the effects of local topography – the narrowing of the valley south of the rock ridge and the entry of a subsidiary ice stream from the Esthwaite valley would renew the force of glacial erosion and bring about the excavation of a second rock basin. The stage of initial formation of lakes, in basins just becoming free of ice, must have been a time of rapid change in land forms, as the recently disturbed surface of the earth began once more to become stabilised. Round parts of the margin of Windermere, particularly just north of the Ferry, a flat terrace indicative of a formerly higher lake level can be seen, believed to date from the time when a mass of dead ice occupied the centre of what is now the lake.

On the rock floor of all the large valley lakes, we know from a combination of echo-sounding and cores taken from the lake sediments that a great thickness of laminated glacial clay – perhaps fifty feet in Windermere – was then deposited. This laminated clay, which is formed by seasonal melt from snowbeds or glacier ice, is also present in many of the moorland tarns, like Burnmoor, Seathwaite Tarn at 1,200 feet, and Blea Tarn which lies at over 1,500 feet on Armboth Fell above Watendlath. It must represent deposits in the lakes from rivers and becks fed by the remnant snowfields of the Lake District, at a time when few, if any, plants had as yet colonised the polar desert left on the disappearance of the ice-cap. At this time there were probably many lakes which soon disappeared; flat valley floors on which shallow lakes were impounded by morainic dams which were soon worn away. The great spread of re-deposited drift which floors Great Langdale between Dungeon Ghyll and Chapel Stile was probably the deposit of a shallow lake about this time. Many of the present boggy flats in the mountain valleys were certainly open water until long after the final disappearance of all ice. The twin lakes Derwentwater and Bassenthwaite, Buttermere and Crummock, were possibly separated as early as this by the very rapid deposition, in the original single lakes, of vast quantities of the rock debris which were so readily eroded from a land surface as yet unstabilised by plant cover.

A landscape feature which has given rise to much discussion is the fresh moraine of the inner valleys and watersheds. This includes the irregular hummocky mounds in Mickleden at the foot of Rossett Gill, the great green tent-like mounds in Deepdale and round Hayeswater, the tumble of ridges and mounds in the Easedale Tarn valley, and the hillocks and saucers on Dunmail Raise, and also the spectacular crescentic ridges which dam the corrie tarns, from the towering hundred-foot wall which stands above Blea Water to the modest bank which used to dam Keppelcove Tarn until it was breached by a great flood in 1927. All these heaps of glacial debris are so fresh in their shape that they give the impression of a much more recent origin. In 1959 Professor Manley published an estimate of the fall in temperature which would be sufficient to produce permanent snowfields in the Lake District mountains, of a size which would account for the fresh moraine at various altitudes, for which he produced a map. He visualised a period of between fifty and a hundred years during which most of the worst features of our present climate might have been accentuated – long snowy winters and summers which became too cool to melt all the snow; this would lead to accumulation of snow in the corries, whither, as Wordsworth had observed for Deepdale, it would be driven by the wind from the summits. Small corrie glaciers would develop, and would tend to produce a terminal moraine on the lip of the corrie. Where, however, local accumulation was very great, the mass of ice would spill over the lip of the corrie on to the floor of the main valley, and form a small glacier tongue. When climatic conditions improved again, and the ice began to waste away rather than to accumulate each year, these tongues on the low floors of the main valleys would lose contact with their source of ice in the corrie above, and waste away where they lay by the process of ablation. The moraine mounds and hollows between them are the result of this wasting; the hillocks are of debris from within the ice, and the hollows represent the sites of those blocks of dead ice which survived longest – another term for this material is 'kettle-moraine'. The corrie glaciers within the corries would last longer; both crescentic ridges which now dam corrie tarns, and spreads of hummocky moraine within corries, represent the last traces of these final glaciers of the Lake District.

In all the time since the end of the last main glaciation, the most likely date for this corrie glaciation seems to be a period of five hundred years during the ninth millennium B.C., when it is well known that an earlier period of milder climate, the Alleröd Interstadial, was followed by five centuries of colder weather during which the vegetation of northern Europe returned to more-or-less tundra conditions, and during which the retreating Scandinavian ice-sheet was halted at the line of the great frontal moraines which cross central Sweden and Finland. Support for this dating of the final glacial phase in the Lake District comes from the sediments of the lakes and tarns.

THE LATE-GLACIAL PERIOD

The period of polar desert with extensive remnant snowfields seems to have ended by about 12,350 B.C. By that date organic mud was forming in a small pond near Blelham Tarn, beneath the present Blelham Bog, and into that mud was shed the pollen of a wide variety of herbaceous plants, together with that of juniper, willows, and the dwarf Arctic birch *Betula nana*. Some pollen of tree birches in small quantity suggests that these trees were growing within perhaps fifty miles, perhaps a greater distance. This type of vegetation, broadly similar to the present high-altitude vegetation of the Jotunheim mountains of Norway, for example, continued in the Lake District for about two thousand years, during which we can suppose a gradual disappearance of all ice and snow from the mountains. A warming up of the climate during the eleventh millennium B.C. – that is, at some time before 10,000 B.C. – led to the spread of juniper scrub over the Lake District valleys and lower hills, and this was followed by the development of birchwoods in at least the southern valleys during the mild Alleröd Interstadial in the tenth millennium B.C. This change in vegetation, and gradual development of a stable soil-covered land surface, can be followed from a study of the succession of sediments in the lakes and tarns. But soon after 9000 B.C., trees and shrubs began to disappear and a more tundra-like vegetation appeared again, and plants such as the least willow (*Salix herbacea*), now confined to the mountain tops, were growing round the lowland lakes, together with some Arctic-alpine plants now no longer found in the district, including *Koenigia islandica*, one of the rarest of Scottish plants. On top of the Alleröd sediments a series of laminated clays was laid down in all the lakes whose drainage basins include high corries and sites of fresh moraine; from this one supposes that permanent snowfields or small corrie glaciers developed in these sites, so that the larger lakes receiving drainage from them became turbid with glacier water.

The most characteristic feature of the vegetation of this final cold period was the abundance of plants typical of open soils and disturbed habitats, and from this it seems likely that frost disturbance of the soils must have been very general. It is from this period of intense disruption of soils and break-up of the vegetation cover that many of the screes and large alluvial delta-fans of the lakes may well date. On the evidence of radiocarbon dating this period lasted from about 8800 B.C. until 8300 B.C. After this a forest cover spread rapidly over the country as the climate improved at the opening of the post-glacial period, and a stable land surface protected by a continuous plant cover developed, up to an altitude of about 2,500 feet.

SOLIFLUCTION

The movement of soils, or 'soil creep', which occurs when alternate freezing and thawing of the water in soil spaces brings about sorting of material of different particle size, comes under the general heading of processes of solifluction. The sorting results in the various forms of 'patterned ground' – polygons on flatter areas, and stone stripes or garlands on slopes – and under certain conditions leads to a general downslope movement which often produces terraces and lobes. These effects, which are now noticeable in many parts of the Lake District above about 2,000 feet, are of course very widespread in Arctic lands and in high mountains in temperate latitudes. During the deglaciation of the Lake District these processes must have been active in shaping the land surface down to quite low altitudes. In the final cold phase which produced the last corrie glaciers, clayey sediment accumulated in all the lakes, and this is thought to have been due to very widespread solifluction movements at all altitudes.

Examples of surface patterns on stony debris can be found on many mountain groups above 2,000 feet throughout the district. Hollingworth studied in particular the Skiddaw–Carrock Fell area, where the bedrock is Skiddaw Slates, a rock which as we have seen weathers into fine particles; such a soil is considered to be particularly susceptible to frost-heaving. Polygons consisting of networks or rings of stones, enclosing areas of small stones or mud, can be found on the higher parts of Skiddaw and Saddleback, ranging in size from two to four feet in diameter. The relation of active movement of these stones to the presence or absence of a vegetation cover has been studied by Hollingworth, who concluded that active movement is going on under present conditions at these high altitudes, for he found that the upland peats and peaty soils, which are of relatively recent formation, are involved in the sorting process. Some of the Skiddaw polygons, however, including some on Broad End at 2,700 feet, are now colonised by a stabilising vegetation dominated by the woolly hair moss (*Rhacomitrium lanuginosum*) and must be regarded as 'fossil' polygons, no longer in movement.

Stone stripes 'consist of alternating bands of fine and coarse material – mud and stones, or bands of stones of different sizes. They are a characteristic form of sorting on slopes and invariably follow the line of greatest slope' (Hollingworth, 1934). Beneath the surface layer of stones is a more-or-less peaty, stoneless soil, 6 to 9 inches thick, and this pattern is often active, preventing vegetation from colonising the stripes. The first colonist is often the grass *Festuca vivipara*, but no plant succession is initiated. Large lobate areas, bounded on the downward side by a steep bank, are often found in this state.

Solifluction terraces, some with patterns of turf and bare debris, and others completely grassed over, are also common on the higher slopes of Skiddaw and Saddleback. 'Active grazing of the banks by sheep doubtless accentuates the terrace form on steep slopes and assists in the movement of material downhill in all bare areas.' (Hollingworth, 1934.) These processes, though especially conspicuous in the Skiddaw fells, can be seen at work on most of the high fells above about 2,700 feet. In the movement of soils down slopes, extrusion of stones, and patterning of the ground, can be seen the kind of soil disturbance which must have been active down to the lowest levels during the colder parts of the late-glacial period.

GLACIATED VALLEYS

The head of Great Langdale, so familiar to all visitors to the Lake District, shows traces of nearly all the ways in which glaciation has affected the landscape. Stickle Tarn lies in a hanging corrie beneath the ice-plucked crags of Pavey Ark and from it Mill Gill comes down as a white streak of waterfall, while Dungeon Ghyll drops in falls to the floor of the main dale from its wider hanging valley between the two Langdale Pikes. The flat floor of the main dale and its steep rocky sides form a most typical U-shaped profile; those who walk up the Mickleden continue along this flat floor until they reach the striking hummocky moraine which was dumped there when the last little glacier tongue from the high corrie of Langdale Combe came to an end. Climbing steeply up the track to Stake Pass, once the ice-fall of that little glacier, they reach the site of the former lake among the steep moraine hummocks of Langdale Combe, where that little glacier was born and finally died. Hardier walkers, who climb out of Mickleden by the steep scramble of Rossett Gill, eventually top a ridge and find themselves looking at Angle Tarn in its corrie under Hanging Knotts, and soon by looking to the right can see the long spread of hummocky moraine which the last glacier from the Angle Tarn corrie left, marking its track down into Langstrath. Even the motorist can appreciate some of the features of this splendid landscape, for the road from Dungeon Ghyll by Wall End zig-zags up the steep southern side of Great Langdale and over a low col at 722 feet to the lovely Blea Tarn in its upland valley (Plate 13, p. 48). Between the col and the tarn are very low hummocks of moraine, quite different from those upstanding high mounds in Mickleden and Langdale Combe. These are much older moraines, dating from a time when, towards the end of the main glaciation, ice which had been flowing over that col from the great bowl at the head of Great Langdale shrank until the main stream no longer overtopped the col, and the ice in the Blea Tarn valley was left as an isolated lump which melted where it lay. The later revival of corrie glaciers did not affect the Blea Tarn basin, and sediments which tell the whole story of the final retreat of the ice from the Lake District can be found in this tarn. Continuing on down Little Langdale, it can be appreciated from the road how this valley hangs with respect to Great Langdale, and near the road is Colwith Force where the Brathay drops from one valley level to the other (Plates 9, p. 96, 12, p. 113, 16, p. 157.)

Borrowdale is another valley where the traces of glaciation are very plain to see, and the U-shaped section of the upper dale between Thornythwaite and Seathwaite is very clear. From the intakes of Seathwaite in Borrowdale two splendid hanging-valley waterfalls can be admired, full and white on any of the 236 days in the average year on which measurable rain falls on this notoriously wet hamlet. Taylor Gill comes down in a beautiful force from Sty Head Tarn, and one of the whitest of Sour Milk Gills comes curdling down from the hanging valley of Gillercombe; this one shows particularly well a characteristic of many of these hanging valleys, where, to quote Marr, 'there is practically no defined bed to the cascading tributary.' There is a rather surprising absence of the most recent moraine from most of this part of Borrowdale; only from Grains Gill, the eastern arm which comes down from the rocky precipices of Great End, can any ice of the most recent glacial episode have come near to Seathwaite. The hummocky moraines can be seen from Stockley Bridge, the graceful 'pack-horse' bridge which arches over Grains Gill, repaired since its partial destruction by the flood of August, 1966. There was no corrie glacier in the Sty Head hollow, for in the sediments of Sty Head Tarn can be found a continuous record of the late-glacial vegetation of the Lake District, which at this altitude (1,400 feet) was a sparse alpine heath of grasses, sedges and mosses all through those four thousand years. But in the other arm of Borrowdale, in Langstrath and Greenup Gill, there is a great spread of the hummocky moraine of the most recent glaciation. Near Rosthwaite there are moraine ridges on the floor of the main dale which appear to represent the frontal moraine of some stage of the main retreat; this is the only place in the Lake District where this type of moraine is found (unlike the Scottish Highlands) and there has been much inconclusive discussion as to the reasons for this.

CHAPTER 4

THE LAKES AND TARNS

I heard the water lapping on the crag,
And the long ripple washing in the reeds.
Alfred Lord Tennyson

THE Lakeland landscape is different from that of any other mountain district of Britain, and one of the main features of this difference is the particular character of all its innumerable and varied sheets of water. These exist, as we have seen in the previous chapter, because of the way in which glaciers of local origin carved the rocky valleys into basins and plastered sheets and plugs of drift in a way which interfered with the former drainage pattern. The diversity of all these lakes, large and small, which is one of the great charms of the district, partly reflects the basic geological division – the great contrast between Wastwater with its high plunging screes and stark skylines of rugged volcanic rock, Bassenthwaite with its tidy woods and fields below the smooth slopes of Skiddaw Slate, and Esthwaite among its gentle green hills of younger slates and grits and its grassy drumlins. Partly, also, the diversity of the lakes is brought about by differentiation of the vegetation pattern, making the contrast between the decorative wooded shores of Coniston Water and Derwentwater, and the mountain grasslands and bare fells of Ennerdale Water and Crummock. Windermere and Ullswater owe their particular charms to such a combination of varied characters that each changing viewpoint offers a different prospect. Even Thirlmere, winding blue among its alien conifers, and often showing the harsh unnatural shorelines exposed by Manchester's thirst, has its attractions, especially when level evening sunlight is falling on Armboth Fell and the slopes of Helvellyn. (Plates 7, p. 80, 15, p. 156, and 16, p. 157.)

There have been many different definitions of what is a lake and what is a tarn; the biological distinction, which has emerged from the work of the Freshwater Biological Association on the plants and animals, particularly from the work of Dr T. T. Macan, is that in a lake, the characteristic emergent plant, where emergent plants are present, is the common reed, *Phragmites australis*, whereas in tarns the common emergent plant is the bottle sedge, *Carex rostrata*. This difference in the emergent vegetation is accompanied by other characteristic differences in the fauna and flora of lakes and tarns respectively. In size, the tarns vary from those like Devoke Water and Burnmoor Tarn, which are not so very different from Loweswater and Brotherswater (undoubted lakes), to minute fragments of water like Boo Tarn beside the Walna Scar track from Coniston, Fox Tarn high on Scafell, and Hard Tarn perched high above Ruthwaite Cove on Helvellyn, which are only distinguished from pools by their permanent outflows.

In the central Lake District, the mountain area within a 15-mile radius of Esk Hause, the lakes and tarns are characteristically rocky, stony-shored and rather straight-sided, comparatively lacking in creeks and bays and without much emergent vegetation, except in rather special areas such as the shallow reedy fringes of Rydal Water, the head of Derwentwater, Pull Wyke bay in Windermere, and the shallow bays among the Esthwaite drumlins. In the outer parts of the district there are tarns more akin to reedy lowland pools, such as Mockerkin Tarn near Loweswater, Helton Tarn near Witherslack, and Skelsmergh Tarn near Kendal, and some tarns in the central valleys have shallow silted shores and an abundance of emergent vegetation. The plant succession, called a hydrosere, takes place where the shores are shallow and sheltered and where aquatic vegetation builds up on the peaty undecayed remains of its predecessors, so that the water becomes progressively shallower. The vegetation changes from plants characteristic of greater depths of water to those of shallower water, so that at any one point there is an upward succession of plant remains from deep-water species to those of shallower and shallower water, until the point is reached where the mud surface has risen above the lake level as a wet fen. This succession is very clearly seen at the north end of Esthwaite Water, where the aquatic communities pass by hydroseral stages through reed swamp to carr woodland on North Fen (page 90). There is proof, set out there, that North Fen is advancing at an appreciable rate into Esthwaite Water, and indeed a boring in any part of North Fen except the landward edge soon penetrates through the fen peat into lake mud, which accumulated before the fen built out over the mud.

This process of gradual reduction in the area of open water in a lake by the hydroseral succession can, of course, lead to complete replacement of the lake by a fen. In time, in the wet climate of the Lake District, a fen of this type may pass from reed-swamp to wet fen carr woodland of willow and alder, and then to a stage in which species of *Sphagnum* (bog-moss) build up the surface to a level at which there is little contact between the surface and ground water. By this time the peat has become extremely acid and only certain species of *Sphagnum*, with a few associated plants, will grow, since for most of its mineral nutriment the vegetation depends entirely upon rain. The fen has become a bog, with complete change in the plants making up the vegetation.

It is certain that many former lakes of the Lake District have been filled in and transformed into bog by a sequence of events on this general pattern. A good example is to be found in the far north-east, at Bowscale

Moss, north of Mungrisdale and under the steep slope of Carrock Fell. In this flat-floored valley there was a shallow lake in late-glacial times. Now a great spread of cotton-sedge, sedges, including *Carex rostrata*, *Sphagnum* species and the beautiful bogbean (*Menyanthes trifoliata*) crosses the floor of the valley from Bowscale to Mossdike. In section through the deposits of Bowscale Moss, organic lake mud passes upwards into reed-swamp peat; then comes wood peat with remains of alders and willows, and this passes upwards into bog peat made up of *Sphagnum*, cotton-sedge and *Carex* species, with *Menyanthes*, similar to the peat being formed today. This is a bog still periodically below ground-water-level, but the water is poor in bases and other dissolved salts. Rusland Moss, in the south, is a raised bog formed as the next stage in such a succession. These must have been shallow lakes, round which the vegetation belts of respectively aquatics, reed-swamp plants and then the fen woodland would slowly advance over the open water until the lake was obliterated. A broadly similar hydrosere can be traced in the deposits filling kettle-holes, both within the central Lake District and on the West Cumberland coastal plain. A kettlehole is a steep-sided hollow within glacial drift, formed by the delayed melting of a block of dead ice incorporated in the drift. In late-glacial and early post-glacial times these hollows contained small lakes; some of these remain as lakes, such as Mockerkin Tarn near Loweswater, but some have been filled in and are now areas of fen carr or *Sphagnum* bog. Blelham Bog, a National Nature Reserve near the north end of Windermere, overlies two filled-in kettleholes (see page 194).

This process by which a lake may be filled in by a hydroseral succession is only operative in small or shallow basins, and of course the infill is of lacustrine peat and not of mineral soil. In the larger tarns and lakes, this hydroseral succession to peaty infill is found only in particularly sheltered bays, such as Fold Yeat Bay, Esthwaite (Fig. 6, p. 69), or in positions such as the North Fen of Esthwaite where a rapid stream carrying a big load of silt is entering the lake and depositing the silt as an underwater delta. The silting is here contributing to the advancement into the lake of the vegetation belts. Each major inflow is building an extensive underwater delta where it drops its burden of alluvial silt on entering a lake. It is commonly stated that lakes are essentially temporary features of a land-scape, because of this combination of alluvial infill with the hydroseral succession which can be observed in some places. The twin lakes of Buttermere–Crummock and Derwentwater–Bassenthwaite have already been mentioned as examples of partial infill of an originally single basin, and in the shoreline of the old Haweswater, before Manchester raised its level by 90 feet, there was a great projection formed by the delta of Measand Beck, which was sometimes cited as an example of an inter-mediate stage in the formation of twin lakes. Many of the valley lakes, particularly Wastwater and Ennerdale, have at their heads extensive flats of coarse alluvium which seem to indicate a formerly much more extensive lake; the most striking example of this is probably Brothers-water, where the straight southern shore of the lake represents the frontal edge of a great mass of coarse alluvium which fills the lower portion of Dovedale and indicates that the lake was once much larger.

There are, however, some difficulties in accepting the view that any appreciable extension of the above-water portions of the deltas into open water is going on, except in places where the delta front is unusually protected from wave action, as at the northern end of Esthwaite. On any part of a lake shore where exposure to wind is normal, without any particular protection from headlands or spits (which are rare in these straight-sided glacial basins) the effect of wave action is to remove accumulating sediment and carry it out into deeper water, where it is deposited as part of a wave-cut terrace. The characteristic feature of such a shore-line includes a steep drop from the flattish terrace into deeper water, and this is the reason why some lake shores are described as dangerous for bathing. On a shore of this character, sufficiently scoured by wave action to prevent the accumulation of fine sediment in the shallow marginal water, no hydroseral succession is initiated. Round the greater part of the shores of the large lakes of the district, wave action normally produces a stony shore where no plants will grow, which forms a discontinuity between the vegetation of land and water. The rocky shore of Windermere below Wray Castle, in Low Wray Bay (Fig. 5, p. 63) has a growth of submerged aquatic plants at appropriate depths, but it has no emergent vegetation and is never likely to be the site of a hydrosere. About twenty yards out from the shore, where the water is about 10 feet deep, a core of the lake sediment shows that the bottom mud, just below the semi-liquid ooze of the actual mud surface, dates from the early part of the post-glacial period, about 6000 B.C. One supposes that the lake sediment built up in this position, which is neither particularly sheltered nor particularly exposed, until it came within the zone of wave erosion, and that thereafter the force of the waves was sufficient to prevent any further permanent accumulation of sediment. This explains why the underwater deltas of the inflows advance without necessarily reducing at all the area of open water, for only when the alluvial burden is of coarse and heavy particles will it build up above water-level in the zone of wave erosion. All this suggests that the existing lakes may retain something approaching their present *area* for much longer than is sometimes suggested; all the lakes are filling up with alluvium and lake detritus *from the bottom*, and gradually becoming shallower, but the lakes which have been obliterated within the fifteen thousand years since the last glaciation were of a particular size, shape and depth (=morphometry) which put them into a separate category from the existing lakes.

It has already been suggested that the separation of the twin lakes

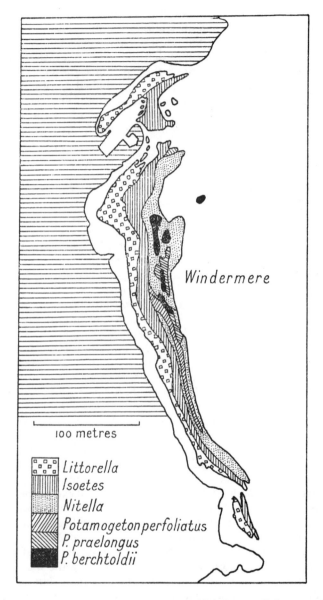

Windermere

100 metres

Littorella
Isoetes
Nitella
Potamogeton perfoliatus
P. praelongus
P. berchtoldii

EIG. 5. The vegetation between Wray Crag and Watbarrow Point, west shore of Windermere, from an unpublished survey by W. H. Pearsall.

probably dates from the time immediately after the glaciation, when a great abundance of coarse and unstabilised detritus would be in process of redistribution; formation of the Measand delta and the great infill of Brotherswater and other lakes may well also date from this period, when remnant snowfields were present on the mountains and great volumes of summer melt-water could transport this unstabilised detritus every year. Under present conditions, the occasional rainstorm of several inches of rain in twenty-four hours (e.g. August, 1966) shows how rapidly swollen watercourses can move great quantities of large boulders.

THE DEVELOPMENT OF A LAKE

In its primitive state, or beginning, a glacial lake or tarn must have had an inorganic floor of glacial deposits, sand and gravel, silt and clay. At that time, at the end of a glaciation, no organic soil would remain on the ice-eroded surface of its drainage basin, and the absence of any microfossils from the basal lake sediments shows that the lakes, too, were quite barren. With the spread of a vegetation cover over the drainage basin, and accumulation of humus in stable soils, plant and animal life began in the waters of the lakes. Through the ten thousand years of the post-glacial period, as silts and eroded soils came down the rivers into the lakes, as plants and animals grew in the lakes and contributed parts of their corpses to the accumulating mud, changes took place both in the chemical composition of rivers and lakes and in the plants and animals which flourished in them.

At the time when these matters were first considered, it seemed likely that it was the lakes in which there is the largest proportion of rocky shores today, and the clearest water, containing the lowest quantities of dissolved nutrients and dissolved organic matter, which should resemble most closely the primitive state of a glacial lake. Wastwater and Ennerdale are both the rockiest lakes and contain the purest water; they are both very 'unproductive' lakes in which comparatively few plants and animals grow, because of the shortage of nutrients such as nitrogen, phosphorus, etc. Buttermere is another lake of this type, as are all except the shallowest of the mountain tarns. At the other end of the scale is Esthwaite Water, the shores of which are almost entirely of drift, with little or no solid rock, and in which the water is very much richer in all plant nutrients, especially in nitrates and phosphates. In these early days, it seemed a possible hypothesis that the rich growth of plankton in Esthwaite was consequent on the higher nutrient status of its water, and that both this and the abundance of aquatic plants were related to the silted habitats available for colonisation, and to the ions dissolved from the silts which were in such abundance in the water. This silted condition was thought of as a more developed, or 'evolved' state, to which a glacial lake probably attained in

PLATE 5 Pines on Castle Crag, Borrowdale: the formation of screes has been accelerated since prehistoric clearance of native woodlands from the mountains.

PLATE 6 The heart of the rugged Borrowdale Volcanics country. *Above*, Scafell, Mickledore and Scafell Pike, from Crinkle Crags. *Below*, Great End and Sprinkling Tarn.

time by silting, at a rate which was proportional to the rate at which silt was produced from its drainage basin. This theory supposed that the unproductive lakes, which lie among the hard volcanic rocks and igneous rocks, intruded into them, remained in their primitive state because erosion of these hard rocks produced coarse material, quickly dumped in the underwater deltas, rather than fine silts which 'fertilised' the lake waters and muds.

This was quite a useful and thought-provoking theory (see in *New Biology*, 1949), but, as so often happens, it had to be discarded when further facts were discovered. The first surprising thing was that it was found that all the lakes, productive and unproductive, silted and rocky, contained a very similar thickness of sediment, which in the middle of the lakes is certainly made of fine silts. This, according to Mr F. J. H. Mackereth, suggested that the degree to which the lake basins were filling with sediment must depend on a general balance between the climatically-determined pattern of erosion of the drainage basins and their prevailing composition of hard ancient rocks. The difference between, for instance, Wastwater and Esthwaite, is not primarily related to a difference in silting rate. Is it entirely related to a difference in the dissolved salt content of the waters? A surprising fact in this connection was the discovery by Dr F. E. Round that in the diatom sequence found in the profiles of several of these lakes, the early post-glacial sediment contained the silica shells of certain diatoms, e.g. *Rhopalodia gibba*, which are not found in the lakes of the district today, because they need a much higher level of dissolved calcium and other bases than is now found in any of these lakes. This discovery came at about the same time that pollen analysts were finding pollen of lime-loving plants such as *Helianthemum* and *Polemonium* in late-glacial lake sediments, and the chemists were realising how much calcium is present in unweathered Borrowdale Volcanic rocks (see Chapter 7). Thoughts had to be adjusted to the realisation that even a lake as unproductive today as Ennerdale Water had had a time of much greater production in the early post-glacial period, when the masses of fresh drift from the Borrowdale rocks had not yet been leached of their soluble bases by the high rainfall of the Lake District. Both Ennerdale Water and Esthwaite Water then declined from this state when their waters could support diatoms which required a high base status, because both Borrowdale Volcanic rocks and Silurian sediments alike were leached of all soluble bases by the continuing rainfall. Waters with a high content of dissolved bases and other nutrients normally support a rich growth of plankton and are often called 'eutrophic' (see page 70). In view of controversies as to the exact definition of this term it is probably better to use the word 'productive' to describe lakes whose water supports a rich growth of plankton and other algae. Certain diatom species are characteristic of productive lakes. In two tarns (Blea Tarn and

Devoke Water) and a former lake in Kentmere, it has been shown how the numbers of diatoms of species characteristic of productive or 'eutrophic' lakes decrease on passing up the post-glacial sediment column. We can therefore feel sure, on the evidence of the sediments, that lakes and tarns of all types were, in the early post-glacial period, both more productive and richer in calcium and other dissolved bases than they are today. Why then is Esthwaite Water at present so much more productive than Ennerdale Water?

Table 1. The lake series (Pearsall 1921)

In broad terms, the present productivity of each lake is positively correlated with the percentage of the drainage area which is cultivable, and negatively correlated with the percentage of the lake bottom, to a water depth of 9m, which is rocky, not silted.

Lake	Percentage of drainage area cultivable	Percentage of lake bottom to a depth of 9m which is rocky
Wastwater	5.2	73
Ennerdale Water	5.4	66
Buttermere	6.0	50
Crummock Water	8.0	47
Haweswater (old lake)	7.7	25
Derwentwater	10.0	33
Bassenthwaite Lake	29.4	29
Coniston Water	21.8	27
Windermere	29.4	28
Ullswater	16.6	28
Esthwaite Water	45.4	12

Two factors are involved. Firstly Esthwaite is a very shallow lake (45 feet deep) compared even with Ennerdale and still more with Wastwater – these unproductive lakes are respectively 148 feet and 260 feet deep. This means that when summer stratification sets in, and the lower stable 'hypolimnion' (Fig. 7, p. 77) is isolated from further supplies of oxygen by the epilimnion with which it does not mix, the respiration of the fauna and micro-flora depletes the hypolimnion of oxygen rather quickly in a lake as shallow as Esthwaite Water, and the mud surface becomes anaerobic. This releases nutrients from the decomposing organic mud surface, as originally demonstrated for Esthwaite by Professor C. H. Mortimer, and steps up still further the potential productivity of Esthwaite. In the deeper lakes the mud surface remains oxidising and this does not happen. Secondly, and even more important, there is a good deal more agricultural land within the drainage basin of Esthwaite than in

Ennerdale, and whereas there are no more than half a dozen farms within the Ennerdale drainage area, the village of Hawkshead (population *c.* 1,000) discharges a sewage effluent rich in nitrogen and phosphorus into Esthwaite Water. It seems very probable that most of the present high productivity of algae in Esthwaite is the direct result of a combination of its shallow depth with the additional fertilisation brought about by sewage pollution and by drainage from fertilised farm land. The chances of other lakes coming to resemble this condition will be discussed by Dr Lund in the next section.

THE ROOTED PLANTS IN THE LAKES

Aquatic plants are able to grow in a rather narrow zone around each lake, limited in their downward extension by the depth to which sufficient light can penetrate, and on most shores limited upwards by the zone of most severe wave erosion. Only in sheltered places, which include nearly all the shore-line of small lakes but only bays and inlets in large ones, do aquatic plants grow right up to the edge of the water and merge with plant communities of the land. The aquatic plants are clearly affected by other factors beyond this primary limitation of the area available for colonisation. One is the type of substratum, whether rocky, stony or silted, or organic lake mud; the other is the nutrient status of the water of the lake. The interaction of these various factors in determining the environment for aquatic plants in each lake is still being actively studied, and different opinions as to the most important factor have been advanced from time to time.

The plants which have either floating leaves or emergent stems and leaves tend to grow in the shallower parts of the available area, and in sheltered places the reeds and sedges of the water's edge pass gradually, though with some change in species, into fen communities. In deeper parts of the marginal zone are found the submerged plants whose leaves depend for photosynthesis on light which passes through the water. These submerged plants include rosette forms like *Isoetes*, the quill-wort, and long-stemmed plants with either linear or broad leaves, such as pond-weeds (*Potamogeton* spp. and *Elodea canadensis*, the Canadian pondweed). It seems possible that at each place in a lake the mosaic of plant communities which is found is determined by local conditions of substratum, wave action and silting, which complicate the basic pattern of zones dependent on water depth, and that for the lake as a whole, some factor in the composition of the water (either total dissolved nutrients or the level of one limiting substance) determines the plant species which are most likely to be found growing in that particular lake.

Plant communities of the more sheltered shores and situations will be described in the section which deals with Esthwaite (page 90). A more generally typical kind of lake shore is shown in Fig. 5, p. 63. This is described as follows by Dr T. T. Macan: 'Down to a depth of about two metres the substratum is stony and so pounded by waves that it supports no rooted vegetation. Presumably the stones are broken into small pieces and renewed by destruction of the rock which bounds the lake, but this is an extremely slow process. In deeper water *Littorella* (shoreweed) is able to withstand the wave action and colonises a stony substratum, and below it on the finer deposits where *Isoetes* grows there is still enough water movement to remove much of the silt and the dead remains of plants.' In still deeper water are found species of *Potamogeton* and *Nitella* (stonewort) down to the limit of the illuminated zone.

Littorella and *Lobelia dortmanna* (water lobelia) are very common rosette plants in the shallow-water communities, especially in the more acid and less productive lakes and tarns. The pale lilac flowers of the water lobelia, emerging from the marginal shallows in July and August, particularly in places where the bottom is peaty, are one of the most characteristic of Lake District sights. Water lilies (*Nymphaea alba* and *Nuphar lutea*), members of the floating-leaved communities, develop only in sheltered bays in the lakes, but are found in some of the shallow and less rocky tarns, and particularly in those which have been artificially enlarged as fishing tarns. The water-milfoils (*Myriophyllum spicatum* and *M. alterniflorum*) are common on rather organic substrata in the more productive lakes, especially in places where dead leaves accumulate along the base of the wave-cut terrace.

Water plants characteristic of the unproductive rocky lakes include *Isoetes* and *Nitella*; *Isoetes* will not tolerate silting, but in unsilted places these plants are also found in the somewhat more productive lakes such as Windermere, but not in highly productive waters. Other aquatic plants which will grow in the rocky unproductive lakes are *Myriophyllum spicatum* and *Juncus kochii*; these four species are the only ones commonly found in Wastwater and Ennerdale Water.

Among the constant relationships which have been found between species and the substratum, *Isoetes* in Windermere and other lakes is found typically on coarse inorganic brown silt, *Potamogeton perfoliatus* on moderately organic brown mud, and *Sparganium minimum* and *Potamogeton alpinus* on highly organic brown mud. In more acid and unproductive lakes and tarns, there is a characteristic association between a peaty substratum and *Lobelia*, *Juncus kochii*, *Potamogeton natans* and *Carex rostrata*.

The aquatic vegetation of Esthwaite Water has been studied in detail. In this shallow lake with silted (not rocky) shores and water of a high nutrient level there is a particularly good development of submerged plants with linear leaves and delicate stems. This is the 'linear-leaved associes' (Fig. 6, p. 69) and includes pondweeds (*Potamogeton* spp.)

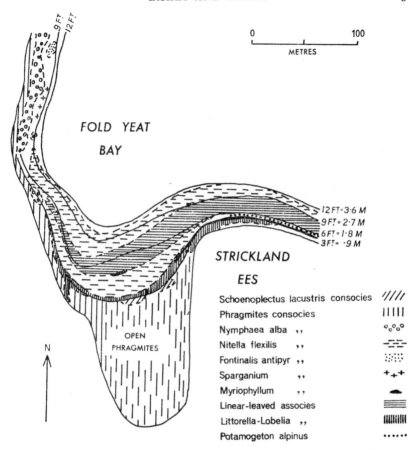

FIG. 6. The vegetation of Fold Yeat Bay, Esthwaite Water. From Pearsall, 1917, J. Ecol., reproduced in Tansley, The British Islands and their Vegetation.

such as *P. pusillus* and what is now known as *P. berchtoldii* (formerly *P. pusillus* subs. *lacustris*); also *Naias flexilis* and the very rare plant which was originally called *Hydrilla verticillata* var. *pomeranica*, now called *Elodea nuttallii*. The introduced Canadian pondweed (*Elodea canadensis*) is also frequent in this plant association.

The shape of Esthwaite Water provides more sheltered bays than are found in the more straight-sided lakes, and Fig. 6, above, shows the vegetation of Fold Yeat Bay on the western shore, typical of these sheltered situations. The reedswamp of *Phragmites australis* at the back of this bay passes gradually into land vegetation, with a small area of willow carr.

On the lakeward side the reeds give way to a belt of the tall sedge *Schoenoplectus* (formerly *Scirpus*) *lacustris*, and off the sheltered shore north of the bay is found a community of plants with floating leaves and sub-aerial flowering stems, dominated by water-lilies, white and yellow (*Nymphaea alba* and *Nuphar lutea*).

Black Beck, the main inflow into Esthwaite, has deposited an under-water delta of silty mud and coarse organic detritus (see page 90). On the richly silted area around its mouth the vegetation zones have been shown to be advancing towards open water (see the maps for 1914 and 1929 in Tansley's *The British Islands and their Vegetation*, 1939). Small submerged plants of deeper water such as the charoid *Nitella flexilis* and the moss *Fontinalis antipyretica* have been replaced in some areas since the first survey by the small bur-reed (*Sparganium minimum*) with floating stems and emergent inflorescences, and both the water-lily and reedswamp belts have advanced lakewards.

RECENT ENRICHMENT OF THE LAKES: EUTROPHICATION

Some sixty years ago the terms eutrophic and oligotrophic were coined to describe lakes which are rich or poor in plant nutrients. The words were used also in relation to the life within the lakes, because the nutrients which are available are likely to be utilised. Thus, a eutrophic lake will have a greater abundance of life within it than an oligotrophic one. Wastwater is oligotrophic and Esthwaite Water eutrophic. Such words, despite their impressive sound, are not exact scientific expressions; no numerical value can be assigned to them. However, they are useful as single words which bring to mind a set of attributes of the lake to which they are applied. When we say that Wastwater is highly oligotrophic we have in mind its rugged mountainous situation, the great screes, the thin, poor soils, unsuitable for intensive agriculture and the vegetation which can only support a sparse population of hardy sheep. On the other hand, when we call Esthwaite Water eutrophic we think of its lowland position, the softer countryside with deeper soils and better agriculture, so that, apart from more sheep per acre, there are also many cattle and the farmers can be seen adding lime and fertilisers to their fields. Lastly there is a village of moderate size, Hawkshead, whose sewage passes into the main inflow to the lake.

From this beginning of the classification of lakes according to the fertility of their waters arose the use of phrases such as 'increasingly eutrophic' or 'eutrophication' meaning that a lake was becoming richer in nutrients and so in plants and animals, or that a certain degree of enrich-ment, that is eutrophication, had taken place. Therefore a change from oligotrophy to eutrophy can be considered a good one. However, as always, it is necessary to ask for what and for whom the change is good.

In the Lake District the change involved qualitative and quantitative alterations in the flora and fauna. If a lake becomes richer in fish, as a result of eutrophication, one might expect this to be considered good by fishermen. However, if, as happens in our lakes, the result is an increase in coarse fish such as perch and pike, or the arrival of new species and a decrease or even the disappearance of char or trout, many fishermen will say that eutrophication is a bad thing. Further, as has also been mentioned, in recent times the process of eutrophication has been accelerated by the increase in the amount of sewage, detergents and agricultural fertilisers passing into rivers and lakes. It is important to emphasise that this is not pollution in the original meaning of the word, although too many people today are using the words pollution and eutrophication as though they were synonymous. It is true that they overlap, because, as we shall see, eutrophication can lead to conditions characteristic of pollution. It can be said that eutrophication is likely to lead to secondary pollution. Primary pollution of water, that is pollution in the original meaning of the word, is the entry of noxious or poisonous substances. Today the entry of untreated sewage in large amounts is becoming less and less common. It is treated sewage with which we are concerned. The treatment consists in the passage of domestic and industrial wastes through a sewage plant. In the sewage works the noxious organic matter is broken down and an effluent is produced which is rich in the mineralised remains of raw sewage. The effluent contains large concentrations of essential plant nutrients such as phosphates and nitrates. These substances are the same as those also passing into waters as the result of the fertilisation of farm land. However, they cannot be called noxious or harmful even though they may lead, in the end, to undesirable results. In addition to these important fertilisers, purified sewage contains other known and unknown substances which promote the growth of plants. Examples are vitamins, such as B_{12} and B_1; humus, and trace elements such as cobalt, molybdenum and boron. The last, a constituent of detergents, is an example of a substance which, as is well known, can be toxic. However, in the concentrations in which it is present today, it is very unlikely to be toxic to any organism in fresh water, and for some organisms, notably diatoms, it is an essential element so that it may well stimulate rather than retard their growth.

The objection to eutrophication lies in the fact that it is possible to have too much of a good thing. Just as we can overeat so can a lake be over-enriched. So far and so fast has the process of eutrophication gone in highly industrialised countries, with their large towns and intensive agriculture, that the enrichment of many water bodies has reached a stage which many people dislike. Those concerned with supplying water object to the troubles caused by the vast number of algae passing into the treatment works. The algae block their filters and produce unpleasant tastes and odours. The capital costs increase because the filtration, clarification and purification plants have to be larger. The running costs increase because of the amount of material which has to be removed and the larger quantities of chemicals which have to be added to ensure that the water supplied is fit for drinking and for many industrial processes. Above all, it is the unpredictability of algae which enrages the waterworks engineer. There is always the possibility that, despite apparently adequate provision for treating water, a set of favourable circumstances for algal growth will cause a bloom of such exceptional size that the works may have to be shut down.

The use of water for recreation is also threatened. Today, amenity is already big business and must become a more and more important part of our lives. It has become common practice to consider what is called the multipurpose use of reservoirs and lakes. By this is meant that the water shall be usable for domestic and industrial purposes, and the water body suitable for recreation such as swimming, boating and picnicking round its shores. Another favourite phrase of the planners of our diminishing countryside is 'visual amenities', a phrase which is very familiar in Lakeland in relation to the effect of new building or roads on the landscape. If a lake is enriched by sewage and agricultural fertilisers, then scums and mats of algae can be expected to appear on its surface and shores. When they decay they will look unsightly and smell unpleasant. Meanwhile their remains will be decomposing during the summer in the hypolimnion, leading to the utilisation of the oxygen in solution in the water and the production of noxious smells and undesirable chemicals. As a result, the enjoyment of the area is reduced and the provision of potable water made more difficult. In the planners' phraseology, the visual amenities are harmed. Fishing becomes poor, even for those who do not object to the replacement of sport fish by coarse fish. The fish find themselves caught between the oxygenless depths and the mass of algae in the upper layers, certain kinds of which are directly or indirectly harmful to them. The fish are hard to catch and when caught may be in poor condition. The fisherman may not catch old boots or cans, but his line may be entangled and fouled by branched, thread-like algae which he calls blanket-weed. The swimmer no longer wishes to wade through slippery and slimy masses of algae and rooted vegetation, nor to swim among the scum covering the open water. Even the picnicker, who may happily ignore the litter, may object to the scene before him and to the odours wafting towards him. Some lakes in other countries have become so unpleasant that people will not even go boating on them.

Such can be the results of man-made eutrophication and, as a result, the word now has a new meaning for many people. No longer is it a good thing, producing a rich and fascinating living world in a lake; it is the cause of the destruction of every reason why man wishes to use lakes for the supply of water or for his enjoyment. This is why the word eutrophication has so largely lost its original meaning and is so often spoken of in the same terms as pollution.

On this background we can now consider what is happening to the Lake District and what may happen in the future. First of all it is necessary to point out that eutrophication has not reached the stage described above in any of our lakes. Many are untouched by it. Manchester uses the waters of Thirlmere and Haweswater because they are so pure, and takes good care to preserve them so. No sewage enters these lakes; no undesirable development is allowed in their catchments. To such a degree has Manchester protected these lakes that a good deal of dissatisfaction has been expressed. The argument against Manchester's protective attitude is that it is carried to unreasonable extremes. Though the visual amenities have been preserved, this preservation has not been for the sake of the Lake District as a holiday centre but for the sake of a cheap source of water. The visual amenities would not be harmed, in some ways, if the precautions were relaxed somewhat. Manchester can reply that what is good for it is also good for the holiday trade in the Lake District. If the lakes were enriched and access to them and their catchments increased, then their beauty and recreational value would decline. Against this is advanced the view that their recreational value is small because recreation is not allowed on them and access to their shores is restricted. So the arguments rage. Recently Manchester has at least partially met the last complaint by increasing public access to Haweswater. Manchester has also had to change its policy of sending water straight through to the consumer without the intervention of treatment works, and only token chlorination. It has permission now to use water from Ullswater and Windermere. These waters are so much richer in plants and animals than those of Thirlmere and Haweswater that some treatment is necessary before passing them on to the consumer. Since the waters of the various lakes undergo mixing in various proportions on their way to Manchester, it is possible that the ever increasing need to use less pure water will reduce the need for restrictions on the recreational use of a lake such as Thirlmere. Haweswater and Thirlmere are not the only lakes used for water supply which are free of artificial enrichment. One example has been mentioned – Wastwater; others are Ennerdale and Crummock Water, as well as remote mountain tarns like Blea Water.

So far, the economic and social implications of eutrophication have been the main consideration, though some reference has been made to the ecological effects on fish. In the final section a return will be made to these matters in discussing the future of the lakes, with special reference to Windermere, but first more strictly biological features are discussed. As with so many features of the present condition and appearance of the Lake District, an understanding of the present and a forecasting of the future are best based on an understanding of the past. A brief description of the development of the lakes has already been given based on chemical, physical and biological investigations of the sediments laid down in them since the end of the Ice Age (see also Chapter 13). In this section, the changes in the algae present in the plankton are considered with special reference to recent times, since these alterations can be related, to a considerable extent, to eutrophication.

Diatoms are microscopic algae whose living matter is encased in a shell or wall of silica (Plate 18, p. 165). Silica has many forms, from the hard lustrous quartz to dull flint. The diatomaceous silica is similar to flint. As silica is a relatively insoluble substance, the remains of diatoms are found, like flinty skeletons, in the sediments on the lake floor. These microfossils are often very beautiful because of the geometric regularity of their sculpturing (Plate 18). The pioneer researches of Pearsall showed that lakes such as Windermere and Esthwaite Water both have more planktonic diatoms than, for example, Wastwater and Ennerdale and that the dominant species are different in each case. One of the diatoms he studied was *Asterionella formosa* (Plate 18). It, too, is a thing of beauty when seen under a microscope. However, a waterworks engineer may not be able to appreciate either its aesthetic or scientific charm, for it is a major pest of British reservoirs. In the Lake District, it is absent or extremely rare in Wastwater, Ennerdale, Buttermere and Thirlmere but very common in Loweswater, Windermere, Esthwaite Water and Blelham Tarn. Its appearance and increasing abundance go hand in hand with an increasing richness of our waters in plant nutrients such as phosphates and nitrates. In all the lakes phosphates are present in small amounts compared, for example, with many lakes in lowland Britain. In Buttermere the amount of phosphate phosphorus in solution is about one tenth of that in Windermere and one hundredth of that in Esthwaite Water or Blelham Tarn. Yet, the amount in the last two lakes is only a tithe of that commonly found in the Shropshire meres and about one hundredth of that in London's reservoirs, which contain a large proportion of treated sewage. An increase in the numbers of *Asterionella* and of certain other diatoms in our lakes could be caused by an increase in phosphates in the inflows. In turn this increase may be the result of growing urbanisation and intensified agriculture.

In 1943, Pennington showed that there was a great increase in the number of fossil *Asterionella* from 20 centimetres below the mud surface, up to the surface, in the deposits of the North Basin of Windermere. She suggested that this change in abundance might be correlated with the opening up of the Lake District at the beginning of the nineteenth century. An improved method for dating deposits developed by Mr F. J. H. Mackereth gives strong support to Pennington's hypothesis. It is clear that the depth of deposit concerned represents approximately the last 150 years. The influence on the district of the poets and writers from the eighteenth century onwards, the arrival of the railway at Windermere in 1847, the building of the town of Windermere and the effects of the invention of the motor car, will be considered in the final chapter. During this period the sanitary arrangements changed. The Wordsworths at Dove Cottage in December, 1801, had a 'necessary' in the garden, but soon after that flush toilets and main drainage (begun for Windermere in 1846) began to send domestic wastes direct to sewage works on the shore of the lakes. Since then, the ever-increasing number of people living around Windermere and coming for holidays has led to an ever-increasing flow of treated sewage into the lake. Recent unpublished work by Dr J. G. Stockner has caused some changes in our views, but the general thesis proposed by Pennington remains unchallenged. In some ways even more striking than the rise of *Asterionella* is the increase of a closely related diatom, *Fragilaria crotonensis* (Plate 18, p. 165), which is characteristic of eutrophic lakes. It was not observed in Windermere by the Wests, father and son, who examined the plankton at the beginning of the century, nor by the Pearsalls, also father and son, who carried out their investigations between 1920 and 1930. For the last quarter of the century it has been a regular and sometimes abundant component of the plankton.

A similar account could be given of Esthwaite Water, though there the effect of urbanisation is less striking. It has always been a richer lake than Windermere because of the richer soils around it. A marked difference from Windermere is that the hypolimnion of Esthwaite Water becomes deoxygenated in summer, and there is good evidence that this has been the case for thousands of years. The hypolimnion of Windermere always contains free oxygen in solution. However, this difference between the two lakes cannot be satisfactorily explained by what has been said above. The urbanisation of the shores of Windermere has been far greater than that around Esthwaite Water. Hawkshead may be larger than it was but this enlargement cannot compare with the creation of the town of Windermere and the enlargement of Bowness during the last 120 years. The study of the deposits presents us with a problem to which we have no certain solution. In suggesting a possible solution in this book, the excuse must be that it has relevance to the final section on the future and underlines the reason why the hypolimnion of Windermere has not yet become de-oxygenated. The volume of water in the hypolimnion of Esthwaite Water is far less than that of Windermere. The smaller the hypolimnion, the less the total amount of oxygen in it and therefore the smaller the amount of decomposable organic remains necessary to deoxygenate it. So, one of the factors determining whether the hypolimnion of a lake becomes de-oxygenated is its size and, especially, its size relative to that of the epi-limnion in which the primary production of living matter takes place. The suggestion made here is that the greater fertility of Esthwaite Water and its smaller hypolimnion have combined to cause the latter to be deoxygenated each summer for the greater part of the lake's existence. A parallel may be drawn with Grasmere, another small lake in which, despite its oligotrophic plankton, the lower portion of the hypolimnion becomes deoxygenated. It is the size of the hypolimnion of Windermere and so its large reserve of oxygen that prevents deoxygenation in summer.

Table 2. Changes in the nutrient content of inflow streams 1948–68

			Nitrate		*Phosphorus*
a. Esthwaite Water					
Black Beck		1948/49	1.0	1948/49	.3
		1968/69	2.0	1968/69	.5
Smooth Beck		1948/49	.15	1948/49	.003
		1968/69	1.7	1968/69	.2
b. Blelham Tarn					
Ford Wood Beck		1948/49	.9	1948/49	.02
		1967/68	1.2	1967/68	.07
High Wray Beck		1948/49	.7	1948/49	.003
		1967/68	1.2	1967/68	.02

What of the future? A published forecast may become a monument to the fallibility of the forecaster, but the description of what eutrophication can lead to raises the question whether any of our lakes are endangered. There can be no doubt that Windermere and its neighbours Esthwaite Water and Blelham Tarn are becoming more eutrophic. Table 2 shows how much greater the concentration of certain nutrients is now in inflows to Esthwaite Water and Blelham Tarn than it was in 1947. The sources of the increase, as elsewhere, are sewage and agricultural fertilisers. Sewage adds particularly large amounts of phosphate, a feature aggravated since the middle nineteen fifties by the universal use of detergents. The chief cause of the increase in nitrates is agricultural fertilisers, notably on grassland. If the inflow of sewage increases, as it will do if the present increase in the population round the shores of Windermere and in the numbers of tourists continues; if the farmers use more fertilisers, as they will do, and if foresters begin to fertilise trees, as they may do, then the eutrophication of Windermere will increase. Then it will be only a matter of time before, in the southern basin, the hypolimnion becomes deoxygenated. The southern basin receives the sewage of Windermere and Bowness and the outflow of Esthwaite Water. Will Windermere become another lake whose beauty and recreational value is reduced by the development of algal scums and tangles together with the products of their decomposition?

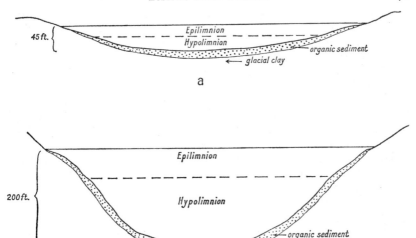

FIG. 7 Lake profiles and summer stratification. Sections across (a) Esthwaite Water and (b) Windermere, North Basin, showing summer stratification and the position of the thermocline, and emphasising the much greater volume of the hypolimnion of Windermere.

It must be borne in mind that the answer to the question is not wholly scientific. Beauty is a personal concept. From the scientific viewpoint, present evidence suggests that the eutrophication of Windermere is mild as yet. The main danger is to the southern basin. The northern basin is deeper, has a larger hypolimnion (Fig. 7, above) and receives less sewage. Even in relation to the southern basin, it is doubtful whether the development of larger growths of algae would be considered objectionable. Deoxygenation of the hypolimnion and the chemical changes resulting therefrom would be invisible to the public. Fishermen might object, but the northern basin would be less altered. Coarse fishermen might be pleased, because sooner or later fish not previously present would appear. Yachting, motor-boating and water-skiing could still be enjoyed, though swimming might not. It is accepted by many people that Windermere is already what might be described as an urbanised lake.

Turning to the other lakes, Esthwaite Water and Blelham Tarn are threatened, the latter having undergone a sharp increase in eutrophication since 1954–6. However, it is not clear that further marked changes will occur. As elsewhere it depends on how the catchment will be developed. The lakes which are loved for their clear pure water and unspoilt surroundings seem to be in no danger, although the attitude taken towards them is different from that towards Windermere. Changes which have long been accepted in and around Windermere would there lead to a public outcry, and, we may hope, will never be permitted. In this group of lakes one can think of Wastwater, Ennerdale Water, Buttermere and Crummock Water. Loweswater is already moderately eutrophic but a major part of its drainage area is poor mountainous ground. Grasmere is threatened by a new sewage scheme due to come into operation shortly, but at present there is insufficient knowledge of how great an addition there will be to the present input of sewage.

The whole position with regard to the lakes may be summarised as follows. Eutrophication is occurring here as elsewhere. The present situation is not as serious as some accounts have suggested, nor does the future look as threatening. On the other hand, there are possible dangers ahead, especially in regard to certain lakes. What is needed is constant vigilance and a knowledge of what is happening in our lakes. So long as the Freshwater Biological Association exists, information and advice will always be available.

LAKE ALGAE AND OTHER ORGANISMS

The algae in lakes are eaten by a variety of invertebrates. Those living on underwater stones, rocks and mud are food for chironomids, snails and crustaceans. In the plankton the main herbivores are crustaceans, rotifers and certain little known protozoa. The latter belong to several distinct groups but as yet not enough is known about them to classify them properly. They are generally grouped together in the Proteomyxa, a heterogeneous order of the Rhizopoda. They have been known for a long time, for they were described by famous microscopists of the last century and early years of this one. However, only recently has it become clear that they often decimate populations of planktonic algae, notably colonial green algae. Plate 17, p. 164 shows such a protozoan moving towards an alga called *Paulschulzia*. Protozoans of this kind possess two unequal anterior flagella or, as in our picture, two pairs just before cell division. It swims freely in water but within the alga, which consists of groups of cells embedded in diffluent mucilage, the protozoan moves in an amoeboid manner. It makes contact with an algal cell, dissolves a portion of the cell wall, and then the internal contents of the cell pass into the body of the animal. This process is well illustrated by *Vampyrella*, another protozoan often found on certain filamentous algae in the plankton of Windermere. A *Vampyrella* approaches an algal cell and makes contact with it by long protoplasmic threads (Plate 17). Next, the threads gradually shorten and become thickened by fusing laterally one with another. (Plate 17). Eventually the main body of the animal comes to rest on the algal cell (Plate 17). In about five to ten minutes the *Vampyrella* has made a hole in the wall of the alga and the contents of the cell have passed into the animal (Plate 17).

The effect of grazing by protozoa on colonial green algae in Windermere has been repeatedly demonstrated. Only about 7–14 days are necessary for the destruction of more than 99 per cent of the algal population. The discovery of the ecological importance of protozoans has solved an apparent paradox of our freshwater plankton. This was that small algae were eaten by large animals but the large algae seemed to escape grazing. So far as large green algae are concerned, it is now clear that they are eaten by these small protozoans which enter their colonies or attach themselves to their filaments and ingest the content of one cell after another. Therefore we have a new paradox; the larger animals depend on the smaller algae and the smaller animals on the larger algae. How true this generalisation is, here and elsewhere, remains to be seen. The diversity of nature is so great that it will be surprising if this generalisation does not have to be modified.

Fungal parasitism can also decimate algal populations. The great majority of the plankton algae in Windermere and nearby lakes is parasitised at one time or another by one or more fungi. Green algae and diatoms are most frequently parasitised. The parasites themselves belong to fungi called Phycomycetes, a group which also includes many of the moulds so common on stale bread, rotting fruit and dung. There are two sub-groups of these fungi which infect our algae. The members of one group are commonly called chytrids. Similar organisms to these cause diseases of agricultural plants, such as potato black wart. The motile cell (zoospore) of a chytrid possesses one flagellum which propels the cell from the rear. In the other sub-group, the zoospore has two laterally inserted flagella of unequal length. These latter fungi may be considered as simple members of the water moulds, which include *Saprolegnia*, a mould often found on diseased fish, and *Pythium*, a gardening pest which causes 'damping-off' of seedlings.

In many species, after a chytrid zoospore has attached itself to an algal cell, it develops into a sporangium on the outside of the alga (Plate 18, p. 165). From this sporangium are liberated further zoospores. In other species, the sporangium develops inside the algal cell. This is always the case in the biflagellate sub-group (Plate 18, p. 165). In both sub-groups thick-walled resting spores (Plate 18) are commonly produced. Presumably the resting spores remain alive between periods of fungal activity. However, little is known about this stage or the part it plays in initiating a fresh epidemic of parasitism.

In general, these fungi are selective parasites, infecting one algal species or a few closely related species. Epidemics produced by such fungi can both reduce the total population of the alga concerned at the time, and play some part in determining its abundance months hence. However, since parasitism affects the growth of algae over relatively short periods, it does not usually alter the whole seasonal picture from year to year. For example, despite very frequent fungal infection, desmids in Windermere increase each summer, but which species predominate may be directly related to parasitism.

The abundance of the protozoans mentioned and of fungal parasites in our lakes will probably be found to be a common feature of temperate regions, once equally detailed studies have been made elsewhere.

LAKE INVERTEBRATES

Less is known about zooplankton than about phytoplankton, but a recent study has been published by W. J. P. Smyly. The composition of the zooplankton community varies little from lake to lake, though numbers, as might be expected, reflect the position of the lake in the 'Pearsall series' (see Table 1). It was common to find only one numerically dominant species in the same genus; there were rarely more than one or two copepods and one or two cladocerans abundant at any one time. There has been little change in species composition since the survey by Gurney (1923) (see Bibliography).

Little is known about the animals that inhabit the mud in the deep parts of most of the lakes, but the animals that dwell on a stony substratum in shallow water have been well studied. Collections made on either side of the outflow of the Bowness–Windermere sewage works into Windermere yielded higher totals of flatworms than any other animal. The water hog-louse (*Asellus*) was also abundant, though the largest catch of this animal was made not at the station nearest the outfall but at the one beyond. Also numerous was the freshwater shrimp *Gammarus* and its American relative *Crangonyx pseudogracilis*, a recent immigrant. The Bladder Snail (*Physa fontinalis*) was associated with these species, which occurred throughout the South Basin of Windermere and in the shallow island region which separates it from the North Basin. At most stations the only insect was a caddis, *Agapetus*. North of the islands the fauna begins to change. The animals already mentioned, particularly the flatworms and *Asellus*, become scarcer and an increasingly numerical contribution to the fauna is made by three species of mayfly, three species of stonefly, and a net-spinning caddis larva. At Red Nab, a mile or so south of Wray Castle, no flatworm has ever been taken during a routine collection and the insects mentioned are often numerous. Farther north the fauna begins to change again, and the community found along the north shore of the North Basin is the one found in the South Basin. In this region the lake is influenced by the Ambleside sewage works.

In Esthwaite Water most of the east side of the lake is floored with

PLATE 7 Windermere and the Langdale Pikes: a reedy eastern bay of the North Basin, with a background of the high Langdale fells.

PLATE 8 *Above*, Great Gable from Pillar: mountain summits which belong to the nation, the property of the National Trust. *Below*, Striding Edge and Red Tarn: a winter view of the popular route up Helvellyn.

stones and the fauna on them consists of flatworms, *Asellus*, *Gammarus*, *Physa* and leeches. The large stonefly *Diura bicaudata* and the flat mayfly nymph, *Heptagenia lateralis*, both abundant in Windermere, have never been taken in Esthwaite.

When the other lakes are arranged in the series (Table 1), which approximately reflects their different productivity, the change in fauna runs closely parallel to the difference seen between the middle of the North Basin of Windermere and the north and south extremities of this basin. Flatworms, common in the two lakes already mentioned, decrease rapidly in numbers with decreasing productivity, being numerous only in Bassenthwaite and Loweswater of the other lakes, and unrecorded from Crummock, Ennerdale and Wastwater. *Asellus* was known only from Bassenthwaite and Ullswater until its recent colonisation of Esthwaite Water – it appears to be extending its range. Professor H. P. Moon was able to keep this spread under observation, and has published an account of it in the *Journal of Animal Ecology* for 1968. The decline in numbers of *Gammarus* with decreasing productivity is less abrupt than that of the flatworms, and only in Buttermere, Ennerdale Water and Wastwater is it scarce or absent. *Physa*, which is absent from these three lakes, is scarce in lakes in the middle of the series. As the numbers of these animals decline, the numbers of various species of mayfly and stonefly rise. They reach a maximum in lakes in the middle of the series, and then decline again in step with the fall in total productivity.

It is not known why the fauna changes. Probably increased productivity means much greater numbers of small worms and chironomid larvae, which provide the main food of flatworms. These and other organisms become numerous, and when in abundance they exterminate the insects by eating them. The distribution of this community in relation to the sewage outfalls of Windermere points to a correlation and to the conclusion that the fauna of this lake has changed markedly within the last century and perhaps less. Once, all over the lake it was the same as it is now in the middle of the North Basin, and in time all over the lake it will be the same as it is now in the South Basin. It is to be hoped, however, that from now on the course of events will be recorded.

THE FISH

The fish most widely distributed among the tarns and lakes of the English Lake District belong to the Salmon family, and are the Salmon, *Salmo salar*, Sea Trout and Brown Trout, *Salmo trutta*, and the char, *Salvelinus alpinus willughbii*, and two kinds of whitefish, the Schelly, *Coregonus laveratus*, and the Vendace, *C. albula*. It is usual to find one or more of these species in a tarn or lake and an angler in the Lake District fishes primarily for 'game' fish, i.e. these Salmonids. There are, however, in the Lake

District, Pike, *Esox lucius*, Perch, *Perca fluviatilis*, Eel, *Anguilla anguilla*, Roach, *Rutilus rutilus*, and Rudd, *Scardinius erythrophthalmus*, species which will also provide sport for the angler.

The tarns and lakes are set amid a diverse landscape and the character of the fish community in any water reflects, to some extent, the features peculiar to its landscape.

Ennerdale Water and Wastwater, the rocky lakes, have brown trout and char; there are minnows and sticklebacks; salmon run through Ennerdale Water. A small tarn, Goat's Water (1,600 ft) on Coniston Old Man, has a similar landscape and holds char (introduced) and trout; and Angle Tarn (1,800 feet) under Bowfell, again with steep sides and rocky shores, holds brown trout (but no char) and it may be taken as typical in its fish fauna of the tarns on the high fells. Some of them, e.g. Stickle Tarn in Great Langdale, hold perch also.

Much of the landscape round Windermere is hilly rather than moun-tainous and there is a fair amount of cultivable land around it; the lake is nowhere markedly steep-sided and much of the shore is wooded. The chief fish are trout, char, pike and perch. Mention should be made of a unique experiment which has been carried out by the Freshwater Bio-logical Association on the perch population of Windermere. Beginning in 1941 and over a period of years, many tons of perch have been removed by traps from the lake, thus effecting a drastic reduction of the population. Early in the experiment the individual perch weighed about 1 oz; today perch taken by angling usually weigh 6 oz. The experiment was initially made possible because the trapped perch were canned to provide food in wartime. A long-term experiment on the pike population of Windermere undertaken by the Freshwater Biological Association since 1944 has involved the removal, by gill net, of one ton of pike per year. Today the numbers of adult pike are about the same as before 1944, but the fish are much younger and they grow faster, but netting allows few to have the chance to live to grow old and therefore large so that the average size is smaller and big fish are fewer.

Buttermere and Crummock Water, like Windermere, have pike and perch as well as trout and char; the presence of these two non-salmonids is somewhat remarkable because the surroundings of both lakes are more mountainous, the shores more rocky and the cultivable area less, com-pared with Windermere. Thirlmere, also amid mountains, with the shoreline of a reservoir, has pike, perch, trout and char.

Coniston Water resembles Windermere closely in its setting of high hills, fields and woods; and its fish, trout, char, pike and perch would seem to bear much the same relative importance to each other as in Windermere.

Ullswater is another of the large lakes and is very like Windermere in landscape and its general physical characteristics; it, too, has perch and trout as important fish, but it differs from Windermere in having a white-fish, the schelly (*Coregonus laveratus*) and also in that pike and char are absent. Char were certainly in Ullswater until about the mid-nineteenth century for G. F. Braithwaite, who knew the lake well, writing in 1884, records catching them but remarks, after a visit in 1872, that the 'char which used to be caught with the rod are extinct'. It is implied that this might be, in part, due to the lead ore washings in Glenridding Beck. There is no evidence that pike were ever in Ullswater and it seems likely that they are also absent from the small lake, Brotherswater, upstream of Ullswater, which holds trout, and perch and possibly schelly; this last fish is also found in Red Tarn (2,356 feet) in the mountains above Ullswater.

Haweswater, which is not far from Ullswater, has a moorland land-scape, with little cultivable land, and a steep shoreline which reflects its conversion into a reservoir since 1938. The species of fish present are the same as before it became a reservoir, namely the schelly (the third and remaining locality for this Coregonid), trout, perch and char, but here, as in Ullswater, there are no pike.

There used to be certain rights for seine netting of fish in Ullswater and Haweswater and from references in nineteenth-century literature, the schelly was much prized. Fish netting was carried out in Windermere and Coniston Water for centuries; it was abolished in Windermere in 1924; the favourite fish were trout and char. At present char are caught by the Plumbline method of angling, which is peculiar to the English Lake District and practised chiefly on Windermere, and to some extent on Coniston Water, Crummock Water and Buttermere. Essentially, the tackle consists of a stout short rod with a bell at the top, an 80-foot line fitted with six side lines (at 4 yard intervals) to each of which is attached a flat metal spinner of silver, aluminium or copper made by the angler, the whole weighted by a plumb. The angler rows slowly over the deep parts of the lake, when his bell rings he lifts in the tackle to net the char caught on the side line.

Char are normally found only in the deeper lakes of the District (those in Goat's Water were introduced by men). The breeding habits of the char in Windermere are of especial interest. After years of scientific investigation it has been established that in this lake there are two distinct and self-perpetuating populations of char isolated from each other by their time and place of spawning; one spawns in November–December in shallow water (3–12 feet) along the lake shore; the other breeds in February–March in deep water (50–70 feet) fairly close inshore. At present this situation is known only from Windermere in British and Irish waters and is not documented from elsewhere in Europe.

Derwentwater and Bassenthwaite Lake, separated by an alluvial plain, differ in their landscape, for that of Derwentwater is the more mountain-ous and there is more cultivable land around Bassenthwaite Lake; both, however, are shallower than the other lakes we have considered and both have a species of whitefish, the vendace, *Coregonus albula*, not found elsewhere in the Lake District; they both contain pike, perch and trout also.

The gentle hills nearby and the pastures along its shores give Esthwaite Water a softer landscape than any of the other lakes. Pike, perch and trout are the main species of fish present (with salmon passing through), but here also are rudd and roach, also rudd/roach hybrids, which are 'coarse' fish of the family Cyprinidae; these same Cyprinids also occur in a small pond cut off at the north end of Esthwaite Water called Priest's Pot.

Up to the present there are only a few authentic records of roach and rudd from tarns (e.g. Tarn Hows) and lakes (e.g. Esthwaite Water, Windermere) in the Lake District, and these have occurred within the past ninety years. These Cyprinids are not usually found in waters where the landscape is rugged and mountainous, but where it is much softer and gentler. Therefore, their apparently recent appearance in what may be regarded as an 'unnatural' environment strongly suggests that the rudd and the roach (and two tench, *Tinca tinca*, from Windermere in 1966 and 1968) have been introduced to the Lake District by man, perhaps when brought to the District to be used as live bait for pike. If then they were 'accidentally' set free in a part of the lake which somewhat resembled their own natural habitat, e.g. in a quiet weedy bay, the introduced species would be likely to survive and if not to become prolific, at least to maintain a small population.

Elterwater and Blelham Tarn in sylvan and pastoral settings, Rydal Water and Grasmere in a more hilly landscape have trout, pike, and perch, the last two tending to be the main species, and Little Langdale Tarn in a similar setting has perch and trout. Loweswater, with a background of mountains as well as woods has pike, perch and trout, the latter being important. None of these waters are deep compared with the larger lakes and none is steep-sided, their shores are not primarily rocky; none of them holds char.

Little has been said about the distribution of the smaller species of fish, the Minnow, *Phoxinus phoxinus*, Three-spined Stickleback, *Gasterosteus aculeatus*, the Bullhead (or Miller's Thumb) *Cottus gobio*, and the Stone Loach, *Nemacheilus barbatulus*, because the occurrence of these fish in the various waters in the Lake District has not been well documented. However, the minnow is known to be in large and small lowland lakes and also high tarns, e.g. Grizedale Tarn (Helvellyn) and Stickle Tarn; the three-spined stickleback is found in lowland waters (in diverse landscapes, too, such as Ennerdale Water and Windermere) and so is the bullhead; although stone loach, which are also of lowland waters, are often found in Esthwaite Water they seem to be absent from Windermere. In so far as the limited information permits, it seems likely that the distribution of these fish has little to do with the character of the landscape. This is certainly true of the eel, which can be found in any lake or tarn (even on higher ground, up to 700 feet), large and small, no matter what the nature of the surrounding countryside.

Salmon and Sea Trout, particularly the former, occur in most of the larger and some of the smaller lakes. They cannot, however, be regarded as members of the community of fish in the lake since as adults they are only passing through on their way to the spawning streams and as young fish on their way to the sea; there is no specific angling for sea trout or salmon in lakes.

The lakes and tarns of the English Lake District occur in various kinds of landscape and some association emerges between the fish fauna of a water and its surroundings. Lakes and tarns where the landscape is decidedly mountainous and the shore is rocky and there is little or no cultivable land round about have trout and char as their fish species (Ennerdale Water, Wastwater). When the landscape is less harsh, the shoreline softer and there is more cultivable land in the area, then the trout and char are joined by the pike and perch (Windermere, Coniston Water).

THE BIRDS OF WINDERMERE

In no way can Windermere be called a favoured resort of wildfowl; it never attracts many surface-feeding duck in winter, and in open winters the diving-duck population may remain small throughout the season. Yet it is a fascinating lake in winter, and in spite of many days when one may see only a few tufted duck (*Aythya fuligula*) or goldeneye (*Bucephala clangula*) there is always the chance that the next bay might hold something unexpected – a velvet scoter (*Melanitta fusca*) or a party of goosanders (*Mergus merganser*). Apart from these there is the perpetual interest of the small bird life along the shore, the gulls, buzzards and hawks flying over, and owls and wood-pigeons among the islands. One very noticeable effect of the north and south alignment of the lake and its position between Morecambe Bay and the central fells is that it forms part of a regular migration highway to and from the southern estuaries of Lakeland and the Solway, and is followed in spring by many small birds making for the passes through the hills, and in the winter months very noticeably by geese. These, though they seldom alight on the lake, are seen flying over as they change their ground from north to south and *vice versa*, which may happen several times between autumn and spring, according to Miss Garnett. On the whole few water birds breed on the lake – until recently mallard (*Anas platyrhynchos*) was the most numerous, together with coots (*Fulica atra*) and moorhens (*Gallinula chloropus*), and a few pairs of resident mute swans (*Cygnus olor*). Shelduck (*Tadorna tadorna*) spread round the lake as a common breeding bird between 1918 and 1930 but later declined

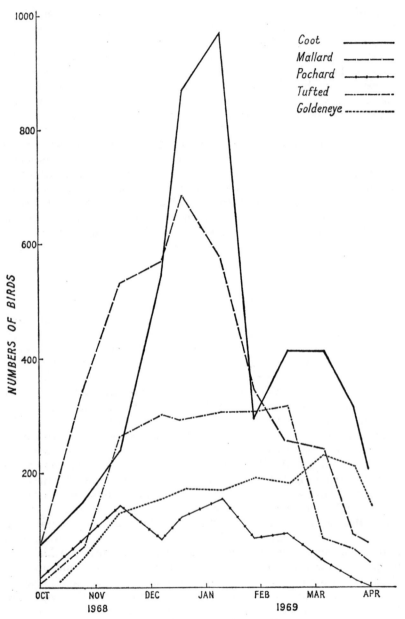

FIG. 8. Wild-fowl counts on Windermere, winter 1968-9.

in numbers, and as we shall see later there has recently been a great increase in the numbers of breeding red-breasted mergansers (*Mergus serratus*) which is now the most numerous nesting species.

Among those birds which feed on the lake, the fish-eaters include cormorants, grebes and divers. Cormorants (*Phalacrocorax carbo*) first appeared regularly on Windermere about fifty years ago, and are now occasional visitors to the lakes at any season, and are common in small flocks between autumn and late spring, often roosting on trees on the islands. They feed on perch, eels and trout. Though 31 feet has been given in bird handbooks as the maximum depth to which these birds dive in pursuit of fish, a cormorant has been found trapped in a Freshwater Biological Association gill net which was set at 39–43 feet. Cormorants nest on the Solway estuary, mostly on the Scottish side but there are a few pairs on St Bees Head; non-breeding birds can be seen on Windermere at most times of year. Grebes and divers are common winter visitors to Windermere, the great crested grebe (*Podiceps cristatus*) nesting on Esthwaite Water and Blelham Tarn, and the little grebe (*Podiceps ruficollis*) on most suitable ponds and tarns up to about 1,000 feet. Regular winter visitors to Windermere, particularly in hard winters, are the great northern diver (*Colymbus immer*), and the black-throated (*Colymbus arcticus*) and the red-throated (*Colymbus stellatus*) divers.

Among the more omnivorous feeders, great numbers of ducks visit Windermere in winter (see Fig. 8, p. 86), but only the mallard and the red-breasted mergansers nest in any numbers. Shelduck appeared as a breeding bird about 1918, but were not usually seen in winter on the lake; they nested in rabbit holes and among rocks in the woods on either side of the lake, and left the neighbourhood when the young left the nest. Most of the breeding shelduck then returned to the lake in March or April. At the end of the war, about 1945, shelduck still commonly nested round the lake in rabbit holes at sites which included places like Watbarrow Point in the North Basin, but soon after that year they decreased in numbers and before long disappeared from the North Basin as the great increase in numbers of tourists took place. Round the quieter shores of the South Basin they continued to breed until myxomatosis put an end to the rabbits and the holes became silted up with leaves and other woodland detritus, whereupon shelduck almost ceased to nest. In 1969 only two pairs attempted to nest round Windermere Of the duck which do not breed on the lake, pochard (*Athya ferina*) and tufted duck (*Athya fuligula*), which are both rare nesters in the district, do not generally visit Windermere until the autumn. Goldeneye (*Bucephala clangula*) appear in October or November, and small numbers of teal (*Anas crecca*) frequent the lake from late autumn to spring. Comparatively rare winter visitors include velvet scoters (*Melanitta fusca*) and shovelers (*Spatula clypeata*); the common scoter (*Melanitta nigra*) appears irregularly but not uncommonly. Wigeon

(*Anas penelope*), which are among the most numerous winter duck in the Lake Counties as a whole, are comparatively scarce on Windermere, as are scaup (*Aythya marila*) and goosanders (*Mergus merganser*).

'Unless they are much disturbed, the different kinds of duck can usually be found in certain places where the depth of water or the kind of bottom are to their liking, or where they are sheltered from the prevailing wind. Nearly all the bays are favourite haunts, especially the deep indentations with reed beds (*Phragmites australis*) at the back, and where the bottom is of sand or mud with patches of weeds, or covered with the short grassy tufts of shore weed (*Littorella lacustris*) and water lobelia (*Lobelia dort· manna*).' (Garnett, 1946.) Such bays are Rayrigg and White Cross on the east, small bays near Waterhead, and Pull Wyke and the inner end of High Wray Bay on the west; much of the shallow part of the lake among the islands provides attractive feeding for ducks. In the South Basin, Parsonage Bay and the bays in the eastern shore from Ferry Nab to Storrs Point, the bay below Cunsey, and Parkhead Wyke at the southern end, are attractive to winter ducks. Of the winter diving duck, tufted duck, often the commonest species, feed by day on both animal and vegetable matter, commonly pulling up tufts of *Littorella*. A sample of the animal food of this duck included caddis-fly larvae, the freshwater shrimp *Gammarus*, and species of *Chironomus*. Goldeneye, though they are found on the *Littorella* beds, also frequent places where the bottom is stony; they feed on *Isoetes* (quillwort) and small molluscs often associated with it, also on *Gammarus* and caddis larvae, but they are also known to feed on the eggs of those char which spawn in November and December. All these duck except the breeding mallard begin to leave the lake towards the end of March.

Flocks of wintering coot frequent the lake from November to March, feeding on species of *Potamogeton* and other aquatic plants, and usually remaining out in the open water over the shallows where they find these plants. Coots nest on all the lakes and on many of the tarns, and leave the higher sites to winter on the valley lakes; on Windermere the nesting birds find sites in the thicker reed beds of the bays. Moorhens similarly nest on all bodies of water up to about 1,000 feet, but tend to congregate on the valley lakes in winter.

Other winter visitors to Windermere include gulls – black-headed (*Larus ridibundus*), herring (*Larus argentatus*) and common (*Larus canus*) – dippers (*Cinclus cinclus*) from the becks, which appear round the lake shores, water rails (*Rallus aquaticus*) and whooper swans (*Cygnus cygnus*). There are few waders on the lake in winter – usually some lapwings (*Vanellus vanellus*) and common snipe (*Capella gallinago*) on the marshy fields behind certain bays such as Pull Wyke, and occasionally redshanks (*Tringa totanus*), oystercatchers (*Haematopus ostralegus*) and dunlin (*Calidris alpina*). Though the lake forms such a conspicuous part of the regular migration routes of many geese in winter, these were seldom seen to alight over the period between 1910 and 1940. Oystercatchers, which commonly nest by mountain lochs in Scotland, are seldom seen and never nest inland in the Lake District, though they are, of course, one of the commonest of birds on the coasts and estuaries within a few miles of Windermere.

One of the earliest signs of spring is the arrival of curlews (*Numenius arquata*) and lesser black-backed gulls (*Larus fuscus*) towards the end of February. The curlews disperse to nesting places in the hills, but those which nest on Claife Heights above Belle Grange come to feed at Calgarth all through the summer. Reed-buntings (*Emberiza schoeniclus*) return in March or earlier to their nesting-places on some of the islands and on marshy places round the shores, and common sandpipers (*Tringa hypoleucos*) arrive in April and spread far up the fells by becks and tarns. A few pairs of kingfishers have been found nesting near the lake from time to time, but at present kingfishers (*Alcedo atthis*) are seen only rarely, and then in winter, on the lake; in summer they can be seen on the Leven after it leaves the lake.

In recent years Miss Atkinson and Mr Shepherd have made regular observations, including detailed counts, of the wildfowl on Windermere. The counts, by boat, were made at frequent intervals through the winters of 1967–8 and 1968–9; Fig. 8, p. 86, shows the numbers of the five major species on the lake for 1968–9. The most numerous species have been coot, mallard, tufted duck, pochard and goldeneye. Although, as Miss Garnett pointed out, for its size the wildfowl population of Windermere is not great, the winter numbers are themselves considerable, with over 1,200 duck seen in December, 1967 and 1968, and approximately 1,000 coots in January, 1968 and 1969, but the summer population is very small, the minimum being 16 duck and 16 coots in August, 1968.

Other birds regularly included in the counts have been little grebes, cormorants, herons, mute swans, moorhens, and various species of gulls which nest on the neighbouring coast – mostly black-headed, herring, and lesser black-backed. The gulls are frequently found feeding and roosting in large numbers; the black-headed gulls have some inland nesting sites on nearby tarns on Claife Heights. Two cormorants recently caught in Freshwater Biological Association gill nets had been ringed as juveniles in the preceding summer, one on the Farne Islands and one in Wigtownshire.

Among the birds seen rarely on the lake, additions to Miss Garnett's list provided by this recent survey have included the bittern (*Botaurus stellaris*), which now nests on Leighton Moss (see page 193), and the common tern (*Sterna hirundo*). Both Canada geese (*Branta canadensis*) and greylag geese (*Anser anser*) have occasionally been seen on Windermere, but only in odd pairs, despite the fact that the greylag has recently become a permanent resident on nearby Esthwaite. A scheme by the Wildfowlers' Association of Great Britain and Ireland to re-introduce the greylag to England was started in 1959, on the Duddon Estuary, and greylag have successfully bred on Coniston Water and on some of the surrounding tarns, including Grizedale Tarn in Grizedale Forest (see also page 291), as well as on lakes in northern Lakeland, in recent years.

An interesting recent development has been the decline of the shelduck as a common breeding species on Windermere, following increased tourist pressure and myxomatosis in the rabbit population, and the increase in numbers of the red-breasted merganser as a summer resident to a level surpassing the mallard in numbers. The first record of nesting of the red-breasted merganser on Windermere was in 1957; in the early summer of 1968 there were 110 adults and at least 14 broods, with a total of 138 young, were raised on the lake in that year. Flotillas of young mergansers have become a regular sight on the lake in late summer. The birds feed on small perch, and are commonly found in those bays where this is the only fish present. On a lake which is becoming busier every year, this increase in a breeding species is in many ways surprising. Observations during this count have emphasised the efficiency of the mergansers as parents, and how they seldom lose a chick, showing great persistence in re-assembling the flotilla of chicks after any disturbance; in this they contrast strongly with the behaviour of mallard as parents.

Other birds breeding regularly on the lake, apart from the mallard, are coots, mute swans and moorhens. Some mallard regularly interbreed with domestic ducks, mostly with Aylesburys and Khaki Campbells, and there is an increasing population of tame hybrids to be seen in such places as Bowness Bay, Rayrigg Bay and Wild Duck Bay, while a few hybrids are also to be found with the winter migrant population of mallards.

Around the lake shores chaffinches and pied wagtails are the commonest summer small birds, and pheasants from the surrounding woods are often seen. The chaffinch (*Fringilla coelebs*) is of course resident and one of the commonest birds of the Lake District; many of those round the lake shores become very tame. The pied wagtail (*Motacilla alba*), which nests at all heights up to about 2,000 feet, tends to congregate in flocks around the lakes before the autumn migration; passage migrants then appear, and though a few birds remain over the winter, numbers are very low from November until February. The return passage begins at the end of February and goes on until April.

ESTHWAITE NORTH FEN

At the point where rivers or large streams flow into a lake, the velocity of the water decreases suddenly and the coarser sediment is deposited on the bottom of the lake to form banks at the sides of the mouth of the river. These banks build up and eventually reach the water-level of the lake, emerging above it when the level is low and continuing to gather further sediment when the level is high. As a result of this process an almost level expanse of alluvium forms through which the river comes to meander.

The process of colonisation of this alluvium by vegetation varies from one lake to another and seems to depend on the rate of sedimentation and the nature of the sediment, and on the dissolved substances in the water. At the head of Ennerdale, for example, the clear waters of the river Liza enter the lake through a swamp formed by extensive carpets of *Sphagnum* and this provides a habitat for many bog plants including *Utricularia intermedia* in the shallow pools. In contrast, at the head of Windermere near Ambleside, the muddy waters of the river Rothay flow in a broad meander through water-meadows with only a narrow fringe of bull-rushes (*Schoenoplectus lacustris*), heavily grazed by cattle, and patches of sedges including, however, the rare northern species *Carex aquatilis*.

In a few sites a fen has developed on the banks of alluvium. The most extensive fen is at the south end of Bassenthwaite but the smaller fen at the north end of Esthwaite Water has been more thoroughly investigated and is now a national nature reserve.

This site was, of course, surveyed for the first edition of the 1 : 10 560 (6 inches to the mile) Ordnance Survey in 1848, and then it was surveyed twice by W. H. Pearsall in 1914–15 and 1929. Pearsall published a detailed description of the vegetation in 1918 and his two surveys show the distribution of the principal types of vegetation. The site was photographed from the air in 1963 and again in 1967. In 1968–69–70 the part of the fen nearest to the lake has been surveyed again by parties of undergraduates from the University of Lancaster under the supervision of C. D. Pigott and Joan F. Wilson. There can be few sites in Britain where the history of the vegetation is known so reliably and in such detail over a period of nearly a century. This is particularly fortunate as the sites provide a fine example of the succession of vegetation during the process of infilling of the lake and its conversion through reedswamp and fen to woodland.

The general structure of the fen and the conditions controlling the distribution of the main types of vegetation were investigated and described by Pearsall (1918). Pearsall emphasised the importance of the Black Beck as a source of sediment. This stream enters Esthwaite Water at its northern end and the North Fen has developed as a result of the silting up of the lake which formerly extended northward and was once continuous with Priest Pot. The map of 1888 on which Pearsall apparently based his estimates of the rate of growth of the fen is in fact identical with the first edition of the Ordnance Survey, surveyed in 1848; presumably the margin of the lake was not re-surveyed in the 1888 edition. This means that between 1848 and 1915 the fen advanced at a much slower rate than Pearsall's calculations suggest. Recalculating the rate it is 25 m in 67 years or an average rate of 37 cm a year. From 1915 to 1965 the fen encroached a further 20 m, so that the rate has remained almost the same at 40 cm a year. Pearsall's description of the vegetation as it was in 1914 and 1929 allows the changes which have occurred in half a century to be exactly identified and their rate measured.

The main burden of sediment brought into the lake by the beck is deposited in two banks which extend into the lake but are separated by a channel. In summer the position of these banks is clearly marked by the floating leaves of yellow water-lilies (*Nuphar lutea*) which are rooted in the sediment where it accumulates most rapidly. In 1914 the white water-lily (*Nymphaea alba*) was the principal species at the mouth of the beck. The submerged banks of 1914 now form the true mouth of the beck and the water is sufficiently shallow to allow replacement of the water-lilies by reed mace (*Typha latifolia*). Following the Black Beck upstream through the fen, the predominantly mineral deposits which form its banks are marked by a distinctive belt of vegetation in which *Phalaris arundinacea*, *Calamagrostis epigejos* (not *C. lanceolata*) and *Filipendula ulmaria* are especially characteristic. When the beck overflows its banks sediment is deposited in this belt of vegetation to form natural levees.

In the shallow water of the lake away from the mouth of the Black Beck, the bullrush (*Schoenoplectus lacustris*) forms the outer fringe of the reed-swamp where the rate of sedimentation is much reduced. The present reed-swamp forms a belt about twenty metres across and must therefore occupy an area which was largely open water in 1914. At its outer edge where *Schoenoplectus* occurs the water is normally over a metre deep even in the summer and the depth decreases away from the lake. Over much of the area reed (*Phragmites australis*) is exclusively dominant but there are patches of *Typha latifolia* and of the very beautiful *Ranunculus lingua*.

Behind the present reed-swamp a mixture of sedges now occupies the area which was reed-swamp in 1929. Towards the lake *Carex rostrata* is the predominant species, mixed with patches of *Carex vesicaria* and scattered young tussocks of *C. elata*, but farther from the lake *C. elata* becomes the dominant species until it dies out in the deep shade of the fen woodland behind. *Phragmites australis* persists in many places in the sedge-fen but its shoots are stunted and sparse.

A few small bushes of a willow which is probably a form of *Salix fragilis* are present in the reed-swamp, and small trees of the same willow, a large thicket of purple osier (*Salix purpurea*) and saplings of alder (*Alnus glutinosa*) occur in the outer part of the sedge-fen. These two willows also occur on the predominantly mineral soils at the mouth of the Black Beck but are no longer confined to these banks as they were in 1914 and 1929. The distribution of alder has also changed because in Pearsall's map of 1929 the first bushes to colonise the sedge-fen behind the reed-swamp were *Salix cinerea* and alder was absent until a later stage. Now it is one of the earliest trees to become established, and there is a mixture of alder and willow over most of the sedge-fen with a few young saplings of bird-cherry (*Prunus padus*) and scattered birches (*Betula pubescens*) in the older but not in the younger woodland. Another striking change is the widespread occurrence of well-grown saplings of ash (*Fraxinus excelsior*) throughout this woodland. In Pearsall's maps of 1914 and 1929 no ashes are shown in the fen, although the large trees on a small mound of glacial drift on the eastern edge of the fen are marked but not labelled.

The development of this woodland is now known in detail. In 1914 there were only scattered bushes of *Salix cinerea* and occasional alders and birches on the eastern part of the fen. These early colonists are now easily identified by their size and spreading growth-forms. The age of the old alders has been confirmed by ring-counts of cores and they prove to have originated at the beginning of the century. By 1929 the number of both alders and willows had greatly increased and now they form an almost continuous canopy beneath which most of the *Carex elata* tussocks are dying but *Carex paniculata* is flourishing. The woodland on the western part of the fen described as old carr by Pearsall in 1914 and 1929 occupies an area subject to a moderate rate of sedimentation in which the soil is intermediate between the inorganic soils of the levees of the Black Beck and the organic peats of the eastern part of the fen. In 1929 the closed carr was dominated by *Salix cinerea* with some alder, birch and much more rarely alder-buckthorn (*Frangula alnus*). The willows are now large and many of them have sunk down into the peat and are dying with their branches often infected by the bracket fungus *Trametes gibbosus*. There has been no regeneration of willow and in much of the woodland, birch has over-topped the willow. The oldest part of the wood is largely composed of birches and beneath it *Molinia caerulea* is plentiful with patches of *Sphagnum palustre* in the wetter parts, and scattered thickets of bramble (*Rubus fissus*). Even this old part of the fen is liable to flooding on rare occasions, as in November, 1968, when the whole wood was flooded to a depth of 20–60 cm and only the eastern edge of the fen remained free of flood water.

The oldest part of the wood has now reached a particularly interesting stage. Some of the birches are now beginning to die and since 1960 a few saplings of oak (*Quercus petraea*) and hazel (*Corylus avellana*) have become established, particularly in the thickets of bramble. Tansley, following Pearsall, believed that in the cool moist climate of the Lake District it was probable that bog would eventually develop as the birches died, but the appearance of oak suggests that the development of oak woodland is also possible.

The eastern and oldest part of the fen remains the least changed over the whole period since 1914. It is the area least subject to addition of sediment and in 1914 it was a meadow of *Molinia* still cut for hay. Although no longer mown, it remains almost free of bushes and consists of a mosaic of large tussocks of *Molinia* with patches of *Sphagnum* containing bog asphodel (*Narthecium ossifragum*) and *Erica tetralix*. Possibly as a result of enclosure and restriction of grazing a few clumps of *Trollius europaeus* have appeared in the edges of the meadow where patches of *Filipendula ulmaria* mark the emergence of springs.

The changes between 1914 and 1929 seem to have been essentially those resulting from the passage of time and the natural successional development. These changes have continued but the recent survey provides evidence that another process of change may now be superimposed on the succession. The change of dominance in the beds of water lilies, the spread of osiers into the areas with a low rate of sedimentation, the early invasion of the reed-swamp by alder, the spread of ash and even the colonisation by oak might all be in response to an increased supply of plant nutrients, particularly phosphate and inorganic nitrogen carried into the fen during periods of flood. Analyses of the water in the lake itself show a rise in concentration of these nutrients and this reflects the increasing use of chemical fertilisers on agricultural land in the lowland part of the catchment area (cf. Table 2). The concentration of phosphate on a dry weight basis (this is not affected by compression) in the peat now forming in the reed bed is over three times that in the peat which formed at the position of the reed bed a half century ago and is now preserved beneath the sedge-fen. The responses of the species are in keeping with their known ecological behaviour. However, until a more detailed investigation, which is now in progress, is completed the explanation suggested remains pure speculation.

CHAPTER 5

RUNNING WATER

. . . the Streams . . .
Pure as the morning, fretful, boisterous, keen,
Green as the salt-sea billows, white and green –
Poured down the hills, a choral multitude!
William Wordsworth: *The River Duddon*

THE FAUNA

An area of impervious rock lying beside an ocean is bound to be well provided with streams. Some rainwater sinks into fissures and emerges lower down from a spring, and much is held in bogs whence runnels flow to unite into a stream which runs down the mountainside to the valley below. Here the various streams combine to form a river, which runs on till it enters a lake. The streams are generally torrential and the rivers sufficiently fast to be floored with stones.

Many animals have established themselves in this environment. Its advantages are that the flow brings a continuous supply of food, and the turbulence keeps the water well oxygenated. The disadvantage is that the colonists cannot venture into the open water without being carried downstream. Probably the hazards of living in a current have been exaggerated, and most stream-dwellers avoid the current by living underneath stones. The current may, of course, turn over a stone, in which case the animals exposed must behave in an appropriate way, and make for the bottom and the shelter of another stone as quickly as possible.

Temperature is variable. Springs are usually cold, but water from superficial layers may emerge warm if the soil is shallow. A small stream warms up in a short distance if exposed to the sun, and may then be cooled considerably by evaporation if it runs through a wood or a gorge shaded by trees.

Anyone who has occasion to watch a stream closely over a few decades becomes aware that the mountains are being broken up and carried down to the plain at an unexpectedly high rate. The upper reaches of the streams that rise on the fells generally consist of cascades and pools. Pieces are continually breaking off the solid rock, and if they are large they come to rest in a pool, or jam in the ravine through which the stream flows. If they are smaller they travel farther, as will the larger blocks also as they disintegrate. Corners are chipped off as the pieces are carried downstream, and as a result at the head of the valley the river bed often consists of rounded stones that shift easily each time the current increases speed. A similar unstable bottom is found where a stream has eroded boulder clay and exposed rounded stones.

Near the spring, where the volume of water is insufficient to move even round stones, and lower down on rock faces and larger boulders, there may be a growth of mosses or liverworts (Fig. 10, p. 104). On unstable bottoms no more than a coating of algae is able to establish itself. This algal covering provides pasturage for some stream-dwelling animals, but the main source of food is thought by many to be the debris washed in by the rain, but possibly the plant material which is the main constituent is not directly available to animals, and their real source of food is the fungi and bacteria that are breaking down the vegetable tissues.

It is evident then that the food supply varies enormously down the length of a stream. High up the rain will wash into a watercourse the remains of the sparse upland plants and a little sheep-dung. Lower down dead leaves from trees make a more substantial contribution to the debris, a contribution that becomes increasingly great with increasing distance downstream. For the algae there is a critical point at which the fertilisers that the farmer puts upon his fields begin to augment the exiguous supply of nutrients leached out of the soil.

Very little is known about the small organisms in streams, and rather few studies of the vegetation have been made, but there have been several surveys of the animals, both in the Lake District and in mountainous regions elsewhere. It is, therefore, possible to list a typical small-stony-stream fauna and to discuss how it changes with changing conditions. Ford Wood Beck, the main inflow of Blelham Tarn, has been extensively studied and may be taken as a point of departure for that reason, though it is not typical, as most of it runs through the sort of farmland that is dressed with fertiliser. It is, therefore, richer than many streams. The first striking feature of the fauna is the preponderance of insects, in both numbers of species and numbers of individuals. Some other groups occur in abundance, but are represented by one or two species only. One of the most obvious is *Gammarus pulex*, the freshwater shrimp, which occurs everywhere in Ford Wood Beck. It is a good example of a species which lacks obvious structural modification for life in flowing water and presumably owes its success to adaptation of behaviour. In contrast is *Ancylus fluviatilis*, aptly named the freshwater limpet, for it resembles a limpet closely in everything but size, though not, in fact, related to it. This snail is found generally wherever there is a hard substratum, though, as might be expected, such a slow creature cannot survive on an unstable bottom. The other animals outside the class Insecta that may be common are the flatworms or planarians. *Crenobia alpina*, formerly *Planaria alpina*, distinguished by its two eyes set close together, is not generally found in

PLATE 9 *Above*, Great Langdale Head – Mickleden and Oxendale: the Band
and Bowfell rise behind the dale-head farms which belong to the National Trust.
Below, Eskdale and Harter Fell: an unspoiled dale landscape of farms and semi-
natural deciduous woodland, part of the proposed and successfully opposed
"Hardknott Forest Park".

PLATE 10 *Above*, Ennerdale Water and Pillar: Forestry Commission spruce forest and (right) a small surviving semi-natural deciduous woodland (The Side). *Below*, Pillar Rock towering above the altitudinal limit of economic forestry.

waters warmer than 12° C and it breeds only at temperatures lower than this. It is confined to the topmost reaches of Ford Wood Beck. The second flatworm, *Polycelis felina*, formerly *Polycelis cornuta*, is found downstream of it.

There are a few other worms, using that term in the most general sense, including some that the lay observer is likely to take for earthworms which have strayed into the water. Around midsummer *Gordius*, the well-named horsehair worm, is often seen. During the rest of the year it lives a parasitic existence but there is still much to be found out about its life history.

The collector will also take a few mites.

Among the insects the Ephemeroptera or Mayflies, and Plecoptera or Stoneflies are well represented. The nymphs of the Ecdyonuridae have flat heads, flat basal segments to the legs and a rather flat body. The whole is admirably adapted to cling to the surface of stones and scuttle over it at speed. These nymphs are found on stony lake shores as well. Another mayfly family is the Baetidae, whose nymphs are stream-lined and able to swim through the water at great speed. The tails, fringed with stout hairs, function as propellers. Species in the genus *Baetis* are confined to running water, apparently because the so-called gills down the side of the body cannot beat, as can those of other genera, and therefore the nymph can obtain sufficient oxygen only from water that is flowing past it. Other nymphs can create a current by waving the gills. Some nymphs of Ephemeroptera are adapted for burrowing.

The Plecoptera nymphs are more uniform and any of them could be taken to illustrate the structure of the typical primitive insect. The larger species, over an inch in length when mature, are carnivores and the smaller ones eat detritus. Fourteen species have been recorded from Ford Wood Beck.

The familiar dytiscid and haliplid water-beetles are largely confined to still water, presumably because it is difficult for an animal that must come to the surface for air to avoid being carried downstream. Some have solved this problem, but none has been recorded from Ford Wood Beck. Another family, the Elminthidae, formerly known as the Elmidae or Helmidae, is commonly found in streams of this kind. The adult is capable of no more than a slow walk, and it spends its life on the bottom of the stream. This it can do because it has become independent of the atmosphere. Its lower surface is covered by a plastron, which is a coating of short fine water-repelling hairs. Air is secreted into the spaces between them at the beginning of adult life, and thereafter oxygen taken from this supply for use in the body is made good by diffusion from the water. As already noted there is always plenty of oxygen in stream water. Beetles that carry a bubble must come to the surface to renew it because the pressure on their bubble causes it to dissolve. There is, of course, the same pressure on the elminthid beetles, but it is not sufficient to force water between the hairs of the plastron and therefore the volume of gas can be maintained only by diffusion.

Eighteen species of Trichoptera or caddis-fly have been found in Ford Wood Beck. Some of the larvae make the protective houses for which the group is noted, using the small stones on the stream-bed. Others are more adapted to life in running water, for they spin nets to trap the debris which the current is always sweeping along. They are sometimes found in great numbers just below a lake, for here the plankton caught in the outflowing current provides a rich supply of food. These net spinners are limited in their choice of sites, which must be in a place where the current is strong enough to inflate and flow through the net but not strong enough to tear it.

The most highly adapted of all British stream dwellers is the larva of *Simulium*, which in the adult stage is known as the Buffalo Gnat or the Black Fly. The flies are not much longer but more robust than the midge which causes so much annoyance on damp windless days, particularly near sunset. British species of *Simulium* rarely bite man, though in other countries they may be not only a nuisance but a carrier of disease. The larva feeds, as do the caddis mentioned above, by straining particles from the water, but it does this by means of a net formed by modification of one pair of feeding appendages. It can spin, as can the caddis larva, but lays its silk on the surface of a stone, here and there connecting the threads to a larger pad. It can attach itself to these by means of circlets of hooks at the rear end, and once safely attached it can hang in the swiftest current in a place where the flow both brings food and keeps away predators.

There are several other fly (Diptera) larvae in Ford Wood Beck, one of them, a daddy-long-legs in later life, among the biggest of all the animals to be found. It is a cylindrical grub two inches long and illustrates decisively that structural adaptation is not essential to successful life in streams.

The only fish in Ford Wood Beck is the trout (*Salmo trutta*) though in larger becks the bullhead (*Cottus gobio*) and the stone loach (*Nemacheilus barbatulus*) occur. Another predator on the invertebrate fauna is the dipper (*Cinclus cinclus*). It can dive into the water and progress along the bottom, half walking and half swimming, and it probably takes a heavy toll of the inhabitants. There are probably few insectivorous birds which do not prey extensively at some time or other on the adults that come from aquatic larvae or nymphs.

Ford Wood Beck is barely two miles long, yet the fauna is not uniform. As already noted, the flatworm (*Crenobia alpina*) is confined to the upper part of the main stream, a restriction which, because the animal has been investigated so often, one can confidently relate to the lower temperature there. Other species, for example *Heptagenia lateralis* (Ephemeroptera) and

Wormaldia spp. (Trichoptera), are distinctly more common in the upper reaches, though in the absence of experimental confirmation it would be premature to assert definitely that the factor concerned is the colder water. The large stonefly (*Perlodes microcephala*) is rarely taken except in Sykeside Beck, one of the three main tributaries. Lower down it is replaced by *Perla bipunctata*. Sykeside Beck, as the name indicates, dries up in a dry summer. *Perlodes* completes development in one year and tides over the period when the stream may be dry as an egg, a stage more resistant to absence of water than later active ones. The development of *Perla* takes three years and the inability of nymphs to survive in a stream bed which, though damp, has no moving water, probably keeps this insect out of temporary streams. *Perlodes* is perhaps barred from the lower reaches by competition with *Perla*.

Ford Wood Beck was the scene of a vast experiment, organised, unwittingly, by the local Council. They brought mains water to a village whose existing source of supply was a pump, and then, when everybody installed baths and indoor sanitation, led the waste water from sixteen houses to a septic tank that had been designed to purify the sewage from four. There was some overloading of the tank, and enrichment of the stream. The spectacular result was an enormous increase in the numbers of *Polycelis felina*. Collections of a thousand specimens were made where previously only two had been found. The steady spread of the big population is shown in Fig. 9, p. 100. Some Ephemeroptera and Plecoptera disappeared or became much scarcer, but the difference between the enriched and unenriched fauna was much less than in lakes where, on the stony shores, the animal community was of the same type. It was thought that, had there been a directly unfavourable effect on any of the species, its decline would have been earlier and more sudden. A more likely explanation was that it was due to predation by the flatworms. Obviously none of the larger animals could have formed the main prey, or extinction would have been inevitable. It is thought that the main food was some small organism whose numbers increased greatly as a result of the enrichment and that some Ephemeroptera and Plecoptera were captured incidentally sufficiently often to make a noticeable reduction of their numbers.

A particularly important study was made by two American visitors during a year's tenure of grants to work at the laboratory of the Freshwater Biological Association. They selected the River Duddon, one of the two draining a main valley in which there is no lake. The highest source of a feeding stream is 2,500 feet above sea level and there is a relatively flat valley in which the main river runs at an altitude of between 500 and 600 feet. At the end of this the gradient increases, and the river runs steeply down to a second valley which ends in the sea. The highest source of a stream running into this lower valley is 1,200 feet. Though the valley floor

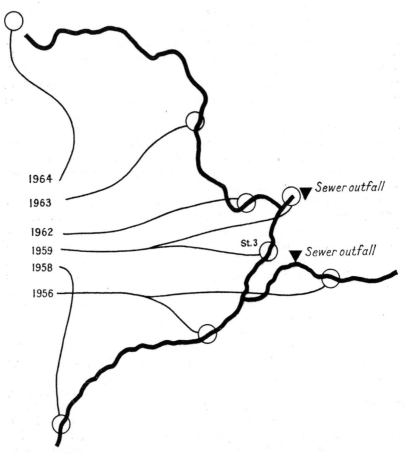

FIG. 9. Diagram of Ford Wood Beck to show the year in which large populations of *Polycelis felina* were first recorded. The circles indicate the positions of the collecting stations.

is flat in comparison with the fell sides, the fall is sufficiently great to maintain torrential conditions right down to the sea. The bottom is of stones and boulders and most of them are rounded, which produces an unstable bottom.

Collections were made often at many stations, and the picture they revealed was unexpected. The fauna of the whole of the upper basin consisted mainly of Plecoptera. Fifteen species were recorded, six of them in abundance. There were also several species of Trichoptera, most of them net-spinners, a moderate population of *Simulium*, various other dipterous larvae, and a small number of *Crenobia alpina* at one or two stations. A few individuals of *Baetis rhodani* were recorded and they were the only representatives of the order Ephemeroptera seen in the upper basin. This, together with the absence of *Gammarus pulex*, was the outstanding feature of the upper basin. In the lower basin the Ephemeroptera typical of streams and, at some stations, *Gammarus*, were numerous, in addition to the Plecoptera found in the upper basin.

That more Plecoptera relative to Ephemeroptera are found in the headwaters of a system had been known for a long time, but their absolute preponderance in so much of it had not been recorded before. An explanation is still to seek. No extensive survey of any other stream at high altitude has been made, but there is sufficient data to make a comparison possible, and from this it is clear that certain explanations that could otherwise have been put forward can be discarded. Much of the information is about Whelpside Gill, which originates in Brownrigg Well at an altitude of 2,800 feet, below the summit of Helvellyn, and flows down the steep side of that mountain into Thirlmere. Many species of Ephemeroptera common in Ford Wood Beck, occur in Whelpside Gill also, though in smaller numbers; so does *Gammarus pulex*, which is abundant in the spring itself though scarce lower down. In addition there are certain species found only at high altitudes. Among the Ephemeroptera there are two of these, *Ameletus inopinatus* and *Baetis tenax*. The latter is indistinguishable from *B. vernus* but, since the nymphs of these species are found either in stony streams above about 1,500 feet or in slow lowland rivers and not in between, they probably are good species. *Ameletus inopinatus* is recorded also in Scandinavia and in the central European mountains through to the east Balkans, but it has not been taken in the Alps or the Pyrenees. A stonefly that is confined to the mountains is *Protonemura montana*, which was discovered in the Lake District by Mr D. E. Kimmins during the war and has since been found in central Europe.

Whelpside Gill and Gaitscale Gill, the highest tributary on the Duddon, appear to be physically similar and have a similar temperature regime, and therefore both those factors can be dismissed from any consideration of the absence of Ephemeroptera and *Gammarus* from Gaitscale Gill. The only possible line of evidence has been gathered during the course of an investigation of the distribution of *Gammarus*, an investigation whose progress has been greatly facilitated by the fact that *Gammarus* is an unmistakable genus which, in the Lake District, contains but one species. It has therefore been possible to entrust the search for it to parties of young men keen to find an excuse for camping in the high fells. *Gammarus* is generally found in streams which, like Ford Wood Beck, run through fields likely to be fertilised. Higher up its distribution is much less regular. It occurs almost everywhere on the range of which Helvellyn is the dominating feature and in some streams immediately on the other side of the rift that bounds the range to the west. Farther west and to the north almost every collection has been negative. There is some correlation between this distribution and calcium, *Gammarus* occurring where there is more than 3 mg/l, but much more work must be done to establish the nature of the correlation. *Gammarus* has invaded fresh water from the sea, and such animals generally take in ions through the body surface. Presumably there must be a concentration below which uptake is not possible and this limits the range of the animal. Insects are less susceptible to limitation in this way because they have invaded fresh water from the land. As land animals they had to develop a cuticle from which little of anything was lost, and also a mechanism whereby ions were taken in with the food and absorbed from the gut. Thus equipped they were in a much stronger position to colonise pieces of fresh water where the concentration of salts was very low, and their preponderance today in such places supports the hypothesis. It has not, however, contributed anything to an explanation of why Ephemeroptera are absent from the upper valley of the Duddon but present in other streams at high altitude. It could be a question of food. Calcium stimulates decomposition of plant remains, and it may affect the distribution of organisms that break down cellulose. However, until work has been done on the digestive processes of mayflies and stoneflies, speculation about the reasons for their occurrence may be all that is possible.

Current speed is rated by many workers as the most important factor shaping the communities that inhabit running water, but this view does not seem to take full account of the fact that most animals live under stones where the current is much reduced. Some of the net-spinning Trichoptera already mentioned, though limited to a narrow range of current speed, are nevertheless widely distributed and to be found in a stream where it is torrential as well as where the flow is only just fast enough to maintain a stony bottom. Many species have been shown to congregate in those places where the configuration of the bottom leads to the settlement of debris. There does, however, seem to be a direct effect on some species. The catches of *Polycelis felina* in Ford Wood Beck have almost always been lowest at Station 3, and Station 3 is in the swiftest part of the beck. A striking example is *Siphlonurus lacustris*, one of the largest Ephemeroptera. It occurs in streams, particularly high up, where they traverse a stretch of flat land and flow slowly. Nymphs are not often taken in tarns but they are sometimes impressively abundant in a small shallow artificial tarn in Brown Cove under the north-east face of Helvellyn. The flight of a crowd of these nymphs as an observer appears may cause a commotion in the water.

As rivers get larger the fauna tends to get richer. For example, among the Ephemeroptera *Heptagenia lateralis* is the only species in becks but lower down *H. sulphurea* is found as well. *Rhithrogena semicolorata* and

R. haarupi are a similar pair. Sometimes one species replaces another: *Ecdyonurus torrentis* appears to be confined to small becks. *E. venosus* occurs with it and lower down, and the river species is *E. dispar* which is joined by *E. insignis*, probably as conditions grow more productive. Of these river species the only one seen in the River Duddon was *Ecdyonurus dispar*. In general the fauna of the main river was poor, probably owing to the unstable bottom, and the fauna was an attenuated version of that found in the side streams.

THE FLORA

The work of Dr Macan and other zoologists on the fauna of Lake District becks serves to emphasise how little we know of the details of the flora of micro-organisms, algae, bryophytes and higher plants which are the other members of this aquatic community. Fig. 10, p. 104 shows the results of an attempt to describe the micro-habitats available in five characteristic reaches of a Lakeland mountain beck, using the mosses found on stones and solid rock as representing the dominant vegetation. As yet there has been no integrated study of the vegetation and the animals in a single stream, but this is clearly something which ought to be done.

Torver Beck, the stream illustrated, rises in springs on the slopes of Coniston Old Man at about 2,000 feet, flows through the tarn Goat's Water at 1,650 feet, and drops steeply in the course of four miles to enter Coniston Water at 143 feet above sea level. Its lower course, which resembles in some ways that of Ford Wood Beck described by Dr Macan, has been so much modified by channelling and straightening through farm land, and by the construction of dams and races for two water-mills, that much of it was not included in the vegetation survey. The upper course is illustrated in transects A, B, C and D in Fig. 10, and resembles in part both Whelpside Gill and Gaitscale Gill mentioned by Dr Macan. Transect E shows a modified section below the sluice of a water-mill which was still in operation until the late 1930s.

The mountain rills feeding Goat's Water, the largest of which has been taken as the headwaters of Torver Beck, rise in springs among the moss *Philonotis fontana* and various submerged liverworts – springs of a kind which will be discussed further in Chapter 9. There is no shade, the water is very cold, and though it flows fast and is therefore well oxygenated, the luxuriant growth of mosses and liverworts in the water must go far to provide a stable micro-habitat where small animals are not washed away.

Transects B and C in Fig. 10 represent the course of Torver Beck where it is similar to that of Gaitscale Gill (p. 101). In the part between the 1,400 and 1,650 foot contours, where the flow of water is very rapid but much broken up by boulders, the bright green cushions of the moss *Dicranella palustris* are conspicuous beside the water, and on the boulders

A

A Transect illustrating zone 1, *Philonotis fontana* zone. Altitude *c.* 1730 ft.; stream about 1 ft. wide. Unshaded, therefore light intensity equal to full daylight.

B Transect illustrating zone 2, *Dicranella squarrosa* zone. Altitude *c.* 1550 ft., stream (partly subterranean among boulders) about 5 ft. wide. Unshaded, therefore light intensity equal to full daylight.

C Transect illustrating zone 3, *Rhacomitrium aciculare* zone, corresponding with the 'upper gill'. Altitude *c.* 1250 ft., stream about 6 ft. wide. Light intensity approximately two-thirds full daylight.

D Transect illustrating zone 4, *Porotrichum alopecurum* zone, corresponding with the 'lower gill'. Altitude *c.* 240 ft., main stream a swift deep channel about 4 ft. wide, with slower side streamlets. Deep shade, light intensity about one-seventh full daylight.

E Transect illustrating sub-zone 4a, *Cinclidotus fontinaloides* zone. Altitude *c.* 200 ft., light intensity equal to full daylight. Stream bed about 18 ft. wide.

FIG. 10. The moss flora of Torver Beck. From Trans. Brit. Bryological Soc., Vol. I, 1949. (for key see facing page)

among which the water makes its way the tufts of *Rhacomitrium aciculare* are dominant within the splash zone. Below 1,400 feet, where the course of Torver Beck descends from a mountain to a moorland environment, and the stream becomes incised into a shallow ravine, the force of the main channel is such as to prevent much growth of mosses on stones below the water level. The most abundant moss is *Rhacomitrium aciculare* on the boulders. This rapid stretch of the upper gills must offer comparatively few micro-habitats to aquatic animals except those which live entirely beneath the loose stones.

Transect D in Fig. 10 illustrates a characteristic profile of the lower courses of many Lakeland becks, where they descend the steep sides of the glaciated valleys in ravines – gills – which are deeply incised into solid rock and often heavily shaded by trees. Dense growth of the moss *Thamnium alopecurum* covers the solid rock from normal water-level to a height of about 5 feet above it, and constantly associated with it is the moss *Eurhynchium riparioides*, a characteristic submerged species of fast-flowing water. These submerged and semi-submerged mats of vegetation must offer a distinct habitat for colonisation by the stream fauna.

Transect E in Fig. 10 shows a type of stream bed which is in some ways comparable with Ford Wood Beck. A peculiar feature, the intermittent flow of this stretch due to the operation of mill sluices, must have been extremely common in Lake District becks through the many centuries when overshot water-wheels, operated by mill races controlled by sluices, were found on the course of almost every stream in the inhabited parts of the district, grinding corn, operating machinery for the woollen industry, turning bobbins, and working hammers and bellows for miners, smelters and smiths. These are the stretches where, though the mills have fallen into disuse, further human modification is now apparent as house drains, farmyard drains and fertilisers from the fields add more and more nutrients to the waters.

Rhacomitrium fasciculare	Brachythecium rutabulum
Rhacomitrium heterostichum	Andreaea rothii
Rhacomitrium aciculare	Barbula cylindrica
Philonotis fontana	Bryum spp.
Hygrohypnum eugyrium	Cirriphyllum crassinervium
Hypnum spp.(section Limnobium)	Isothecium myosuroides
Hypnum cupressiforme	Hygroamblystegium fluviatile
Dicranella palustris	Fontinalis antipyretica
Thamnium alopecurum	Mnium hornum
Eurhynchium riparioides	Mnium punctatum
Cinclidotus fontinaloides	Blindia acuta

Scapania   Pellia   Grasses

Falling or rapidly flowing water   Boulders

Smoothly flowing water   Solid rock

Soil or glacial drift

CHAPTER 6

CLIMATE

On stern Blencathra's perilous height
The winds are tyrannous and strong;
And flashing forth unsteady light
From stern Blencathra's skiey height,
As loud the torrents throng!
Samuel Taylor Coleridge

LYING between 54° and 55° N, the climate of the Lake District is that of a small group of mountains and valleys which more often than not finds itself to leeward of a wide expanse of ocean that is distinctly warm for its latitude, and beneath those upper westerlies whose sinuous flow above 20,000 feet girdles the earth. From winter to summer there is a great change in the amount of daylight; the slow unfolding of the long cool spring is a delightful concomitant. Northern Labrador and Moscow lie near the same parallel, but our mobile humid air and our mild winters ensure that adjacent to the ever-open sea the coastal fringe today provides some remarkable ecological niches, for example in favourable sheltered locations on the well-drained limestone slopes that fall to the southward, adjacent to Morecambe Bay. Yet, within a very few miles, the relatively cool and breezy summer ensures that the altitudinal limit for tree-growth is remarkably low. Latitude, moreover, implies not only a great change in day-length, but also in the intensity of radiation on slopes of varying aspect, most noticeable to the visitor in the immense variety of light and of colour from season to season and indeed from day to day and hour to hour, under the lively mobile skies that are proper to a mountainous country so placed. For 200 years the stimulus arising from the resultant variety and accompanying changes of mood has been welcomed by visiting artists, poets and scientists alike, many of whom have come to live amid the mountains and lakes to savour it all throughout the year.

Were it not for the mountains the climate would be much like that of the Fylde of Lancashire or the Cumberland plain. Inland, the mean temperatures in the colder winter months lie a little above those of south-eastern England at the same level; while the prevalence of westerly winds ensures that the summer months, especially August, are somewhat cooler and inclined to be more cloudy. Over the low country there is distinctly more wind; from the Climatological Atlas of the British Isles it is seen that the mean wind speed inland is about half as great again as in the south-east. The frequency of strong winds, often reaching gale force on the coast,

is distinctly higher in the north-west. The northbound traveller begins to
see the evidence in the leaning trees as soon as the train has crossed the
Mersey. To the homing Lancastrian the little oak trees of the Fylde tell
the tale of that cheerful, fresh sea-borne wind that gladdens his heart, in
spite of the rude buffeting that so often goes with his more boisterous
winter air. And when in early May his Westmorland neighbour drives
eastward into the Pennines, soon he will behold the characteristic
struggling ash-tree on the windward side of the fellside farms, the long
march across the upland pastures of those effortful stone walls that can
give welcome shelter for the sheep, the tell-tale remnant snowdrift among
the rocks above 2,000 feet. It is at about 600 feet that we find today the
limit for those hawthorn hedges that betoken the kindlier arable lands
below, where the grass grows well and the dairy cattle thrive. Even today
the occasional arable farming reminds us how, not long ago, the countryside raised its own grain; wheat here and there along Edenside or towards
the coast where the average annual rainfall is less than 38 inches or so; but
oats predominating where the presence of the hills meant more rain, more
cloud in the late summer, and a shorter growing season. To this we must
add the effect of diminished evaporation in the cooler upland air; hence,
a land of porridge and good tweed, and manifest regard by animals, plants
and men for the well-drained slopes and the helpful presence of limestone
or the glacial drift derived therefrom.

On the lowland bordering the Lake District proper the annual rainfall
is much the same as that of lowland Devon or Somerset, between 37 and
40 inches towards the coast in Furness; between 32 and 35 inches along
Edenside to the north-east; but, with the later spring and the cooler
summer, growth is not quite so lush. Inland, the overall risk of frost in the
spring and autumn is not seriously greater than that for most of lowland
England, but night frosts tend to be a little sharper in spring. Furthermore,
the diversified drift-covered landscape provides important local hazards
and some very acute frost-hollows can be found. The sunshine record,
having regard to the latitude, is quite good, accompanied as it often is by
the clear unpolluted air from the nearby sea and correspondingly high
intensity of solar radiation. It is, moreover, important to recognise that
with the high Northern Pennines to the eastward, and Scotland to the
north, the whole area often becomes decidedly dry and sunny when the
wind goes into that quarter. As winds from between north and east
provide about a quarter of the annual total, the vegetation in the Lake
District suffers more frequently from drought than is commonly realised,
especially on south slopes where very free-draining soils often prevail,
underlain as they commonly are by the shattered hillside screes that were
left after the Ice Age.

The specific character of the Lake District, therefore, so much a part of
northern England, arises from the presence and particularly the disposi-

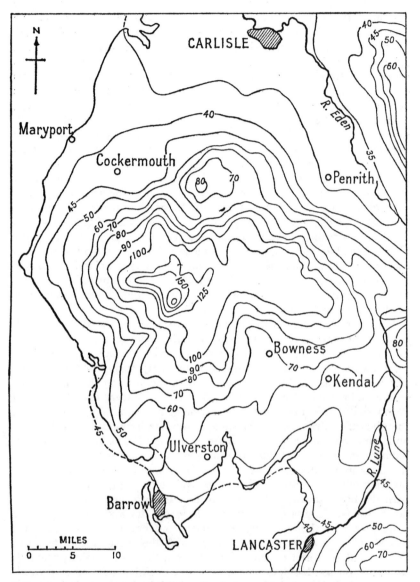

FIG. 11. Average annual rainfall (1916-50) shown by isohyets in inches.

tion of the mountains. The primary result is to increase not only the amount of cloud but also very notably the amount of precipitation, whether as rain or snow. Annual precipitation totals increase very rapidly between the coast and the heads of the several valleys that so conspicuously radiate, and thus cause marked convergence of the upflowing airstream, especially from between south and west whence, in an advancing depression, the humid air with a long fetch over the sea so commonly arrives. Accordingly, compared with Low Furness, five times as much rain falls in a small patch near Sprinkling Tarn beneath Great End, where it is thought that the annual total averages 185 inches. About a dozen square miles around the heads of Eskdale, Langdale and Borrowdale catch more than 150 inches. That convergence of the surface airstreams plays a part in adding to the normal orographic rainfall, that is rain caused or intensified by the forced expansion and cooling of the air as it rises over mountains, has long been recognised, for minor wet areas which get more than 100 inches are found between Fairfield and Helvellyn and around the headwaters of the river Kent. Diminution of the rainfall to leeward is, however, quite rapid. Coming down Borrowdale, Seathwaite averages 131 inches, Rosthwaite just over 100, Grange about 90, Keswick about 57 and Cockermouth under 45; and to the north-east the decrease is more marked. Penrith and Appleby average about 35 inches, and on the lighter well-drained soils beyond Ullswater arable fields appear; even today a good deal of land is there devoted to feed grain and root crops, in addition to the hay crop so characteristic of the whole of north-west England.

Among the mountains, parts of the valleys are relatively sheltered and the trees retain their leaves, for example, along the west side of Windermere, well into the autumn by comparison with the more windy coastal lowlands. The effect of the diminution of rainfall from south-west to north-east is evident from the character of the land use. In Dunnerdale at Cockley Beck the highest reclaimed fields lie at about 700 feet, with a rainfall nearly twice that which prevails at 1,300 feet beside the highest farms in Matterdale, on the more sheltered and drier north-eastern flank of the district; although Matterdale is much colder, and the winter snowfall borne on the north-easter is both deeper and more persistent, covering the pastures on an average of 45 days yearly, against 20 or less in Dunnerdale.

Not only do we find that the spell of continuous rain characteristic of the approach of the warm front of a depression is much intensified among the mountains but that a day with half an inch at Barrow may give three inches in Langdale. Much of the air that passes over northern England is conditionally unstable with the result, for example, that a cloudy late autumn day that may remain almost rainless on the coast will give a number of sharp showers among the mountains. This explains the increase in the frequency of days with measurable rain from between 190 and 200 on the coast to upwards of 225, rising to 236 at Seathwaite. Nevertheless the number of rainy days does not increase in conformity with the amount. Evidently, on the rainy days it rains in greater amount and for a longer time; measured in hours, the annual total is probably about 700 on the surrounding lowland, but it may well exceed 1,500 hours in the wet centre. The number of dry days is very nearly as great among the mountains, and drought is far from unknown. In February, 1932, no measurable precipitation whatever fell at the head of Borrowdale; and other phenomenally dry months were April, 1938, May, 1909, August, 1947, September, 1865 and 1959.

The effect of these radiating dales of varied aspect with their well-drained slopes, a very irregular rocky terrain, a series of flat-floored valley-bottoms sometimes partly occupied by lakes, and diversified elsewhere by a very irregularly deposited drift-cover is to provide a great variety of micro-climates. To all this there can be added the consequences of man's efforts, manifest in the numerous patches of woodland, the walls and buildings, that can affect the local radiation balance and the air movement, together with the effects of drainage that can influence the conductivity of heat from the ground. It is readily seen that plants, animals and man can find very different conditions within short distances. Even from the standpoint of the impression gained by the visitor, the aspect of the several valleys is important. Local effects of the heavy rainfall are, moreover, intensified by the very variable detailed relief. Within a few yards of the very free-draining slopes that can so readily burn in May, there may lie a patch of very wet peat-bog, the result of the filling of one of the many irregularly-disposed dimples of the underlying rock surface that are so characteristic of a glaciated country. Indeed, many of the larger hollows of this type are still occupied by tarns.

TEMPERATURE: FREQUENCY OF FROST, AND EXTREMES

Instrumental observations have been kept by many individuals throughout the district: from 1756 onward temperature and rainfall data of some kind can be found.

Monthly means adjusted to the period 1931–60 are given below, for Keswick. They are not dissimilar to those of north-west England generally. Approximate average extremes, and the absolute extremes on record for each month are also given. The station at Keswick lies within a mile of two extensive lakes, and is well exposed on the valley-floor which is partly wooded and partly open grassland and is thus well representative of the inhabited valleys. Averages have not yet been published for Ambleside, but its temperature records compare closely with those of Keswick (which ended in 1958).

	Jan.	Feb.	Mar.	April	May	June	July	Aug.	Sept.	Oct.	Nov.	Dec.	Year
Keswick (254')													
Mean °C	3.7	3.8	5.8	7.8	10.9	13.7	15.2	15.0	12.8	9.8	6.7	5.0	9.2
Fahr.	38.7	38.8	42.4	46.2	51.6	56.7	59.4	59.0	55.0	49.6	44.1	41.0	48.6
Mean Max. °C	6,7	6.8	9.3	11.7	15.3	18.0	18.9	18.8	16.4	13.0	9.7	7.9	12.7
Fahr.	44.0	44.2	48.7	53.1	59.5	64.4	66.0	65.9	61.5	55.6	49.5	46.2	54.9
Mean Min. °C	0.6	0.7	2.2	4.0	6.5	9.5	11.6	11.1	9.2	6.5	3.8	2.1	5.7
Fahr.	33.1	33.3	36.0	39.0	43.7	49.1	52.8	51.9	48.5	43.6	38.8	35.8	42.3
Approximate average extremes Fahr.	52	52	58	64	72	76	78	75	70	64	57	53	80
	21	22	26	29	33	40	44	43	37	31	27	23	16

Absolute extremes 1904–58: 91° in July 1948, 0° in January 1940. On the same night in January 1940 −6° was observed at Ambleside.

The effects in more sheltered valley locations, not close to the larger lakes, are demonstrated by comparing the observations at Appleby with those at Keswick, making allowance for the difference in level between the two stations:

Differences between the mean monthly *maxima* at Appleby and Keswick: reduced to the same level and rounded to 0.5° F (Appleby is the lower in winter and higher in summer.)

Jan.	Feb.	Mar.	April	May	June	July	Aug.	Sept.	Oct.	Nov.	Dec.
−2.5	−2.5	0	+0.5	+0.5	+1.0	+1.0	+0.5	0	−0.5	−1.5	−2.0

Differences between the mean monthly *minima* at Appleby and Keswick: reduced to the same level and rounded to 0.5° F (Appleby is the lower throughout.)

Jan.	Feb.	Mar.	April	May	June	July	Aug.	Sept.	Oct.	Nov.	Dec.
−2.5	−2.5	−2.0	−2.0	−1.5	−2.0	−2.0	−2.0	−1.5	−2.5	−2.5	−2.5

It becomes evident that proximity to the larger lakes has an appreciable ameliorating effect throughout the winter, and that although in the summer months, the maxima are likely to be a little higher in a well-sheltered position, such as Appleby, this is not sufficient to offset the cooler nights that prevail throughout winter and summer alike.

On cloudy and windy days and nights both the maxima and the minima are likely to be very similar in either location. This means that on clear, calm and starry radiation nights the minima in a well-sheltered valley location are likely on many occasions to fall by 4° to 6° F, and occasionally more, below those at more favoured sites. Accordingly, the average annual frequency of night minima below the freezing point, which may be very significant for vegetation, varies considerably.

This is well demonstrated at the new Forestry Commission station at Grizedale. The station lies at the foot of the slopes adjacent to the broad flat valley and in the seven years of its operation the mean minima average about 2° F below those of Ambleside. As cloudy nights will give much the same minima, clear nights (about two-fifths of the total) are likely to give minima around 5° lower at Grizedale. Since 1956, the annual number of days with a minimum in the screen at or below the freezing point ('air frost') has been published, and if we take the available somewhat interrupted records from the several stations, the average annual expectation of such nights, standardised throughout to the 12-year period 1956–67, can be given:

Sellafield (length of record 7 years, 40 ft)	42
Keswick (3 years only, 254 ft)	55
Ambleside (12 years, 151 ft)	62
Newton Rigg (by Penrith) (10 years, 560 ft)	72
Urswick (12 years, 130 ft)	56
Grizedale (7 years, 330 ft)	90
Appleby (based on the mean minima quoted above: 440 ft)	84
Upland and Mountain	
Moor House (extreme upper Tees basin: 1,825 ft)	130
Dun Fell (Pennine summit, 2,780 ft)	160

For comparison: a coastal location (Morecambe) averages 38, and is similar to Barrow. Stations in the Fylde of Lancashire average 54 to 58, comparable with Urswick, or with Keswick; farther inland, averages vary from 55 to 70 and are comparable with Ambleside or Newton Rigg; but frosty valley locations give averages up to 85 or 90, comparable with Appleby or Grizedale. It is probable that unusually favoured slopes around Grange-over-Sands might give only about 30 such days as an annual average.

Continental writers commonly quote the average number of 'ice days' (maxima not rising above the freezing point). At inhabited levels in the Lake District these do not average more than one or two yearly.

Extremes of temperature for Keswick have already been quoted; but the possibilities in the more exceptional locations should be added. Temperatures below zero Fahrenheit have quite often occurred in the inland valleys, in general on occasions when with Arctic air a calm clear night has followed a heavy snowfall. There have been 'unofficial' reports on several occasions in the region of −10° F, the first being by John Dalton from the Friends School at Kendal in December, 1791. But the likelihood that such extremes are confined to the valley-floor is evident; G. F. Braithwaite's long record on the rising ground at the south end of the town, 1872–1935, gives extremes of 92° in July, 1921, and −2° in February, 1895. In December, 1961, the local minimum in Rosthwaite fell just below 0° F, although at Ambleside the minimum was 8°, at Urswick in Furness 7°, at Sellafield close to the coast 17°. Such comparisons serve to demonstrate the character of the local variations that can occur, that can affect the vegetation. Much depends, too, on whether

PLATE 11 *Above*, Small Water and Haweswater: here a dam of moraine has diverted the outflow from the tarn to the left, over a lip of rock. The upper part of the enlarged Haweswater lies over the drowned village of Mardale. *Below*, Grasmoor End: arable farming of marginal land in the valleys – a pause during the sowing of oats.

PLATE 12 Mickleden, Pike o'Stickle and glacial moraine: hummocks on the dale floor were left by the last glaciers to descend Rossett Gill and The Stake. Axe factory sites lie on the upper screes below the crags of Pike o'Stickle.

the lakes happen still to be unfrozen; once they have become well frozen, minima are likely to fall lower at places such as Keswick or Ambleside. For those who wish to make comparisons over a longer period, the monthly means for the Lancashire plain have been compiled (1753–1945) by the present author, and are reasonably representative of the adjacent Lake District (see Bibliography, page 300).

Upland and mountain temperatures: For most of our deductions it is necessary to make use of the neighbouring high Pennine stations at Moor House (1,825 feet) in extreme upper Teesdale, and on the summit of Dun Fell (2,780 feet). Records at both places were initiated by the present author, and can be found discussed in *Q. J. Roy. Met. Soc.* for 1936, 1942 and 1943: more recently official observations have been maintained, since 1952 at Moor House, 1963 on Dun Fell. There have also been stations at and near Alston (1879–86, 1950–56).

The most notable feature is that the rate of fall of the mean daily maxima with altitude above sea-level is considerably more rapid than that of the minima. This is the result of the characteristically windy climate of the summits, together with the greater frequency of cloud. The overall mean temperature falls by 1° F for about 275 feet (0.66° C per 100 metres). Rather rarely, in calm anticyclonic weather, the upland minima remain, even above 2,000 feet, higher than those in the valley below; but very commonly the lapse-rate by day in cloudy windy weather is close to the adiabatic, 1° F for 185 feet (or 1° C per 100 metres). As the summit of Dun Fell (2,780 feet) has a July average of about 9.4° C (49° F) tree-growth is not to be expected. At Moor House, where the July mean is close to 11.5° C (52.7° F) a small experimental plantation in such shelter as the landscape affords is beginning to succeed. Not far away, there is evidence that a belt of trees planted about 1846 virtually fails, in spite of slight shelter, at 2,000 feet.

In the Lake District few trees remain at higher levels, on account of many centuries of grazing by sheep, but here and there, among crags difficult of access, occasional rowans and sometimes birch can be found up to 1,900 feet with occasional rare individuals above. Examples can be seen near Codale Tarn above Easedale; at the head of Grains Ghyll; and near Sheffield Pike east of Helvellyn.

In a maritime climate the rapid fall of temperature with altitude means that the length of the growing season, conventionally regarded as the period with a mean temperature exceeding some value often stated as 6° C, or 43° F, diminishes very rapidly, by about ten days for each 250 feet of altitude; although some allowance can be made for local effects of shelter among the hills, together with areas of better drainage and exposure to the sun.

The summarised temperature statistics from two high-level Pennine stations (see table below) are generally applicable throughout the Lake

D.—H

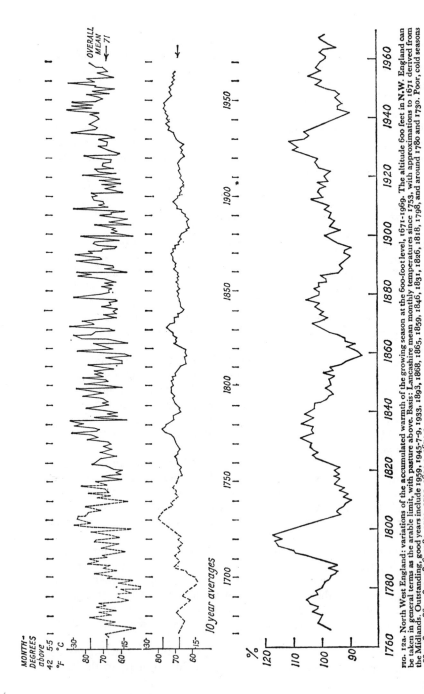

FIG. 12a. North West England: variations of the accumulated warmth of the growing season at the 600-foot level, 1671-1969. The altitude 600 feet in N.W. England can be taken in general terms as the arable limit, with pasture above. Basis: Lancashire mean monthly temperatures since 1753, with approximations to 1671 derived from the Midlands. Outstanding, good years include 1959, 1945-7-9, 1933, 1868, 1865, 1859, 1846, 1831, 1826, 1818, 1798, and around 1780 and 1730. Poor, cold seasons 1885, 1879, 1860, 1823, 1816, 1784, 1740, 1725, 1694-5, 1674-5.

FIG. 12b. Fluctuations of the rainfall by decades over the Lake District from 1757-66 to 1960-69. Percentage deviations from the average for the period 1916-50. Basis: Kendal rainfall measurements since 1788, standardised; supplemented by estimates derived from other N.W. rainfall records from 1757. Wettest year 1792 with 159% of average. Driest year 1887 with 62% of average.

District. One very important feature of the high-level climate is the very great frequency of temperatures oscillating about the freezing point. A quite pitilessly raw, windswept, bitter freeze-and-thaw climate prevails for long periods every winter, with a high frequency of alternations between cold rain, sleet or driving snow and very persistent low cloud; throughout the winter, sunny intervals that are really calm are very rare, and one of the most characteristic features is the rime-deposit from low cloud with abundant 'frost feathers' on the windward side of all obstacles; on one occasion a growth of 18 inches within 24 hours was observed on Dun Fell by the present writer.

Moor House (1825 ft) Estimated monthly means for 1931–1960 (for comparison with Keswick, based on records kept 1932–47 and 1953–65, the latter by courtesy of the Nature Conservancy).

Jan.	Feb.	Mar.	Apr.	May	June	July	Aug.	Sept.	Oct.	Nov.	Dec.	Year
31.5	31.8	35.0	38.8	45.0	50.3	53.3	53.0	49.2	42.8	37.6	34.2	41.9

Dun Fell (2780 ft) Estimated monthly means for 1931–1960, derived from 6 years of available data; these must be regarded as approximate only.

Jan.	Feb.	Mar.	Apr.	May	June	July	Aug.	Sept.	Oct.	Nov.	Dec.	Year
28.0	28.0	31.3	35.0	40.5	46.3	49.5	49.0	45.5	39.5	34.5	31.0	38.2

Recorded extremes at Moor House, 80° and −2°. Annual average rainfall 81.3 inches. Average annual number of days with snow cover, approximately 70. Average annual number of 'days with frost' (screen min. 32° or below) 130.

HUMIDITY

Although rainfall is abundant, the average moisture content of the atmosphere, or the humidity, does not differ from that prevailing over north-west England generally. South-westerly winds are often more humid, but east winds are dry; and, for example, in June the average relative humidity in early afternoon at Keswick compares with that at Norwich, and is less than that over the greater part of Wales.

RAINFALL

The general characteristics have been described; it will be sufficient here to summarise the monthly average totals at some notable stations, quoted from the Meteorological Office, *Averages of Rainfall, 1916–1950*. Measurements are in inches; the heights of stations are given.

Spells of rain can be long; quite recently, for example in October, 1967 – which at some stations was the wettest month of any name for over 100 years – 29 inches of rain was reported to have fallen in 29 days in Great Langdale, at a station where the annual average (1916–50) is

	Jan.	Feb.	Mar.	April	May	June	July	Aug.	Sept.	Oct.	Nov.	Dec.	Year
Barrow (20 ft.) (Sewage Works)	4.2	2.8	2.5	2.3	2.7	2.5	3.3	4.0	4.0	4.5	4.3	4.0	41.1
Windermere (175 ft.) (Brockhole)	8.5	5.5	4.3	3.7	3.7	3.6	4.9	5.7	6.1	7.6	7.4	7.6	68.6
Keswick (254 ft.)	6.7	4.2	3.4	3.3	3.2	3.3	4.4	5.1	5.6	6.8	6.1	6.0	58.1
Seathwaite in Borrowdale (420 ft.)	16.0	10.6	8.3	7.5	6.8	7.5	9.5	11.1	12.6	13.7	14.2	13.7	131.6
Appleby (440 ft.)	4.1	2.4	2.3	2.1	2.4	2.2	3.3	3.7	3.3	3.8	3.5	3.5	36.5

The range of variation can be summarised; the totals are rounded to allow for minor changes of gauges and the like.

Seathwaite (1845 onward)   88″ in 1855, 182″ in 1861; average 1916–50: 131″
Kendal (1788 onward)   34″ in 1855, 84″ in 1792; average 1916–50: 51″

108 inches. Over 50 inches in one month (December) has been recorded on the Sty-head above Seathwaite, where the 1916–50 average is given as 173 inches, and there have been several occasions when between 7 and 8 inches have fallen in one day. Drought, implying negligible rain (not greater than 0.01 inches or 0.2 mm) has, however, been reported on several occasions for upwards of 30 days, even from much of the mountain area. It is most likely to occur in late spring and early summer, when the sun is strong and evaporation is high.

EVAPORATION: WIND

Direct measurements are almost lacking. Some use can be made of records maintained in the Forest of Bowland, near Slaidburn, under somewhat similar climatic conditions; and there are a few measurements of run-off. Some measurements of rainfall and discharge on the small Greta basin by Keswick indicate an annual evaporation loss of about 18 to 20 inches. About five-sixths of this occurs through the months April to September, with a likelihood of just over four inches in May and June, decreasing in July and August. Hence at Keswick evaporation loss frequently exceeds the rainfall in May and June, but is much less likely to do so thereafter.

Wind frequencies overall are those of the north of England generally, roughly 55 per cent from south to west, 25 per cent from north to east, about 10 per cent from west to north and the remainder from between east and south, with a very few calms. But the surface winds are very noticeably canalised along the valleys, and their strength and gustiness varies locally, depending on the extent and character of the obstacles met. With a gale blowing in the Irish Sea, winds can be very strong along the larger lakes, and gusty elsewhere, but in the valleys their overall strength is considerably less than on the outer coast. On the mountains they may be very strong indeed, especially across the smoother rounded summits. On Dun Fell it appears that the average speed of the wind is about force 5, 20 per cent greater than at the same height in the free air. A gust of 134 m.p.h. and an hourly wind of 99 m.p.h. have been recorded in the short period during which observations have been maintained. Violent eddies, with consequent gusts and lulls are common in the lee of the summits; as a result, snow accumulations after a storm are very variable in depth.

The 'helm wind' is in essence the result of the development of standing-wave phenomena, on many occasions when a wind from north-east to east blows over the Crossfell escarpment; the necessary condition is that an inversion-layer should exist at no great height above the summits, probably not more than about 6,000 feet above sea level, and the pressure gradient should suffice to maintain a wind of the order of force 4 upward on the Northumberland coast. Considerable acceleration of the flow takes place over the summit and down the escarpment on the lee side. In the Lake District, in these circumstances, the phenomenon is not so well defined, as the trend of the ranges is more irregular; but from time to time a decidedly strong wind from the north-east can be observed locally at the foot of the slopes, e.g. at Grasmere. In such conditions it is commonly very cloudy to eastward, but on the west side of the district the sky is quite clear with abundant sunshine and a decidedly drying wind. As winds from the north-east quarter are most common from March into May, the dry harsh air is not very welcome as it often imposes a serious check to the growth of grass. From time to time it is accompanied by drifting snow, but as a rule it causes much less trouble in the Lake District itself than along the Pennines farther to the east.

SUNSHINE

Bright sunshine has been registered over varying periods of years at a number of stations. In spite of the high rainfall, generally speaking the amount compares well with other English stations in similar latitudes, making some allowance for the fact that at Keswick and Ambleside a certain amount of the low sunshine, especially in winter, is cut off by the surrounding mountains. On the outer flank of the district the south-west Cumberland coast can be quite well favoured, especially with the wind between north and east.

Averages for the period 1931–58 are available for Keswick and run as follows, noting that from September to April a small amount is cut off by surrounding objects:

Keswick: Duration of bright sunshine by hours, average for each month, 1931–58

Jan.	Feb.	Mar.	Apr.	May	June	July	Aug.	Sept.	Oct.	Nov.	Dec.	Year
34	56	102	139	192	181	146	140	103	72	39	28	1232

Duration in May is about 39 per cent of 'possible', in December and January about 12 per cent of 'possible'. Ambleside, surrounded more closely by hills, records about 60 hours less than Keswick; Newton Rigg appreciably more. The decline in late summer is noticeable.

There is some evidence of an increase in recent years towards the averages that appear to have prevailed earlier this century; and additional stations have come into operation. Over the 17-year period 1951–67, Newton Rigg, by Penrith, has averaged 1,310 hours, which may be of the order of 2 per cent below the longer-term average. For 1951–67 the averages derived from shorter overlapping records, with the number of years available in each case, are given below; this will enable comparisons to be drawn between the different parts.

	hours
Newton Rigg, 1951–67	1310
Silloth (Cumberland coast to north) 9 years (reduced to 51/67)	1425
Sellafield (Cumberland coast to west) 11 years (reduced to 51/67)	1515
Keswick (9 years), partly screened in winter (reduced to 51/67)	1270
Ambleside (11 years), partly screened (reduced to 51/67)	1140
Moor House, 1825 feet (High Pennines) 12 years (reduced to 51/67)	1150
Dun Fell, 2,780 feet (Pennine summit) 7 years only (reduced to 51/67)	840

The range of variation between extreme years is of the order of ±25 per cent. In the phenomenal August of 1947 Keswick enjoyed nearly 70 per cent of its 'possible' sunshine, more than double the normal August expectation; the rainfall being 0.02 inches (0.5 mm). The 'summit' record kept on Dun Fell gives an indication of the decidedly cloudy climate of the higher fells. For comparison, the average for 1951–67 on the flat Lancashire coast at Blackpool was 1,548 hours.

SNOWFALL AND SNOW-COVER

The valley-floors around Keswick and Ambleside are likely to experience about 25 days each year when an alert observer keeping constant watch would record the fall of some snow or sleet; and at the morning observation, the ground is likely to be covered on about 12 days. To the westward, beside the coast, or beside Morecambe Bay, this last figure decreases to less than five. Of the 25 days on which, by keen observation, sleet or snow will be observed to fall, six are likely in January and February, nearly four in December and five in March, two in April, and the odd one in November and May, or possibly in October; in recent decades this last has been unusual.

On the summits above 2,500 feet the first powdering may come about the second week in October, the last in mid-May. The greater part of the mountains above 2,500 feet is likely to be 'white' for about a hundred days; this means that ski-ing can be fairly regularly enjoyed by those who are prepared to climb first, although the severely windswept and crusted snow near the summits is not always congenial and the leeward slopes are to be preferred. At Moor House (1,825 feet) the annual average is of the order of 70 days with snow-cover; on Crossfell, about 105 days.

Drifts accumulate beneath the crags and in the gullies and may be espied in a normal year until nearly the end of May. But rather rarely they have been known to last well into July, for example on Helvellyn in 1951, or in summers such as 1879 and 1816.

Duration of snow-cover in an exceptional winter may attain 50 days more than the average in the valley-bottoms, and up to 60 or even 70 more than the average on the summits. A great deal depends on whether there are incursions from time to time of heavy and 'warm' rain, borne on a strong south wind from far down the Atlantic; such a rain will remove practically all the snow within a day or two. Enormously wide variations from year to year can thus be expected. Snowfall on the summits lasting for a few hours is far from unknown in June; but in July it is decidedly rare. Dorothy Wordsworth mentions it in 1802, and in 1888 an early morning cover was reported on Skiddaw down to below 1,500 feet.

Drifting in strong winds is severe; and may affect the roads at lower levels, for example on the Kirkstone Pass and by Dunmail Raise. Level for level, the occurrence and persistence of snow-cover decreases very markedly to the westward; it seems likely that the number of days when the summit of Black Combe is covered is less than half that which occurs at the same level around Haweswater. This is because the majority of heavy snowfalls come from north-east and east and are heavier to the windward; indeed, the Pennines are conspicuously more snowy than the Lake District. West Cumberland is, however, not free from occasional south-easterly blizzards, as in March, 1947, when the Furness Railway was blocked by drifts beside the seashore, and by Barrow, January 1940.

MISCELLANEOUS PHENOMENA

Fog of sufficient density seriously to impede traffic is quite rare. Morning mist beside the lakes, and occasional valley-fog, is free from pollution and may slow the traffic but gives little real difficulty; while between about 400 and 800 feet, especially towards Edenside, the air is prevailingly clear. At higher altitudes low cloud may affect some of the main roads, but as it is commonly accompanied by wind the layer beside the ground is not too dense.

Smoke-pollution is occasionally borne from South Lancashire, generally in the base of low stratus cloud; it is not unknown from Glasgow and Teeside, and on quiet winter mornings the spread inland of an appreciable murk even from Barrow and Whitehaven can be noted. But it does not as yet appear to be sufficient to check the general growth of the lichens (though for another view see page 143), and is probably diminishing.

Thunder is heard on 10 to 12 days yearly, considerably less than in the South Midlands, but more than in the greater part of Scotland. Catastrophic deluges when slow-moving thundery rains develop great intensity over the mountains have occurred, as in Borrowdale and Great Langdale in August, 1966. But the frequency of hillside scars and other evidence suggests that such devastating thunderstorm-rainfall may be more frequent on the Pennines.

In conclusion: in spite of its reputation for heavy rainfall, the climate of the Lake District does not differ to the extent that some are prone to believe from that of other parts of northern England. Because of the mountains, in wet seasons the extremes of rainfall and the persistence of cloud may be a little greater. But the presence of the mountains also increases the liability to drought when the wind goes easterly, and it leads to noteworthy local variations, especially in regard to the incidence of frost, the accumulation of snow, and the local exposure to damaging wind. Climate indeed plays its part in adding to that superb diversity which in an age of increasing monotony and uniformity becomes so great an asset.

CHAPTER 7

SOILS AND SOIL HISTORY

SOIL TYPES

BEFORE it is possible for anyone to understand the background to problems of changing land use in the Lake District, such as the conversion of great old sheep farms like Gillerthwaite in Ennerdale, and Lawson Park above Coniston, into Forestry Commission plantations, and the limitations set to husbandry in those valleys which, as Professor Manley has shown in *Climate and the British Scene* (Chapter 10) are far wetter than most of the world's inhabited and farmed lands – it is necessary to understand something of the history and present character of the native soils.

In the previous chapters we have seen how, in the closing stages of the most recent glacial episode, the land surface would consist either of bare rocks, like those now found on the summits of Scafell and other mountains, which had been scraped clean by the action of the ice, or else of 'skeletal soils' – accumulations of coarse or fine glacial drift, gravels, sands, silts and boulder-clays, dumped by the ice when it melted. These drifts, derived mainly (except in the north of the district) from the Borrowdale volcanic rocks, must have had originally a much higher base-status, in particular much more lime, than is now found in Lake District soils. Rocks of the Borrowdale Volcanic Series in their fresh, unweathered state may contain over 4 per cent calcium, whereas most soils in the district today, inside the limestone fringe, are rather poor in calcium and acid in reaction (pH often 4 to 5). The calcium in the Borrowdale rocks is in some strata visible as frequent veins of white calcite ($CaCO_3$) and in places where these are particularly abundant the soils are less acid than the average. One such place is the Mardale valley, where soil samples around the tarns Blea Water and Small Water have an average pH of 5 to 6.5, and many plants of neutral or rather base-rich soils can be found (see Chapter 9). Another such place is the eastern cliffs of Helvellyn, above Red Tarn, where many of the Lake District records for those few Arctic-alpine plants which do occur locally have been made. In general, however, soils derived from the Skiddaw Slates, the Borrowdale Volcanic Series, and the Silurian sedimentary rocks of the south, are now all rather poor and acid, because in the course of the last ten thousand years, since the last glacial episode, the very high rainfall of this western mountain district has leached out of the soil most of the more soluble mineral elements such as calcium. If a fresh surface is exposed on Borrowdale Volcanic rock by striking with a hammer, the freshly exposed rock will fizz if hydrochloric acid is applied to it, indicating the presence of calcium carbonate, but the weathered surfaces of this rock exposed to the air have lost all their calcium carbonate by the leaching action of rain, and will not show any reaction with hydrochloric acid, except where white calcite veins are present. This explains why the rocks of the Late-glacial period, more than ten thousand years ago, were more base-rich than the present soils, so that plants like the beautiful Jacob's Ladder (*Polemonium caeruleum*) and the rock-rose (*Helianthemum canum*), now found in the district only on the limestone of South Westmorland, grew near to Seathwaite Tarn at 1,200 feet above sea level, where today there is only acid moorland.

The soils derived from the other old rocks of the central Lake District – the Skiddaw Slates, the acid western intrusions of granite and granophyre, and the Silurian slates and grits, are in general even poorer in bases, and so more acid, than the soils on Borrowdale Volcanic rocks or drift derived from them. Both intrusive igneous rocks and most of the sedimentary rocks were always from the beginning poorer in bases than the Volcanics. There is a sudden change to more fertile soils on passing on to the surrounding ring of Carboniferous Limestone, and the difference in the native flora is often very clearly marked. Even on parts of the limestone, however, as on Moor Divock between Penrith and Ullswater, comparatively high altitude, and therefore rainfall, combined with land use by prehistoric settlers who appreciated the greater fertility of the limestone, has produced poorer soils, with acid-tolerant plants such as heather (*Calluna vulgaris*) on soils above the limestone.

At the end of the last glacial episode, these soils would all consist of purely mineral material and be what are called 'skeletal soils'; the building up of organic matter and nitrogen would take place as a result of the growth of plants. Lichens and mosses will grow on skeletal soils, and contribute to the humus which accumulates as time goes on. As the climate warmed up at the end of the last glacial episode, lichens and mosses would be followed first by a carpet of herbaceous plants, and then by the spread of trees across the landscape. The first stages in the process of soil development, or 'maturation', can now best be studied on the high ridges and peaks of the central mountains, where a moss-lichen grassland, most nearly approaching the original soil-forming plant communities, can be found. High on the summits the walker can see how the mats of lichens and woolly hair-moss (*Rhacomitrium lanuginosum*) and other mountain-top plants are building up humus, in the form of a rather black and crumbly peat, among the blocks of mountain-top detritus. The mountain soils where peaty humus directly overlies the bedrock are called 'ranker' soils. One may deduce, from evidence as to which plants were growing, that in the first stages of soil formation in the lowlands, about ten thousand years ago, temperatures were comparable with those now found only on the summits such as Great Dun Fell. As temperatures rose rapidly and a stable soil developed, however, forest spread over the landscape covering all but the steepest slopes and crags, up to about 2,500 feet above sea level. With the accumulation of forest humus, with its characteristic bacteria, moulds, protozoa and other invertebrates, and favourable temperatures for the activity of these micro-organisms, a true fertile forest soil would develop.

The soils of the Lake District, like those of any upland area, can be regarded as belonging to a developmental series. In places where the surface is unstable, either rocky or covered by rock fragments in various stages of disintegration, the soils remain in a comparatively early stage of this series. Both the mountain-top soils and those of the scree slopes come into this class; though more stable, the latter are still subject to soil-wash and soil-creep. All soils of this type are alike in possessing a high base-status, because they consist mainly of rock particles as yet not greatly modified by chemical change. Some scree soils tend to lose more bases by leaching than are added by weathering and breakdown of rock fragments: these form a transitional group of slightly leached soils, and on older and more stable screes may support a characteristic type of Sessile Oakwood, as in the well-known high-level oakwoods of Keskadale in the Newlands valley where the pH is not less than 5.0 (Chapter 8, page 137).

On slopes where finer rock material is present, and on the shoulders of the fells above the steepened valley-sides, up to about 1,000 feet but commoner below 700 feet, the typical soil profiles fall into the type known as 'brown earths' from their ochreous brown colour. The surface layers have been somewhat leached of bases, but retain a brown colour due to the presence of oxidised iron, and the humus in the surface layers is crumbly and incorporated into the mineral soil, forming *mull*, in which earthworms are active; such soils have a base-status sufficient to give moderate fertility. This is the characteristic soil type of much of lowland Britain, but in the uplands with their higher rainfall, this condition can only be maintained under certain conditions. These are found where the original rock type was particularly base-rich (an example is found in one of the Borrowdale woods described in Chapter 8 by Dr Ratcliffe) or where 'flushing' of some sort, by water or continuous soil breakdown, maintains the base supply, or where the vegetation is such as to renew continually the base supply in the surface layers. Such a vegetation is oak woodland, for the lime content of oak leaves is high – about 3 per cent, compared with only about 1.5 and 1.0 per cent respectively for birch and pine. The roots of oaks absorb more lime than most trees from the lower (mineral) layers of the soil, and return it to the surface soil with their fallen leaves each autumn; rapid decomposition of these leaves restores the base supply of the soil. Thus an oakwood vegetation maintains soil fertility and tends to retard the effects of leaching. The surviving good brown-earth soils in the Lake District, up to between 1,000 and

1,200 feet, were almost certainly under mixed-oak woodland until well into the historic period and so their fertility was preserved. Now they are very widely cleared and carry grassland of various types, and the conditions essential for the maintenance of their fertility are no longer there. It is these soils which are now so extensively invaded by bracken, though in past centuries, when cattle in considerable numbers (as observed, for instance, by Dorothy Wordsworth) trod the bracken, and when more and cheaper labour than today was available to cut it regularly, many of the fell-sides which are now so unproductively covered with bracken were some of the best grassland, with partial survival of the stored fertility of the old forest soils. Even today, bracken on these fells indicates the presence of deep and comparatively well-drained soils of which the profile approximates to a brown-earth.

On other parts of the fell-sides between 800 and 1,500 feet above the sea, soils now under *Calluna* or mat-grass (*Nardus stricta*) show a different profile – one in which the humus is not mixed with the underlying mineral soil, but forms a separate black layer on the surface, in which there are no earthworms and a poor soil fauna in general, so that no mixing of the humus takes place, and an acid humus, or *mor*, builds up in layers. In the sort of mineral soil in which free drainage takes place (typically a sand) humic acids produced by such acid organic layers rapidly leach the underlying mineral soil of all bases and produce a grey leached horizon, beneath which redeposited layers of iron and humus compounds can be found. This is the podsol profile, found in its most characteristic form under *Calluna* or coniferous trees on a sandy soil, but rare in the Lake District, where the bedrock and drifts weather into stony soils with much clay and fine silt, and where the relief is such that much of the soil drainage goes laterally down slopes, rather than vertically downwards through the soil profile. The common upland soil type in the Lake District is a somewhat leached stony clay, often irregularly stained brown with iron, under a thick accumulation of black mor humus. Transitions between humus types can be found in some of the existing woodlands, where in less base-rich areas, oaks and birches are surrounded by mor humus with its characteristic mosses and herbs. Ash, elm and alder trees are never found in such acid parts of the woodlands, nor is the herb dog's mercury.

Gley soils, the soil type of waterlogged ground, are of course very common in the damper and ill-drained parts of the fells and valleys. In these the mineral soil has a characteristic blue-grey colour due to ferrous iron salts. 'Peaty gleyed podsol' is a term sometimes applied to those wet soils in which leaching alternates with periods of flooding during which the soil is anaerobic. True gley soils in which the water-table is always high do not, of course, become leached. Soils of the gley types usually underlie the spreads of rushes (*Juncus* spp.) on damp slopes and on the marshy meadows of the valley bottoms. The Skiddaw Slates weather into a comparatively stiff soil in which drainage tends to be impeded, and these spreads of rushes are very characteristic of the Skiddaw Slate country and those areas where the soils are formed from the rather tenacious boulder-clay derived from Skiddaw Slate rocks.

SOIL FERTILITY

Some soils with acid mor humus have always been shallow and rather poor; those at higher altitudes were formerly birch or pine woodland, but some of the heather moorland and acid grasslands of the Lake District have undoubtedly replaced former oakwoods with accompanying soil degeneration. Prehistoric clearance of the oakwoods for pasture, on moorlands such as those round Devoke Water and Burnmoor Tarn on the fells between the Duddon, Esk and Irt valleys, must have started the soils on the downward trend towards acid infertility, for the heather and shallow-rooted grassland herbs which replaced the oak trees failed to renew supplies of lime and other bases in the surface layers, and so the original forest brown earths have been progressively depleted of their accumulated store of fertility.

It is when the vegetation no longer brings about recycling of the soil nutrients that, under relentless leaching by the Lake District rain, surface soils inevitably become acid except where natural flush effects due to crumbling bedrock or the flow of comparatively base-rich water operate. The effects of this leaching reduce the activity of soil micro-organisms and change the composition of the fauna and micro-flora of the soils, so that mull and mor soils can be distinguished by the animals found in them, as well as by their plants and their chemical composition. Good forest leaf-moulds – the mull soils – contain earthworms, snails and millipedes, and these can be found in the old woodlands of the Lake District where the presence of ash or elm trees indicates comparatively base-rich conditions. Mor humus soils, found on acid grasslands and also in the higher and more strongly leached parts of oak-birchwoods, carry the wavy hair-grass (*Deschampsia flexuosa*) as the characteristic grass in the woodlands, and mat-grass (*Nardus stricta*) on the open grasslands; heather and bilberry (*Vaccinium myrtillus*) are also typical plants. Often the pH of these mor soils is below 3.8, nitrates are absent and there is little ammonia nitrogen. The animals characteristic of mor soils include certain mites, the larval stages of two-winged flies (*Diptera*), click-beetles (*Elaterideae*), and often centipedes and predatory beetles. The absence of earthworms from mor soils is one of the main reasons why the humus of such soils builds up in layers, for want of the activities of earthworms in comminuting and distributing organic matter added to the soil surface.

When considering land use in the Lake District fells, it must be remembered that the potential productivity of mor soils is very low

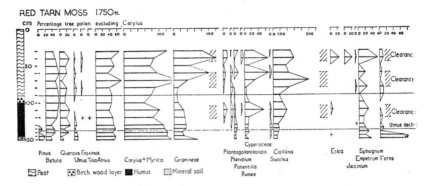

FIG. 13. Pollen diagram from peat overlying old woodland soil at Red Tarn Moss. Date of birchwood layer *c*. 1900 B.C. From *Proc. R. Soc.* B, Vol. 161, p. 319. The change from acid forest humus to peat coincides with a great increase in percentage representation of pollen of *Myrica* (Sweet Gale), grasses, sedges and *Calluna*: that is, the proportion of tree pollen to non-tree pollen is very much reduced in the peat above the wood layer.

compared with brown-earth soils under bracken at similar altitudes. The bracken-infested intakes which are now of practically no agricultural value can be restored to usefulness by the planting of native trees or of accepted aliens, notably the larch, but the *Nardus* grasslands on mor soils, of which many acres are now required to support one sheep, can be usefully afforested only by undemanding alien conifers like the lodgepole pine and the Sitka spruce. The Forestry Commission do not plant these trees from sheer contrariness, as some of their opponents would almost suggest, but from economic and ecological necessity.

PEAT

The peaty nature of upland soils is one of their most easily observed attributes. It is by no means confined to waterlogged areas, but it is equally noticeable on leached soils with mor humus of the podsolic type, and even in the early stages of soil formation on mountain-top detritus. This clearly indicates that the climatic effects characteristic of these three extreme types of habitat – waterlogging, leaching and low temperatures – are alike in leading to humus or peat accumulation in the soils affected. They do so in a generally similar way by reducing the activity of the soil micro-organisms. In the Lake District, wherever free drainage is impeded, either by clayey and impermeable drift deposits or by lack of slope of the land surface, soils of the podsolic type tend to accumulate a thicker and thicker layer of mor humus, which in time passes into peat. Many of these peat deposits are quite shallow, but they are distinguished by further changes in the vegetation as the substratum becomes more and more acid – dry heather and *Nardus* communities on the mor soils give way to wet communities of heather and bog-moss (*Sphagnum*) with cotton-sedge (*Eriophorum*). This is the process which has led to the development of wide areas of boggy wet ground on Lake District hillsides: the tract of high moorland on Armboth Fell between Thirlmere and Blea Tarn, at 900 to 1,500 feet, is a good example (p. 185). Though paths may be marked on the 1 inch O.S. map across such morasses, there are few landmarks to trace them by, and except in very dry summers it is difficult to cross dry-shod. This type of peat is not, however, usually very deep, and rock outcrops in the form of ridges and knobbles protrude through it. Only on very wide areas of flat or gently sloping ground above about 1,500 feet does true blanket-bog develop, as on the western fells such as Lank Rigg, on Matterdale Common in the north, and on the long summit plateaux of High Street and other eastern ridges. Here the thick mantle of peat covers all the rock features of the original surface and extends over gentle slopes and ridges. Remains of the forest which grew on these high plateaux several thousand years ago can frequently be seen, buried at the base of three to five feet of blanket peat (cf. Fig. 14, p. 128). The wood, branches and trunks, is mostly of birch, though willow, alder and occasionally pine can also be found. A good example, at a height of about 1,600 feet in Far Easedale, is the subject of comment in Wainwright's Guide to the fells.

Apart from shallow peat and blanket peat, there is basin peat, which develops in wet hollows, and raised-bog peat, which develops in great domes over the sites of former lakes or on coastal clay flats. North, north-west and south of the Lake District mountains there are some of the finest remaining raised bogs in Britain, covering old lake basins on the Cumberland lowland and built up round the coasts on the marine clay of the latest marine transgression. Foulshaw Moss and Meathop Moss on the Kent estuary, Stribers Moss and Ellerside Moss on the Leven, Heathwaite Moss on the Duddon–Lickle estuarine lowland, Bowness Moss on the Solway and Scaleby Moss on the Carlisle plain, are all splendid raised bogs, some of which have provided in their profiles most valuable evidence as to the ecological history of the Lake Counties. But within the Lake District mountains, the only raised bog is at Shoulthwaite Moss near the foot of Thirlmere, and this is not at all typical, for Shoulthwaite Beck seems to have flowed across it at times in the past.

The peat of both blanket and raised bogs is ombrogenous – that is, it is built up above the ground water level, so that plants growing on its surface derive their mineral nutrient only from the rain. The peat surface is very acid indeed, and only a restricted range of plant species, chiefly species of *Sphagnum*, will grow. Much Lake District peat is periodically flushed with drainage water from higher fell-sides and so is less acid than

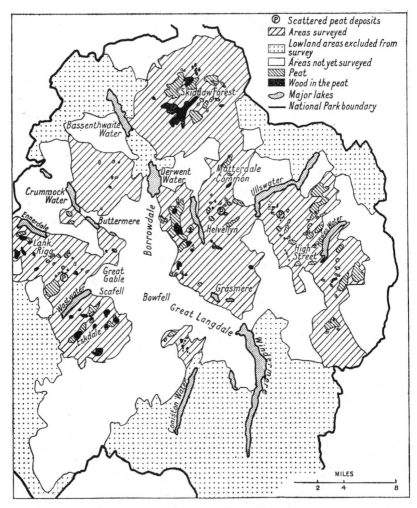

FIG. 14. Remains of former forest in peat. Map prepared from surveys made by the Brathay Exploration Group and the Eskdale Outward Bound Mountain School, by Dr John Barkham.

ombrogenous peat. All raised bogs in Britain have been modified to some extent in the past by the enormous demand for peat for fuel, so the bogs in their present state are to some extent dried out by the drainage consequent on peat-cutting. Nevertheless the larger bogs provide some of the least modified areas of British vegetation.

The other kind of peat, topogenous or basin peat, is found in hollows, and there are, of course, very numerous examples of this in both the main and smaller valleys. The surface of these valley bogs, watered by ground water with its dissolved minerals, is less acid than ombrogenous peat, and carries rather different vegetation. In many of the main valleys are stretches of fen, with a vegetation of tall reeds (*Phragmites*) and alder or willow carr, resembling in many respects Esthwaite North Fen (Chapter 4). It is certain that before man cleared and drained the valley floors, swampy carr woodlands must have been very extensive, both in the main valleys and in innumerable higher valleys among the fells which are now peat mosses, but which below the surface have a thick layer of alderwood peat.

SOIL EROSION

'Soil' includes both predominantly *inorganic* soils, into which a certain amount of organic matter or humus is well mixed, and *organic* soils consisting entirely of acid humus (mor) or peat. Agricultural soils form the major division of the first category, and peat bogs the extreme type of the second. Forest soils, as we have seen, can include soils of both categories, and differences in the tree species making up the forests can be correlated with differences in soil type. Comparatively few trees will grow on soil which is so organic as to be a peat, but pine, birch and some alien conifers will do so, under certain circumstances. The problem of soil erosion in a mountain country such as the central Lake District applies to both inorganic and organic soils, and both categories are subject to both natural and anthropogenic influences which tend to bring about erosion. These influences are discussed in *Mountains and Moorlands*, with a special section giving the various current views on the causes of peat erosion, but it is appropriate at this point to give consideration to the question of how soil erosion is affecting the landscape of the Lake District.

The steep slopes of the intensely glaciated mountains of the Scafell–Gables–Glaramara–Bowfell groups have thin stony soils or bare rock, with no extensive tracts of deep soils or deep peat. Consequently the rain runs off very quickly, and the intense rainstorms which occur from time to time cause very severe flooding. Anyone who knows Great Langdale Beck will have seen it many times as a practically dry bouldery bed during the droughty Lakeland May or June, but knows how quickly it can swell to a raging torrent flooding many of the flat fields of the valley floor. Indeed, anyone who saw it during August, 1966, when the floods coming down Oxendale and Mickleden flattened every wall between Stool End, Wall End and Dungeon Ghyll and gouged out their torrent beds three to four feet deep, so that the Brathay, normally clear as gin, flowed bright haematite red for two days with suspended matter from the red soils of Great Langdale, will understand the problem of soil erosion.

This potential for intense soil erosion must always have been there in valleys of this character. In the words of one Langdale man, while the River Board officials were contemplating the devastation of August, 1966, and the carpets of the New Dungeon Ghyll hotel were drying in the wind, 'Langdale always has had floods and always will'. Nevertheless, the activities of man over the last five thousand years have increased this potential for soil erosion, and it is now one of the Lake District's problems. As soon as destruction of the primeval forests began, the soils began to erode very much more rapidly and were deposited in the lakes at a much faster rate. Where the forest was not destroyed, there was no acceleration of deposition in the lakes. When Manchester acquired Thirlmere and its catchment area, the trees were planted not primarily to produce timber but to regulate the run-off, to minimise the erosive effects of such intense rainstorms (such as that of 1966) and so to slow down the rate of silting in the reservoir and keep the soils in place on the catchment area, where soils and peat function as a sponge to soak up the rain and prevent rapid run-off. The roots of trees serve to bind the soil and hold it in place, and the clearance of forest, particularly on the steep slopes so common in the Lake District, is always followed by increased erosion. Clearance of the native forest led to the development of screes on many of the steep hillsides – beneath these screes the old forest brown-earth soils have been preserved in a few places, but on many hillsides the forest soils were carried away to lakes or the sea. This downgrading of soils can be seen on stony fell-sides in every valley of the Lake District from which the primeval forest was cleared, but there is convincing evidence that re-afforestation of a valley such as that of Thirlmere can halt this process, so that there it is possible now to see spontaneous colonisation by trees of the screes which have been stabilised by the initial planting and protected from sheep (see page 154). At the same time, the waterworks management is satisfied that silting of the reservoir has been minimised and the water is as clear as possible of suspended sediment.

Though the initial destruction of the forest was followed by an increased rate of soil erosion, in most drainage basins an equilibrium was reached as a new vegetation cover – grassland or heather moor – became established. What can be seen very plainly in many parts of the Lake District at present is the intense erosion that follows any break in the present vegetation cover. For instance, a skin of peat protects a land surface from erosion so long as it is intact, but as soon as the continuous plant communities of its surface are broken up by any factor, surface drainage begins to cut into the peat rather than run over its surface, drainage channels are initiated and cut back rapidly, and the peat is soon eroded away. The Lake District, with its steeper topography, never had the wide areas of peat of the neighbouring Pennines, where the results of peat erosion are so striking, but small areas of peat such as that beside Red Tarn above Wrynose, show the process of peat erosion at work – another example is Quagrigg Moss, high on Scafell above Eskdale. Similar rapid gullying and erosion can be seen to follow any destruction of the surface vegetation of *Nardus*, *Juncus squarrosus*, heather and cotton-sedge which covers peaty soils on many fell-sides. Any forms of land use which involve the passage of wheeled or tracked vehicles over steep fell-sides carry this hazard.

In addition to the problem of erosion which follows any break in the continuous cover of vegetation protecting a peat or peaty soil, there is a good deal of evidence in the Lake District of a recent increase in the rate of erosion of mineral soils. One cause of this can be trampling, either by human feet or those of sheep; excessive trampling destroys the grassy vegetation of shallow well-drained soils and allows erosion to begin. Sheep scuffle out places where they like to settle, often under little sheltering overhangs, and once the turf cover is destroyed, the area of bare soil rapidly extends. Overstocking with sheep on fell-sides where the grassland is a mosaic of good and palatable grasses interspersed with areas of mat-grass, often originally reflecting differences in soil type, will bring about excessive trampling by the sheep on the areas of palatable grass, where they all tend to congregate. Human trampling produces its effects: those of us whose memories go back for half a lifetime are aware of how much soil has been eroded away from the popular walkers' tracks – not only the well-worn tracks up to the most frequently visited summits, but paths like the Corridor Route from Sty Head to the col between Lingmell and Scafell Pike have changed from grassy tracks to bouldery ladders in many places.

The only real solution to the problem of increased soil erosion with increased pressure on the land surface of the Lake District is, of course, re-afforestation – to restore the forest cover which not only maintained the fertility of the soils, but kept them in position. The central 300 square miles of the Lake District – that is, all the central mountain core – has been preserved from afforestation since 1936 by an agreement between the Forestry Commission and the Council for the Preservation of Rural England. Therefore it would be good if all users of this uniquely splendid landscape would remember the care with which the Manchester Corporation Waterworks authority cherishes the soil of the Thirlmere and Hawes-water catchment areas (see the leaflets which they issue: *A guide to the Launchy Ghyll Forest Trail, Thirlmere* and *A guide to the Swirls Forest Trail, Thirlmere*). The problem of public access to water catchment areas is not entirely one of preserving the population from typhoid and other water-borne diseases. There is also a problem of preventing the public from undoing this careful preservation of the skin of vegetation over these catchment areas, by driving wheeled vehicles where no vehicles should go, indulging in the sort of carefree camping which leaves areas of bare soil, and other thoughtless activities which result in increased erosion when the next torrential downpour descends.

Before leaving the subject of soils, it should be emphasised that the farmed soils of the inhabited valleys are only maintained in their present state by constant liming and draining, and were it not for this they would have a constant tendency to revert to peaty 'moss' land. The development of an efficient system of field drains and the improvement of farm land by liming at the beginning of the nineteenth century will be discussed in Chapter 15.

THE HABITATS: THE NATIVE WOODLANDS

I bid ye mourn not for the death of beauty,
For, though the Springtide fades from Cumberland,
Her streams and tarns, there is eternal spring
In heaven. And, on my island where I live,
I dream that heaven is very like this land,
Mountains and lakes and rivers undecaying,
And simple woodlands and wild cherry flowers.
At least I know no better. But weep not.
For, though this land is but the shadow of heaven,
It yet is heaven's shadow.
'Casson' quoted by Hugh Walpole: *Vanessa*

THE OAKWOODS

THE remaining representatives of pure or mixed sessile oakwood, the climax vegetation of the Lake District, fall into three general groups. *Firstly,* fragments of almost pure sessile oakwood survive in some of the more remote dales, and by some botanists have been thought to be the nearest surviving approach to 'natural' woodland. Later in this book we shall see how, even in the remotest parts, there can have been no true primeval woodland in the Lake District since Early Neolithic times, about 5,000 years ago. We have no real means of knowing what kind of woodland would develop in the various parts of the Lake District today if all interference by man and his grazing animals were to be removed. Climate and soils are possibly very different now from what they were at the time of the last untouched forest, 5,000 years ago. So it is true to say that the different opinions as to the relation of the almost pure remaining oakwoods to the 'natural' forest of the Lake District, which have been advanced by different botanists, represent opinions and not established fact. *Secondly,* there are the mixed woods of oak, birch, hazel, alder, elm and ash, which include the extensive woodlands formerly exploited for woodland industries and managed for centuries as enclosed coppice, but now mostly allowed to grow up into a semi-natural condition. Mixed woodland of this type is found in most of the dales, and the biggest woodland area of the Lake District, that of High Furness between the Duddon and Windermere, is of the grown-up coppice type though modified in places by planting of alien trees. *Thirdly,* there are the 'amenity' woods, developed and planted by private landowners either from downgraded woodlands or from old coppice, along natural lines and often so successfully that it is difficult to distinguish them from woodlands of the second type except by the presence of those aliens which were not planted before the eighteenth century – larch and beech. Many of the woods in the Windermere–Rydal–Grasmere valley and in lower Borrowdale are of this amenity type, and they are found everywhere on the larger estates, including the lovely Graythwaite Woods south-west of Windermere.

A fourth type of woodland, completely non-native, has been provided by afforestation both by the Forestry Commission and private landowners; this will be discussed in the final chapter.

The mixed deciduous woods of oak, ash, birch and hazel, which often contain the two characteristic and widely distributed wild cherries, the gean (*Prunus avium*) and the bird cherry (*Prunus padus*) which Dorothy Wordsworth called by its local name, the heckberry, as well as hollies and yews which relieve the winter bareness, are one of the loveliest features of the Lake District, and many of them have been listed by the Nature Conservancy as sites of particular conservation value. These include Naddle Forest by Haweswater, Scales Wood by Buttermere, Baysbrown woods in Great Langdale, Glencoyne and Hallin Fell woods by Ullswater, Low Wood by Brotherswater, the Longsleddale woods and the Borrowdale woods described on page 138. Other attractive examples can be found in Eskdale and Ennerdale. The great green forest of the southern Lake District between the Duddon and the Winster rivers, where it was said that a squirrel could once travel from Low Furness to Langdale without touching the ground, remains as extensive areas of formerly enclosed coppice oakwoods which for centuries were cut on a regular 15-year rotation. The Grizedale Forest of the Forestry Commission has restored the forest cover to one valley of this region (page 146) although in modified form.

The greatest enemy of Lake District woods has been and remains the sheep – the inoffensive animal on which local prosperity depended for so long. Sheep nibble down and destroy all tree seedlings they can reach, and browse on the shoots from coppiced stools, and a long local practice of wintering sheep in the woods, combined with the present expense of maintaining a sheep-proof fence, has led to the present situation where very little regeneration of these woods is going on. Only in the very few areas from which sheep are efficiently excluded is regeneration found; on the Thirlmere catchment, fenced 50 to 70 years ago (page 154) oak saplings are only now becoming well-established. Of the old coppice woodlands it is only those which were well-managed which survive, for if sheep were allowed into them too soon after cutting, the browsed stools deteriorated rapidly. These pleasant mixed semi-natural woodlands which add so much to the beauty of the Lake District are almost certainly doomed unless they can be efficiently fenced against sheep for periods long enough to allow natural regeneration. The expense of efficient fencing is so great that this policy would probably be economic only for large blocks of woodland.

Wordsworth has given us an admirably lucid account of the Lake District woodlands as he saw them at the beginning of the nineteenth century, at a time when 'amenity' woods were being actively developed, with planting of both native and introduced species. In his *Guide to the Lakes* published in 1820 he says: 'The Woods consist chiefly of oak, ash and birch, and here and there wych elm, with underwood of hazel, the white and black thorn, and hollies; in moist places alders and willows abound; and yews among the rocks. Formerly the whole country must have been covered with wood to a great height up the mountains; where native Scotch firs must have grown in great profusion, as they do in the northern part of Scotland to this day. But not one of these old inhabitants has existed, perhaps, for some hundreds of years; the beautiful traces, however, of the universal sylvan appearance the country formerly had, yet survive in the native coppice-woods that have been protected by enclosures, and also in the forest trees and hollies, which, though disappearing fast, are yet scattered both over the enclosed and unenclosed parts of the mountains. . . . Other trees have been introduced within these last fifty years, such as beeches, larches, limes, etc. and plantations of firs, . . . but the sycamore, (which I believe was brought to this island . . . not more than two hundred years ago) has long been a favourite of the cottagers; and, with the fir, has been chosen to screen their dwellings: and is sometimes found in the fields whither the winds or the waters may have carried its seeds.'

It is impressive that Wordsworth perceived so clearly that the woodlands must once have covered the mountains up to a great height. The most obvious evidence for this is found in the timber remains – branches, roots and stumps – now exposed near the base of peat sections in the fells. The buried branches and stumps of these ancient trees are familiar to every fell-walker, at altitudes between 1,200 and 2,000 feet. For a long time there has been speculation about this change from forest to bog. John Gerard said in his *Herball*, in 1597, 'firre trees in Cheshire, Staffordshire and Lancashire, where they grew in great plentie as is reported before Noah's floud, but being overturned and overwhelmed have lein since in the mosses and waterie moorish grounds very fresh and round, untill this day.' (p. 1181, quoted by C. E. Raven in *English Naturalists*, 215, Cambridge, 1947). Most of the buried timber in the Lake District peat is of birch, but alder, willow and pine are also represented. The development of the peat blanket which entombed these high-level forests was clearly related to the slope of the ground, rather than to rainfall, because in the wettest area of the district, the steep fells round the heads

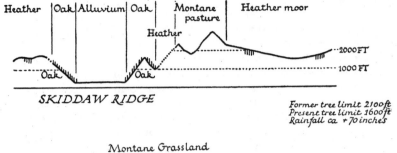

Heather | Oak | Alluvium | Oak | Montane pasture | Heather moor
Heather
Oak .... Oak
2000 FT
1000 FT

SKIDDAW RIDGE

Former tree limit 2100 ft
Present tree limit 1600 ft
Rainfall ca. +70 inches

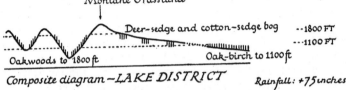

Montane Grassland

Deer-sedge and cotton-sedge bog
1800 FT
1100 FT
Oakwoods to 1800 ft
Oak-birch to 1100 ft

Composite diagram –LAKE DISTRICT   Rainfall: +75 inches

FIG. 15. Composite diagrams comparing slopes and altitudes of present high-level woodland and timber buried in peat. Lake District: rainfall 75 inches. Vertical scale x 2. Buried timber shown as vertical lines below the profiles.

of Great Langdale, Borrowdale, Wasdale and Eskdale, there is very little of this blanket of deep peat with its remains of former forests. Peat has developed most extensively on the flatter fells in all parts of the Lake District, irrespective of the local rainfall. Fig. 15, above, is a generalised diagram comparing slopes and altitudes of the present high-level woodland in the district, and timber buried in the peat. It illustrates that ancient woodlands in the Lake District were buried in peat on gentle slopes, averaging 1 in 10 or less, down to a level of 900 feet. On steeper slopes, averaging 1 in 2 or 3, more or less natural woodland still persists in places up to about 1,800 feet. These effects are associated with an annual rainfall exceeding 70 inches. Clearly the differences could be ascribed to the beneficial effects of increased 'soil creep', or flushing, and the decreased chance of waterlogging, on the steeper slopes. In contrast, on the areas of gentle slope, we might anticipate that leached conditions and water-logging could become established at a comparatively early date in the high-level soils, no doubt extending downward through seepage as time went on. The map on page 128 shows the area of the central Lake District where such remains of the ancient high-level forests can be found.

Those mixed oakwoods which are open to sheep have a ground flora which, though including many mosses, is predominantly grassy, often with bracken, except where the substratum is of block scree sufficiently rough to deter the sheep, when ferns, mosses and liverworts often cover the boulders. Where sheep and deer are excluded or are not numerous, a more varied ground flora including brambles, bilberry and many herbs will be found (see page 140). Local variations in soil base-status are reflected in the presence of different herbs – dog's mercury and wild garlic (ramsons) indicate a richer soil and will usually be found in places where ash and elm trees are relatively frequent. Daffodils, primroses, wood anemones, bluebells and wood sanicle are all characteristic herbs of the semi-natural woods where grazing has been either absent or light.

One of the most beloved and familiar of all Lake District plants, the wild daffodil (*Narcissus pseudo-narcissus*) grows in the more open and damper parts of many of these mixed oakwoods, as well as in the damp grassland developed from former woods, especially by becks, rivers and lakes. Since it is very unpalatable to sheep it resists the effects of grazing. (Plate 23, p. 208.)

'When we were in the woods beyond Gowbarrow Park we saw a few daffodils close to the water side . . . as we went along there were more and yet more; and at last, under the boughs of the trees, we saw that there was a long belt of them along the shore, about the breadth of a country turnpike road. I never saw daffodils so beautiful. They grew among the mossy stones about and about them; some rested their heads upon these stones as on a pillow for weariness; and the rest tossed and reeled and danced, and seemed as if they verily laughed with the wind, that blew upon them over the lake; they looked so gay, ever glancing, ever changing.'

Dorothy Wordsworth: *The Grasmere Journal*, April 1802

The Keskadale Oaks

Of the fragments of almost pure sessile oakwood which are found in the more remote dales, the Keskadale and Birkrigg Oaks in the Newlands valley are well-known examples. These woods, now unfenced and open to grazing animals, lie at an altitude of c. 1,000 to 1,400 feet on steep slopes of stabilised small scree. The shallow soils are well-drained and have a pH of about 5.0. The oaks, all *Quercus petraea*, are rather small, with an average height not more than 17 feet and a girth of about 36 inches, but there are larger individuals. Many of the trees, especially in the lower parts of the Keskadale Oaks, have multiple stems. This has been attributed by some botanists to fresh suckering from the stools after burning or disease, rather than to coppicing, but there is no documentary evidence for either, or for planting in the woods. The presence of many larger and single-trunked trees in the higher and less accessible part of the Keskadale wood suggests the possibility of a human factor in the origin of the multiple stems along the lower margin of the wood. Leach, who studied the woods in 1925, believed that the height of the oaks is limited by wind strength, since in many places those trees which are in comparative shelter below the crags reach a greater height than those in more exposed parts of the wood.

Occasional rowans (*Sorbus aucuparia*) are the only trees present other than *Quercus petraea*. The ground flora is dominated by grasses, mainly *Deschampsia flexuosa* and *Anthoxanthum odoratum*, in addition to mosses, bilberry and bracken. There are few signs of regeneration of the oaks; a few oak seedlings were found in the Birkrigg wood in 1925, Yapp records that acorns were being produced in the Keskadale wood in 1950, and they were found in 1968. The open and grazed character of the woods suggests that regeneration of the oaks would be unlikely even if acorns were produced in plenty; however, the absence of signs of regeneration in conjunction with the stunted size of the trees suggested to Tansley that this altitude may be near the limit for oakwood in northern England today. The grassland with bracken which constitutes the vegetation of the hillsides outside the lower edges of the woods passes into communities dominated by *Calluna* on ascending the steep slopes. In the upper parts of the Keskadale wood there is a very strong contrast between the abundance of bryophytes within the trees (mainly *Dicranum scoparium*, *Pleurozium schreberi*, and *Hypnum cupressiforme*) and the almost complete absence of bryophytes outside the wood; the effect of this bryophyte carpet in stabilising the stony scree on these steep slopes of more than 40° is very apparent. It makes clear how much more liable to erosion such slopes must have become when the woodland cover was removed.

There is therefore insufficient evidence, either biological or historical, on which to decide whether the Keskadale and Birkrigg Oaks are indeed remnants of a native type of forest, or whether they represent the descendants of trees once planted for oak coppice. Yapp (1953) has described an un-named oakwood near Whinlatter Pass at about 1,100 feet which has a similar appearance and soil to the Keskadale Oaks, and also several high-level woods in Borrowdale, but the presence in these woods of pines and larches provides more definite evidence for recent planting than is apparent in the two high oakwoods of the Newlands valley. The species lists for the Keskadale and Birkrigg Oaks (Leach, 1925) can be found in Tansley's *The British Islands and their Vegetation*, pp. 322–4.

Borrowdale Woods

Borrowdale probably has a greater extent of semi-natural woodland, composed of native trees, than any other Lakeland valley. Evidently virtually all these woods are planted and growing on the site of former forests exploited for timber and charcoal during earlier centuries, but as the replanting was largely with native trees, perhaps they show some approach in character to the original, natural woodlands of the district. The dependence of tree composition and woodland type on soil conditions is well illustrated in Borrowdale, especially in the woods around Seatoller at the dale head. Although the valley contains local examples of alderwood and willow carr on wet peaty soils beside the River Derwent and Derwent-water, most of the Borrowdale woods are 'hanging', on steep, well-drained and often rocky slopes. The parent rock belongs to the Borrowdale Volcanic Series, but in its soil-forming properties this is a very variable material, being mostly hard, acidic and deficient in available minerals, yet with local occurrences of more friable, easily weathered and markedly calcareous rock.

Johnny's Wood, covering the two sides of a low spur just north of Seatoller, is situated mainly on the hard, acidic type of rock; whereas the steep, wooded slope of Steel Fell south-west of Seatoller has a good deal of the lime-rich material in places, especially towards Seathwaite. Where the rock is poor, the soils are base-poor brown earths, locally with acid humus at the surface, and sessile oak is the dominant tree. Its growth varies according to age, past treatment and soil depth. Some of the oak has regenerated from coppiced stools, giving multiple-stemmed trees which seldom reach a great height, and on steep, rocky ground with a thin soil the trees are often of a gnarled and stunted form. Yet in places there are numerous fine, straight trees reaching 60–70 feet in height, with stout boles and good crowns. In Johnny's Wood are patches of introduced larch (*Larix decidua*) and scattered sycamore (*Acer pseudoplatanus*). The oakwoods here seldom have a good shrub layer, and there is merely a sparse scatter-ing of holly (*Ilex aquifolium*), rowan, hazel and birch (*Betula pubescens*). This absence of underscrub is generally regarded as an artificial feature, resulting from the way the woods are managed. There is also a scarcity of climbing shrubs such as ivy (*Hedera helix*) and honeysuckle (*Lonicera periclymenum*), which are common enough in many lowland Cumberland oakwoods.

The floor of these Seatoller oakwoods has either an essentially grassy type of vegetation or a rocky terrain in which ferns, mosses and liverworts are more conspicuous. The grassy community has sheep's fescue (*Festuca ovina*), bents (*Agrostis canina* and *A. tenuis*), wavy hair grass (*Deschampsia flexuosa*), vernal grass (*Anthoxanthum odoratum*), soft fog (*Holcus mollis*) and Yorkshire fog (*Holcus lanatus*). There is typically an abundance of herbs such as heath bedstraw (*Galium saxatile*), tormentil (*Potentilla erecta*), earthnut (*Conopodium majus*), cow-wheat (*Melampyrum pratense*), wood sorrel (*Oxalis acetosella*), wood anemone (*Anemone nemorosa*), wood sage (*Teucrium scorodonia*), greater stitchwort (*Stellaria holostea*), foxglove (*Digitalis pur-purea*) and golden-rod (*Solidago virgaurea*). More locally are slender St John's wort (*Hypericum pulchrum*), bitter vetch (*Lathyrus montanus*) and climbing fumitory (*Corydalis claviculata*). There is typically an abundance of dwarfed shoots of bilberry (*Vaccinium myrtillus*), and experiments else-where have shown that when sheep grazing is excluded from this type of woodland community this small shrub increases greatly in stature and quantity, coming eventually to dominate the grasses and herbs. The more natural field communities of these hill sessile oakwoods are thus likely to include dense stands of bilberry.

All these woods around Seatoller are open to sheep, and their grazing is a profound influence in maintaining the present character of the vegetation. The presence and performance of other species beside bilberry on ungrazed crag ledges within the woods gives further indication of the effects of grazing. One infers that species such as great woodrush (*Luzula sylvatica*), honeysuckle, and even heather (*Calluna*), would be a good deal more abundant on the poor oakwood soils in the absence of grazing; though heather does not tolerate too deep a shade and might be restricted to more open places. Sheep grazing is probably the main reason for lack of natural regeneration of the trees and the scarcity of tall shrubs within these woods, for the seedlings of woody species are cropped down relentlessly as soon as they have grown more than a few inches tall. Overgrazing of the adjoining open fell-sides has probably contributed largely to the present ascendancy of bracken, and this fern also occurs in dense patches within the woods, especially where the tree growth is more open. Bracken does, however, probably have a natural place in the dry sessile oakwood community, though not necessarily as a dominant species. Small hollows receiving much water seepage have small marshes with common rush (*Juncus effusus*), jointed rush (*J. acutiflorus*), purple moor grass (*Molinia caerulea*) and bog moss (*Sphagnum palustre, S. recurvum, S. inundatum*).

Locally, there are patches of poor woodland soil with a cover of birch instead of oak. One of these, in Johnny's Wood, is a wet hollow with a *Sphagnum* carpet which would probably not support oak. Yet elsewhere in Borrowdale the difference in tree cover seems unaccountable in terms of soil conditions, and it is more likely that birch is a seral type of wood which has taken over on the site of former oak. In this area birch regenerates more freely than oak, given a measure of protection from grazing, and may form pure stands, though it is not regarded as a climax forest tree here. Birch is a constant though subsidiary species in most of the Borrowdale woods.

Where the lime-rich rock outcrops, and especially where the ground below is periodically flushed with drainage water from this material, there is a relatively fertile, base-rich brown soil. It varies in depth according to the slope and rockiness of the ground, but the deeper good woodland soils often have earthworms and moles, and humus in damper sites is of the 'mull' type. The characteristic woodland of these situations is a mixture of ash (*Fraxinus excelsior*), wych elm (*Ulmus glabra*) and birch (*Betula pubescens*), with an understory of hazel scrub. Ash is the most abundant tree, but much is of only modest height (40–45 feet), perhaps due to immaturity or shallowness of soil on the steep slopes; in some of the

Lakeland woods ash grows to the same height as oak. In places this type of mixed deciduous wood has the coppice with standard structure, and locally the hazel scrub is fairly dense with only scattered taller trees. Other tall shrubs of lesser abundance are bird cherry, hawthorn (*Crataegus monogyna*) and blackthorn (*Prunus spinosa*), but rowan and holly also occur in the mixed woodland. Remnants of the famous Borrowdale Yews occur by the woodland edge at Seathwaite, but yew is relatively infrequent in this valley, in contrast to its abundance in the woods of the Coniston–Windermere area.

The mixed woodland field layer is again predominantly grassy, but the species here are slender false brome (*Brachypodium sylvaticum*), wood melick (*Melica uniflora*), and, especially in damper places, tufted hair grass (*Deschampsia cespitosa*). Less abundant grasses include cock's foot (*Dactylis glomerata*), wood poa (*Poa nemoralis*), red fescue (*Festuca rubra*) and bearded couch grass (*Agropyron caninum*). The grassiness of the woodland floor, and the sparseness of bramble (*Rubus fruticosus* agg.) are again probably a reflection of the heavy sheep grazing. Nevertheless, these richer soils have an abundance of herbs such as dog's mercury (*Mercurialis perennis*), herb robert (*Geranium robertianum*), primrose (*Primula vulgaris*), self-heal (*Prunella vulgaris*), common buttercup (*Ranunculus acris*), sanicle (*Sanicula europaea*), wild strawberry (*Fragaria vesca*), barren strawberry (*Potentilla sterilis*), wood pimpernel (*Lysimachia nemorum*), germander speedwell (*Veronica chamaedrys*), heath violet (*Viola riviniana*), broad-leaved willow-herb (*Epilobium montanum*), lesser celandine (*Ranunculus ficaria*), wood avens (*Geum urbanum*), wall lettuce (*Mycelis muralis*), hedge woundwort (*Stachys sylvatica*), nettle (*Urtica dioica*) and wavy bittercress (*Cardamine flexuosa*). Damper places, with 'mull' soils, have bugle (*Ajuga reptans*), meadowsweet (*Filipendula ulmaria*), marsh thistle (*Cirsium palustre*), golden saxifrage (*Chrysosplenium oppositifolium*), creeping buttercup (*Ranunculus repens*) and wood sedge (*Carex sylvatica*). Rarer species on rock ledges include woodruff (*Asperula odorata*) and tutsan (*Hypericum androsaemum*).

In places the two main woodland types intergrade, and the mixed deciduous kind often contains a fair amount of oak. In some Lakeland woods, ash-elm-hazel stands occur mainly as vertical bands or strips within oakwood, and thus mark the distribution of flush lines on the slope.

Where the floor of the oakwoods is rocky, with areas of block litter and scree, there is often a profusion of ferns, notably male fern (*Dryopteris filix-mas* and *D. borreri*), buckler fern (*D. dilatata*), lady fern (*Athyrium filix-femina*), mountain fern (*Thelypteris limbosperma*) and, more locally, oak fern (*T. dryopteris*) and beech fern (*T. phegopteris*). In the ash-elm-hazel woods the fern flora of scree tends to be similar, but rock outcrops have additional species such as hard shield fern (*Polystichum aculeatum*), brittle bladder fern (*Cystopteris fragilis*) and maidenhair spleenwort (*Asplenium trichomanes*).

The extremely heavy rainfall in the vicinity of Seatoller (90–120 inches average annually) gives to all these woods their most distinctive ecological feature, namely a profusion of mosses and liverworts, including many 'Atlantic' species confined to the extreme west of Europe. Lakeland as a whole is rich in Atlantic bryophytes, and compares closely in this respect with North Wales, the Western Highlands and Western Ireland. Several species occurring in the Seatoller Woods are rare even in Lakeland, and unknown elsewhere in England. There is, however, a general abundance and luxuriance of common mosses and liverworts as well. On poor rocks and soils a typical list from the woodland floor would include the following species: *Rhytidiadelphus loreus*, *Hylocomium splendens*, *Hypnum cupressiforme*, *Pleurozium schreberi*, *Plagiothecium undulatum*, *Thuidium tamariscinum*, *T. delicatulum*, *Isothecium myosuroides*, *Sphagnum capillaceum*, *Dicranum scoparium*, *D. majus*, *Polytrichum formosum*, *Mnium hornum*, *Lophocolea bidentata*, *Diplophyllum albicans* and *Calypogeia muelleriana*. These occur both as a subordinate component of the grass and herb field layer (where they are encouraged by sheep grazing) and as pure growths over blocks and sloping rock faces. The moss *Leucobryum glaucum* is locally abundant, mainly in drier, rocky situations, and the northern species *Ptilium crista-castrensis* occurs in places. Barer and steep-sided outcrops and blocks have an abundance of rock-loving mosses and liverworts such as *Andreaea rupestris*, *Rhacomitrium heterostichum*, *R. fasciculare*, *R. lanuginosum*, *R. aquaticum*, *Marsupella emarginata* and *Diplophyllum albicans*.

The common mosses and liverworts of the more basic woodland soils are *Brachythecium rutabulum*, *B. plumosum*, *Eurhynchium praelongum*, *E. striatum*, *Isothecium myurum*, *Hylocomium brevirostre*, *Rhytidiadelphus triquetrus*, *Mnium undulatum*, *Fissidens taxifolius*, *Ctenidium molluscum*, *Atrichum undulatum* and *Plagiochila asplenioides*. In wetter places there is a good deal of *Acrocladium cuspidatum*, *Cratoneuron commutatum*, *Bryum pseudotriquetrum*, *Breutelia chrysocoma*, *Dichodontium pellucidum*, *Fissidens adianthoides*, *F. osmundoides*, *Hookeria lucens*, *Mnium punctatum*, *Rhytidiadelphus squarrosus* and *Pellia fabbroniana*. On rocks, especially outcrops, are *Tortella tortuosa*, *Neckera crispa*, *N. complanata*, *Amphidium mougeotii*, *Fissidens cristatus*, *Bryum capillare*, *Bartramia hallerana*, *Homalia trichomanoides*, *Pterogonium gracile*, *Grimmia apocarpa*, *Camptothecium sericeum*, *Isopterygium pulchellum*, *Pohlia cruda*, *Anoectangium aestivum*, *Metzgeria furcata* and *Riccardia multifida*.

The bryophytes of markedly Atlantic distribution mostly grow in base-poor habitats and are thus more typical of the oak stands than the mixed deciduous woods, but some species range through both types. Many of these plants depend on high atmospheric humidity – hence their need for the shade of tree cover – and they are thus most abundant on shaded slopes of north to east aspect. This aspect effect on the bryophyte flora is well shown by a comparison of the north-east and south facing sides of Johnny's Wood. Atlantic and western species of general distribution in these woods are *Sphagnum quinquefarium*, *Hylocomium umbratum*, *Scapania gracilis, Bazzania trilobata, Plagiochila spinulosa, Saccogyna viticulosa* and *Mylia taylori*, which grow in pure patches or mixed with the more common bryophytes. Some of these are part of the bryophyte layer over soil on the woodland floor, but they mostly occur in greatest abundance where the ground is rocky, with outcrops and block litters. More local species of this type are *Anastrepta orcadensis, Bazzania tricrenata* and *Herberta straminea*, whilst those confined to open rock surfaces include *Hypnum callichroum, Rhabdoweissia crenulata, Sematophyllum novae-caesareae, Radula voluta* and *Adelanthus decipiens*, the last three being very local. The tiny filmy fern *Hymenophyllum wilsonii* is common on the rocks in these woods and forms patches with more resemblance to the bryophytes than to the ferns.

Other, tiny drought-sensitive liverworts occur on the rocks. There is a tendency for most bare rock surfaces in these woods to be continually colonised, first by small bryophytes and lichens, then by larger species, which gradually accumulate humus and soil particles. Depending on the steepness of the rock surface, a closed mat may or may not develop. Where the slope is steep, the developing mat often eventually sloughs off, and the process starts again; but where the slope is less steep, as on the crowns of large blocks, the moss and liverwort mat becomes dense and there may be further invasion by vascular plants. It is a small-scale succession which may be arrested at any stage by gravitational instability. Professional moss-gatherers have stripped the mats from the crowns of blocks locally, and here regeneration will be slow.

The trees themselves support growths of other lowlier plants. The common polypody *Polypodium vulgare* is usually the only vascular epiphyte, but grows on many trees. Mosses and liverworts typically cover the lower parts of the trunks, and include *Hypnum cupressiforme, Isothecium myosuroides, Dicranum scoparium* and *Frullania tamarisci*. Ash trees often have a greater variety of species than oak, but most of the trees in Borrowdale, as elsewhere in Lakeland, have a rather poor lichen flora, with a scarcity of the large foliose species of *Sticta* and *Lobaria* so typical of West Highland woods. The tree lichen flora here has probably been impoverished over the last century or more by atmospheric pollution (mainly sulphur dioxide) from the industrial and urban areas of northern England. Fallen and rotting logs are an important habitat for certain small liverworts, and are in places coloured red by sheets of *Nowellia curvifolia*.

The future of the woods around Seatoller is a matter for concern, as they are not regenerating and are unlikely to do so naturally under the present system of management, with grazing by sheep. Their richness in drought-sensitive mosses, liverworts and filmy fern suggests that they have never been entirely clear-felled in the past, for many of the rarer species do not readily recolonise lost ground. The maintenance of at least some tree cover is essential to the survival of these delicate plants. It is to be hoped that the National Trust, who own most of these woods, will manage, as they have elsewhere in the district, to perpetuate tree cover in the future. Regeneration by native species is desirable, however, in order to maintain the essential character of these distinctive hill woodlands.

Atlantic bryophytes of the woods around Seatoller, Borrowdale

Mosses
*Bartramia hallerana
*Dicranodontium denudatum
*Grimmia hartmanii
Hygrohypnum eugyrium
*Hylocomium umbratum
*Hypnum callichroum

Hedwigia integrifolia
Rhabdoweissia crenulata
Sematophyllum novae-caesareae
*Sphagnum quinquefarium
*Trichostomum tenuirostre

Liverworts
Adelanthus decipiens
*Anastrepta orcadensis
Aphanolejeunea microscopica
*Bazzania trilobata
*B. tricrenata
Douinia ovata
Frullania fragilifolia
*Harpanthus scutatus
Harpalejeunea ovata
Herberta straminea
*Jamesoniella autumnalis
Lejeunea lamacerina
L. patens
L. ulicina
Lepidozia pearsonii

*Metzgeria conjugata
M. hamata
Mylia taylori
*Nowellia curvifolia
Plagiochila punctata
P. spinulosa
P. tridenticulata
Radula voluta
Riccardia sinuata
Scapania gracilis
*S. umbrosa
Saccogyna viticulosa
*Sphenolobus helleranus
*Tritomaria exsecta

* Species thus marked have an Atlantic distribution in Britain but not, or less markedly so, in continental Europe.

Lichens in Lake District woods†

The bryologically most interesting woods in this area, the Longthwaite and Johnny's Woods were rather poor in the total numbers of corticolous lichens, although the final list from all habitats was 106 species. Included in this were *Arthonia cinnabarina, Arthopyrenia cinereopruinosa, *Cetrelia cetrarioides*, (Duby) Culb. et Culb. (=*Parmelia cetrarioides*), *Haematomma elatinum, *Lecidea cinnabarina, Normandina pulchella, Parmelia laevigata* (which was often dominant), *Parmeliopsis hyperopta, Pannaria pityrea, Porina chlorotica* var. *carpinea, Peltigera horizontalis, Stenocybe pullatula, S. septata, Sphaerophorus fragilis, S. globosus,* and *Tomasellia gelatinosa.* The woods to the south of Seatoller village were rather similar but still

†Reprinted from; *A lichenological excursion through the north of England,* by F. Rose, D. L. Hawksworth and B. J. Coppins, *The Naturalist,* 1970.

poorer in species numbers. On the trees here a characteristic, probably un-described, community occurs in this, probably the wettest woodland area in England (mean rainfall *c.* 150 in. p.a.) which is characterised by the codominance of *Parmelia laevigata* and *P. taylorensis*, with *Ochrolechia tartarea* (fertile) and *Myco-blastus sanguinarius* also common. Other 'atlantic' species not encountered previously on this excursion but seen here were *Parmeliella corallinoides* and *Sticta sylvatica*. Particularly interesting was the absence of *Lobaria* species and *Pachyphiale cornea* in these two woods which would have been expected here if they were species as strongly 'atlantic' as some authors have suggested. . . .

The Keskadale oak woods were rather uninteresting except in their upper parts where *Alectoria chalybeiformis* occurred on the horizontal branches of one ancient oak, and *Usnea fragilescens* was frequent. The saxicolous flora of the crags immediately above the wood included *Bacidia citrinella*, *Lecidea dicksonii*, *Lepraria neglecta*, and *Cornicularia muricata*.

Scales Wood, Buttermere, also a site famous for its bryophytes, had 72 species of lichens, including those on trees and walls by the lake and Buttermere village. Among the latter were *Bacidia affenis*, *Candelariella aurella*, *C. xanthostigma*, *Lecidea berengeriana*, *Parmelia elegantula*, *Protoblastenia rupestris*, *Rhizocarpon ob-scuratum* var. *reductum* and *R. petraeum*. Near Brackenthwaite, at the north end of Crummock Water a group of roadside trees had *Xanthorion* developed and in this community *Sticta limbata* (generally thought of as a nitrophobous species), *Parmelia caperata*, *P. perlata*, *P. exasperatula*, and *Physcia pulverulenta* occurred.

In Great Wood, 1·25 miles south of Keswick the best *Lobarion* communities we had seen anywhere in the British Isles or Brittany were discovered. *Lobaria amplissima*, *L. laetevirens* and *L. pulmonaria* were all common and dominant on *Ulmus glabra* and *Quercus*, forming sheets extending from the base often continuously to at least 35 metres up the trunks. This site was of exceptional interest for the trees them-selves, though fine mature specimens, were not ancient ones, and were obviously regenerate rather than relic, yet the lichens found were those considered as typical of 'relic' forest in other parts of England. It seems probable that these species have been able to spread from older trees which have since disappeared, and develop communities similar to those which must once have been widespread in the British Isles. The occurrence of *L. pulmonaria* has been documented last century in all English counties except Norfolk, Huntingdonshire, Northampton-shire, Middlesex, Hertfordshire, and Staffordshire, which suggests that it was once generally distributed throughout England, and it appears still to be widely distributed in Continental Europe. The finding of *Lobaria* species in open situations in areas of relatively low rainfall in parklands in south-east England, north-west Herefordshire, south Northumberland and Westmorland, together with our observations of their distribution in the Borrowdale and Keswick areas (where they avoid the areas of highest rainfall), together with the evidence of their European and former British distributions, makes it clear that *L. amplissima*, *L. laetevirens* and *L. pulmonaria* are indicators of ancient forest rather than of 'atlantic' habitats. Truly atlantic species such as *Pannaria pityrea*, *P. rubiginosa*, *Parmelia taylorensis*, *P. laevigata*, and *Sticta sylvatica* always appear to be very rare or absent in localities where *Lobarion* is optimally developed. *Pachyphiale cornea*, *Haematomma elatinum*, *Lecidea cinnabarina*, and *Thelotrema lepadinum*, on the other hand, are probably similar to these three *Lobaria* species in indicating relics of ancient forest. Other interesting taxa noted at Great Wood, which had 77 corticolous lichens, were *Arthonia spadicea, Buellia disciformis, *Catillaria sphaeroides, *Cetrelia cetraroides, Dimerella diluta, *Haematomma elatinum, *Lepraria candelaris, *Lecidea cinnabarina, Pachyphiale cornea, *Parmelia crinita, *Pertusaria flavida, *P. hemisphaerica, *Thelopsis rubella, Thelotrema lepadinum, Stenocybe septata, Sticta sylvatica, S. limbata, and S. fuliginosa. Thelopsis rubella is of special interest: thought to be confined to the west Scottish Highlands and south-west Ireland, it has recently been discovered by one of us (F.R.) in Herefordshire, the New Forest, Devon and Sussex, and this new locality helps to bridge the disjunction in its known distribution.

*Species thus marked have not previously been published as occurring in particular vice-counties.

Grizedale Forest and the High Furness woods

The formerly coppiced mixed oakwoods which cover so much of Furness Fells in the southern Lake District resemble in many ways the Borrowdale woods but differ in certain respects. Regular coppicing in the past is probably the reason for the comparative poverty of the southern woods in those bryophytes which require high humidity. The economic value of these regularly coppiced woods led to efficient management and exclusion of sheep while the coppiced stools produced new shoots, and this is reflected in the particularly high quality of some of the present trees, produced as single oaks on old coppiced stools (page 147). The presence of the small-leaved lime (Tilia cordata) in apparently native situations in some of the southern woods suggests that they are near the northern limit for that tree. In Grizedale Forest the Forestry Commission is preserving a fine area of semi-natural deciduous forest of this type.

Grizedale in High Furness runs south between parallel moorland ridges of Silurian sediments, Coniston Grits and Bannisdale Slates, which are in the main about 700 to 900 feet in height, but reach 1,000 feet in a few summits. From certain viewpoints in Grizedale in high summer, when the fells to the north make a blue back-drop, one can imagine more vividly than anywhere else in the Lake District what the landscape looked like when the cloaking mantle of leafy forest ran over fells and dales alike, up to the feet of the high crags and peaks.

The semi-natural woodlands which still run up the sides of Grizedale, between the dale meadows and the rough broken ground of the high ridges, are of sessile oak, with birch, alder, hazel, bird cherry, rowan, wych elm, gean and the rare small-leaved lime. These woods have been used by man since the time, before the twelfth century, when Norse-speaking people ran their pigs in the woods and called the valley Grizedale (Old Norse griss=pig) and cleared the dale bottom at Satterthwaite for the summer shielings (saeter=shieling, thwaite (tveit)=clearing). During the twelfth century the land became the property of the monks of Furness (see Chapter 15) who established local woodland industries and began a systematic exploitation of the woods, partly as enclosed coppice worked on a 14-year rotation. The monks had the rights over the deer, and in 1516 much of the tributary valley of Dale Park was made into a deer park, five miles in circumference, where woodland would be preserved as browsing and cover for the red deer. At the Dissolution, some of the Grizedale coppices which passed to William Sandys were supplying enough charcoal for three bloomsmithies, and in the seventeenth century they continued to contribute to the demand for charcoal of some of the local furnaces, including that at Backbarrow which went on smelting with charcoal until 1921. This local demand for charcoal which continued into quite recent times made the coppices more profitable than any possible agricultural use of this rocky land, and so they were preserved, with their woodland soil and its fauna intact, as economic assets. The present state of the deciduous woods in Grizedale results mainly from the end of the local demand for charcoal, whereupon the woods were allowed to grow up, the oak stools (some of great antiquity) being singled and stored to produce one trunk of good quality each. The woods have also, of course, been modified to some extent by planting of scattered alien trees, of sycamore, larch and beech – at the time when extensive planting of larch took place in the early nineteenth century on the high and windswept ridges where the native forest had probably always been thin. In the 1930s Grizedale was acquired by the Forestry Commission, and in spite of extensive felling during the 1939–45 War, the woods still contain 'some of the finest mature oaks that are still left in the Furness Fells, with all their natural associates, including the very rare small-leaved lime. . . . The first step taken in management was to close these areas to sheep and put them under a separate Working Plan which provided for the maintenance of their deciduous character and the gradual conversion of the crop to uneven-aged high forest by a system of group fellings. These fellings are to favour the natural regeneration of oak and larch where the sites are suitable . . .' (Chard, 1967). The Grizedale oakwoods, though they are clearly no more than 'semi-natural', therefore provide one of the best examples of woods whose history is known and which are now under enlightened management which makes regeneration possible (Fig. 21, p. 291).

In general the Grizedale woods resemble the pattern shown in Figs. 24 and 25 of *Mountains and Moorlands*, by W. H. Pearsall, but a distinctive character is the amount of small-leaved lime in addition to ash and elm, in the flushed habitats. Ashes and elms are found along the stream courses, for instance in Hall Beck and Farra Grain Beck, in the same way in which they are generally distributed in these woods but the habitat of small-leaved lime is rather specialised. Mature trees are found here either on the edges of small crumbling rock faces or beside rocky waterfalls in the course of these two becks (J. S. R. Chard, 1967 and personal demonstration). The presence of larch and beech trees throughout the Grizedale woods is, of course, evidence for the planting of alien trees in the past, but the constancy of the habitat of the small-leaved lime is strong evidence for the descent of the lime trees from members of the primeval forest and not from planted trees, for it is most unlikely that lime trees would have been planted only in those two particular habitats. It is not quite certain what factors determine the distribution of the small-leaved lime in other southern woods, but its presence in the gill of Appletreeworth Beck (near to the farm Lind End where the place-name indicates its presence in the past) may be linked with the generally rather base-rich habitat provided there by a narrow outcrop of Coniston Limestone (cf. p. 221).

The amenity woods dominated by the oak

These form the third type of oakwood, and, planted and well-maintained by private landowners, are an important element in the Lake District landscape. Usually they differ from the grown-up coppice woods in the more uniform age of the trees and often in the absence or scarcity of a shrub layer of native species, while the rhododendron (*Rhododendron ponticum*) is often planted and subsequently naturalised in them. The ground flora is often poor in species compared with the lists given by Dr Ratcliffe for the Borrowdale woods, and there is usually a higher proportion of alien trees. These include beeches, European larches, pines and sycamores, though some of the amenity woods have been developed as almost pure oakwoods. As one example we may take the Muncaster woods in Lower Eskdale, through which the main road to Whitehaven from the south runs, in a stretch contrasting strongly with the bare fields of the coastal plain to north and south. A list of the trees planted on the Muncaster estate between December, 1793, and April, 1794, includes larch (more than 6,000), beech, oak, birch and sycamore.

THE ALDERWOODS

Alder (*Alnus glutinosa*) is very common as a stream-side tree in nearly all the mixed woods of the Lake District, and is frequently found as individuals or narrow belts along the lake shores, as well as in the remaining areas of fen as at Esthwaite. Formerly the alder must have been much more common, for the flat floors of the glaciated valleys, up to at least 1,200 feet altitude, must have been swampy alderwoods until they were cleared and drained. Whenever the valley bogs of these areas today are sampled with a peat borer, pieces of alder wood are found at a certain horizon.

From the pollen record it seems likely that hillside alderwoods must have been present in the past. Surviving fragments of such woods are

PLATE 13 *Above*, Blea Tarn, Side Pike and Lingmoor Fell: amenity planting of pines and rhododendrons. *Below*, Tarn Hows: naturalised larch round the largely artificial tarn; Bowfell and Langdale Pikes in the background.

PLATE 14 *Above*, Elterwater: a reedy lake shore, semi-natural deciduous woodland including birch, and the crag of Pavey Ark above Mill Gill. *Below*, Buttermere, a stony lake shore with no hydrosere. Planted pines.

found in Martindale, on the fell-sides between 900 and 1,100 feet. These woods are of well-grown trees, with a ground flora dominated by rushes (*Juncus* spp.) and *Anthoxanthum odoratum*; the other tree species present are ash, wych elm and holly, bird cherry and rowan. The ground is wet and the soils flushed, with a pH between 5.5 and 6.0. Both from this and from the species present, it is clear that the Martindale woods are occupying a habitat which is more base-rich than that of most of the hill-side woods. It seems possible that these woods are near the altitudinal limit at which the alder can set good seed, for this limit is about 1,000 feet in Scotland at present. There are no signs that these woods are regenerating, but since they are not fenced this may be due to grazing.

As part of the Dalemain estate, Martindale and the alderwoods have been owned by the Hasells for several centuries, and there is no suggestion in Major Hasell's estate records that the woods were ever planted. He regarded them as surviving fragments of native forest. Mr Chard has pointed out that deer do not browse on alder, and that long-continued browsing by red deer exerts a selective effect favourable to the alder in a mixed wood. Since Martindale has always been managed as deer forest, and this selective effect may have operated over many centuries, it is possible that these woods owe their unique character to this factor. Areas of woodland would be left standing to provide shelter for the deer, and within them, on suitable soils, alders would come to dominate the wood as browsing by the deer prevented the regeneration of other trees.

ASH-HAZEL WOODS WITH ELM, OAK AND LIME

These are the lovely woods of the Mountain Limestone of South West-morland and its borders with Furness – Yewbarrow, Whitbarrow and Underbarrow Scar within the National Park, and the woods of Arnside, Yealand and Silverdale between the National Park and the sea. The abundance of ash, hazel, elm and lime distinguishes them from the mixed woods of the Silurian sediments, for whereas base-rich soils are found only in local pockets and flushed habitats on the Silurian slates and grits, the Carboniferous Limestone and the drift which covers it in places provide a base-rich soil which in spite of leaching continues to carry neutral mull humus in general, instead of only in flushed habitats as on the Silurian rocks. The bare limestone pavement of clints and grykes (rock pavement and intervening fissures, representing areas ground bare by the passage of ice and on which no soil has subsequently formed because, being nearly pure calcium carbonate, the limestone in those places dissolves almost completely on weathering) alternates with areas where good mull soils provide habitats for a wide range of lime-loving plants which are not found in the central Lake District. The flora of the limestone, which is described in Wilson's *Flora of Westmorland*, is to many naturalists one of the greatest attractions of the National Park. Species of the limestone flora provide the food plants for the caterpillars of certain butterflies found locally, notably the Scotch Argus (*Erebia aethiops*) which feeds on the grass *Sesleria albicans*, and the Brown Argus (*Aricia agestis*) which feeds on the rock-rose (*Helianthemum chamaecistus*).

The woods include some birch (*Betula pendula*) as well as ash, hazel, oak, elm and lime, and in many places there is yew, often rooted in fissures in the limestone. Larch, beech, hornbeam and pine have been planted. The native shrubs include rowan, bird cherry, hawthorn, blackthorn, two species of whitebeam (*Sorbus rupicola* and the local *S. lancastriensis*), and the typically limestone shrubs spindle (*Euonymus europaeus*), privet (*Ligustrum vulgare*) and purging buckthorn (*Rhamnus catharticus*), all three of which are here at about their northern limit.

The ground flora of the woods is commonly dominated by dog's mercury or ramsons, and includes much *Brachypodium sylvaticum*. Daffodils are common in some of the woods, and lily-of-the-valley (*Convallaria majalis*) in a few. The long species list of the flora of these woods includes the broad helleborine (*Epipactis helleborine*) and the dark-red helleborine (*E. atrorubens*), two species of Solomon's seal (*Polygonatum multiflorum* and *P. odoratum*), and the rare long-leaved helleborine (*Cephalanthera longifolia*). Where the woods thin out into open hazel scrub on limestone pavement, a characteristic vegetation dominated by the wood sage (*Teucrium scorodonia*) and including ploughman's spikenard (*Inula conyza*) is found. In short semi-open turf at the edge of limestone cliffs such as Scout Scar, the rock-roses *Helianthemum canum* and *H. chamaecistus* and the very local sedge *Carex ericetorum* are found, in a community which on deeper soils passes into grassland dominated by *Sesleria albicans*.

Brigsteer Woods, now owned by the National Trust, are an area of limestone woodland open to the public. Scout Scar, the high limestone ridge on the eastern side of the Lyth valley, opposite Whitbarrow on the west, has the charming village of Brigsteer along its skirts, just above the black peat of Helsington Moss which represents a fragment of the great mosses which formerly covered the flat floor of the Lyth. Brigsteer Woods, on the limestone slopes below the bare pavement of Scout Scar, have been famous daffodil woods for more than a century, since they were described by the Victorian novelist Mrs Humphry Ward in *Helbeck of Bannisdale*: 'A Westmorland wood in daffodil time – it was nothing more and nothing less . . . The golden flowers, the slim stalks, rose from a mist of greenish-blue, made by their speary leaf amid the encircling browns and purples, the intricate stem and branch-work of the still winter-bound hazels. . . . They were flung on the fell-side through a score of acres, in sheets and tapestries of gold – such an audacious, unreckoned plenty as went strangely with the frugal air and temper of the northern country, with the bare-walled fields, the ruggedness of the crags above, and the melancholy of the treeless marsh below.'

These are much modified but not heavily grazed woods of the limestone fringe, of hazel, ash, birch and some oak, with yews and many introduced trees – sycamores, beeches, larches and other conifers. Their spring glory of daffodils, windflowers and violets is followed by the more sheltered and hidden blossoming of lily-of-the-valley, at the time when outside the wood the famous damsons of the Lyth are in bloom in every valley orchard.

Roudsea Wood: a National Nature Reserve

Two parallel ridges, of respectively Carboniferous Limestone and Bannisdale Slate, crop out side by side on the east of the Leven estuary. This island of solid rock, lapped round on the seaward side by alluvium and to landward by a complex of raised bogs – Fish House Moss, Stribers Moss and Deer Dike Moss – includes within its bounds both oakwood on the slate, and yew, ash and hazel woods on the limestone. On the drained mosses along the eastern edge of the wood, birch and pine are seeding and are rapidly colonising the peat. Roudsea Wood, a National Nature Reserve, therefore includes within its boundaries a great variety of habitats; it is being intensively studied by the Nature Conservancy's scientific staff at Merlewood, and experimental forestry is going on. There is some particularly attractive hazel coppice where roe deer feed. On one side the woodland vegetation grades into salt marsh, and on the other into the *Calluna–Eriophorum–Sphagnum–Andromeda* communities of a drained and partially drying bog surface. Some curious juxtapositions of species and habitats can be found – for instance dog's mercury, a plant generally indicative of base-rich or flushed habitats, is growing on raised-bog peat, but this will be found to be periodically flushed by water draining from the limestone.

One of the most interesting plants in Roudsea Wood is the yellow sedge (*Carex flava*), a tall handsome plant which grows in rather open situations, in places where somewhat peaty soil overlies the limestone but near to outcrops of solid limestone; in these places the soil is flooded at intervals by the backing-up of freshwater drainage at times of the highest spring tides. These places, where the water-table is so near the surface, are near an overgrown tarn which provides still other habitats, for a rich aquatic and marsh vegetation.

JUNIPER SCRUB

Thickets of well-grown junipers, *Juniperus communis*, locally known as savin, are a characteristic Lake District vegetation type, both on the mountains, lower fells and some lowland commons. The high-level juniper scrub of this type is thought to occupy the sites of former forest, and the soils in most of these thickets are good well-drained mull humus. Juniper does not have the podsolising tendency of many conifers, but on such soils it continues to give rise to mull humus. Other examples of high-level juniper can be seen in many parts of the mountains, such as on Place Fell by Ullswater, in parts of the Caldew valley in Skiddaw Forest, and on both sides of the upper part of Little Langdale. A somewhat different type of tall juniper scrub is found at rather lower altitudes, well seen round Blea Tarn and below it, and on what might be called the knoll and hollow type of semi-moorland where heather crowns the knolls and damp grassland, usually now with bracken, fills the hollows. In this type of country the juniper is, again, growing on the better-drained, more flushed and less acid soils. The Silurian moorlands between Blawith and Torver, west of Coniston Water, are of this type, with abundant juniper together with scattered oaks, birches and hollies. Scattered junipers, many of great age, are common on the moorland ridges of the Forestry Commission's land in Grizedale. Juniper does not tolerate shading by trees, so that where oaks and birches have grown to maturity in this type of marginal woodland–moorland country, junipers have been shaded out and become moribund – this can be seen in a wood on the south side of Oxenfell, east of the Coniston–Ambleside road near Yew Tree Tarn. Other moorland habitats of juniper are on peaty soils, and, of course, it is a characteristic shrub of the Carboniferous Limestone hills.

Since in the Lake District no trace of the natural tree limit remains, it is not possible to know whether juniper naturally occupied a belt of mountain country above the former forest limit.

In Dr Ratcliffe's opinion: 'The dwarf form of juniper, *Juniperus communis* subsp. *nana*, grows on cliffs and broken ground on several hills, mostly above 1,500 feet, but is linked by intermediate forms to the ordinary shrub which produces thickets on many lower hillsides. *J. communis* subsp. *nana* is not merely the montane habitat form of *J. communis*, for equally stunted plants, still clearly nearer to the latter, commonly occur in exactly the same kind of place as the true dwarf, and even alongside it, up to fully 2,500 feet. The high-level juniper populations are evidently mixed and there is a taxonomic and ecological problem to be solved.' (1960.)

The factors responsible for the present distribution of the tall shrub *J. communis*, in the areas which were formerly oak-woodland, must be complex, for no direct relationship between distribution and any single factor has emerged from field surveys. We have seen that it is a plant of wide tolerance as regards soil type. It can resist considerable grazing pressure, though this usually prevents regeneration, as Chard has pointed out for Furness Fells: 'Some of the larger junipers are 300–400 years old and have been browsed all their life; regeneration failed under sheep, but is now appearing again in older plantations in spite of the deer.' (Chard, 1966.) It appears to be sensitive to burning, which would explain its absence from those parts of the fells which have been in the past systematically managed as grouse moor. It is possible that in parts of the southern fells and valleys it may have been at one time protected and encouraged because of the special use of savin charcoal in the manufacture of gunpowder (see Chapter 16). The gunpowder works at Elterwater and Bouth and Haverthwaite were all in areas where juniper is now common on the open fells, and they paid a higher price for juniper charcoal than for any other.

THE PINE IN THE LAKE DISTRICT

The pine is regarded as an introduced alien in the mixed woods derived from the native oak forest. Where it has been planted over the last two centuries it is often now well naturalised, having reproduced and spread by seeding. In woods such as those in the Duddon valley and on the west shore of Windermere below Claife Heights, pine has come to occupy an ecological niche on the summits of rocky knolls where the soil is thin and particularly subject to leaching (Gorham, 1953). On the drying peat of the valley raised bogs – Rusland Moss, Deer Dike Moss and Meathop Moss, for instance, pine is seeding and regenerating so rapidly as to have changed the character of the vegetation within the last twenty years (p. 193). We know from the pollen record that during the early post-glacial period, about 8,000 years ago, pine must have been abundant in the Lake District – this is confirmed by the presence of pine wood at the base of peat profiles in the hills. The still unanswered question is whether or not the native pine had entirely died out by the time that pine began to be planted. (Plate 5, p. 64.)

During early post-glacial time, the frequency of pollen of the native pine varied considerably from site to site, in a way which shows that distribution of this tree was almost certainly controlled by soil type. Pine seems to have been abundant on peaty soils in the uplands, and on lowland peat in the southern part of the Lake District, but in the north it was present only very occasionally. Its abundance must have declined very greatly after about 5000 B.C., when its pollen becomes progressively scarcer. By about 2000 to 1000 B.C. there is either very little or no pine pollen in the lake sediments. Some ecologists believe that the native pine must have died out, and that the occasional pollen grains subsequently found in sediments and peats must have travelled on the wind from distant sources. If this were so, all pine trees in the Lake District today would descend from trees re-introduced in the last two centuries from Scottish or European stock. Oral tradition in the southern Lake District suggests that when the planting of pines became fashionable, in the seventeenth and eighteenth centuries, seedlings were obtained from the lowland mosses where the trees were then growing on drained peat as they do today. Rusland Moss is said to have been one such source. Foresters at Grizedale can produce evidence suggesting that pines from Rusland Moss today are a distinct form, for under parallel conditions seed from these pines produces different growth from that obtained from Scottish seed. It therefore seems possible that native pines did survive on lowland mosses and that these were a source of seedling pines when it became fashionable to plant this tree. This fashion spread widely in the eighteenth century, but may have begun earlier, for in *The Lake District and the National Trust* Mr B. L. Thompson notes that in an Award of 1535 referring to the old mill at Low Millerground, Windermere, there was reference to a 'Scottyshe bushe' as a landmark, and he thinks this must have been a pine.

THE LAKE DISTRICT WOODS TODAY

The various woods of the Lake District offer material for endless discussion on the question of which of them are nearest to the truly 'natural' forest of north-west England. As yet there has been no long-term experiment on what could happen to any of these woods if all grazing were to be excluded and all commercial exploitation to cease, though the work of the Nature Conservancy at Roudsea Wood and elsewhere may be expected in time to yield answers to some of the questions involved. Meanwhile a great deal of interest can be learned from the history of the Thirlmere catchment area since it was planted by the Manchester foresters at the beginning of the present century. The leaflets provided for the Forest Trails at Launchy Ghyll and Swirls, Thirlmere, contain this information and notes on where to look for the examples quoted.

A little more than fifty years ago, the waterworks authority fenced a great part of the western side of Thirlmere to exclude sheep and deer. At that time only very small fragments of native birch-oak wood remained there. The Manchester foresters were primarily concerned to conserve the soil on the treeless fell-sides of their catchment area. They planted the bracken-covered slopes with larch and beech, and the peaty plateau with spruces, and on good deep soils on the lower slopes they planted the Douglas firs which are such fine noble trees today. On bare screes hitherto kept unstable by the continual passage of sheep, they planted young conifers of various species including the native Scots pine, in bucketfuls of soil carried to the spot. Two good results of this can now be seen from the Forest Trails.

Firstly, from mother trees which were included in the fenced areas, natural regeneration by seeding of birch, hazel and oak has taken place since the sheep were excluded. These native trees are springing up on areas which were left unplanted; much of the ground is steep and rocky.

Plate 32, p. 289, shows the way in which the birch has grown up, and among these birches are oak saplings, which will eventually grow up and shade out the shorter-lived and light-demanding birches. It is clear that natural deciduous forest is re-establishing itself here because grazing has been prevented. When the oaks are grown up, it would be possible to open this wood to winter grazing of sheep in the traditional manner, but, of course, no further natural regeneration of trees would then go on.

Secondly, on screes which were fenced and planted with young Scots pine, the soil-forming succession described on page 122 has taken place, and the formerly bare and unstable stony slopes now carry a thick ground vegetation of grasses and mosses, and the carpet of pine needles is adding humus to this developing soil. Instead of running off rapidly from the bare screes, rain is now absorbed by this newly formed soil, so the run-off into the lake is stabilised and the water is comparatively free of sediment. Natural regeneration of conifers can now be seen on these stabilised screes.

THE WOODS AS A HABITAT FOR MAMMALS AND BIRDS

This book is primarily concerned with the landscape and its history, and cannot attempt any detailed account of animal life. But just as it was not possible to consider the lakes and becks without taking account of the trout and char and the ducks and dippers, which an observant visitor to these habitats may see, so it is appropriate in considering the woods to think a little about the habitats which they provide for animals large and small. Most of what follows will refer to the southern Lake District, particularly to High Furness with the largest continuous area of semi-natural woodland in the north of England. The continuity of the woodland habitat granted to this area by the economic importance of its coppices has preserved the fertile forest soil and much of its indigenous flora and fauna. According to foresters, some of the oaks in High Furness began their growth in the days when pack ponies were the only means of transport, and 'the grandparents of those trees could have been contemporary with the wolf and the wild boar' (Chard). So, though some historical records tell of times of timber shortage when, particularly in the late sixteenth and seventeenth centuries, there was scarcely a standing tree of any size in all Furness, the soil and the old rootstocks (stools) go back to the days when the forest was almost virgin, and though the wolf and the wild boar have been gone for many centuries, and the wild cat for about 200 years, the red deer and roe deer, red squirrels, badgers and foxes, have maintained themselves in the woods of Claife, Grizedale, Graythwaite, Dale Park and Rusland, and continue to flourish there under the present enlightened management of the Forestry Commission, together with the pine marten which had gone but is now coming back.

Though great parts of these woods have now, of course, been transformed into conifer plantations, we have already seen that the deciduous woods of Grizedale are being managed under a special plan for hardwoods (p. 147). In the woods round Satterthwaite, for example, the humble little invertebrates of the forest floor, including mites and springtails which suck and chew over the rotting leaves, the earthworms which digest this annual harvest and mix it with the mineral soil and so play their part in maintaining soil fertility, the millipedes and the centipedes, must trace their ancestry back to the primeval forest as surely as do the lordly stags whose heads adorn the Grizedale Deer Museum. The microfauna of these soils of native deciduous woodlands has been studied and described in detail by soil scientists of the Nature Conservancy at Merlewood, and detailed accounts can be found in the Merlewood publications.

Red deer and roe deer (*Cervus elephas* and *Capreolus capreolus*) are both found native in the woods of Furness Fells and on the rocky ridges which rise above them. Both were originally forest animals, and their distribution must have been contracted by destruction of the native forests. Two factors combined to maintain the stock of red deer in Furness – preservation of woodlands for economic reasons during the medieval centuries, and subsequent preservation of deer on the Graythwaite estate after the Dissolution. The other herd of native red deer which has survived in the Lake District, in Martindale, has been similarly protected by the Dalemain estate. In other parts of the district, notably Ennerdale, red deer were protected in deer parks through medieval centuries, but disappeared after the seventeenth century.

Chard states (1966): 'The red deer of Furness Fells are very uniform in colour and markings, according to season, sex and age, and are remarkable for their weight. A mature stag will scale 25 stone clean and up to 30 stone has been reported. The weights of young animals and hinds are in proportion. The antlers are massive but of no great length, 36 inches being the maximum recorded, and about 32 inches average. The tops are formed early in life and there is a tendency for the bay tines to appear late, and sometimes to be missing. A fully attired mature stag is typically a 14 pointer with double-forked tops, but 16 pointers are not infrequent.

'This pattern of antler can be traced not only in old trophies at Graythwaite Hall, and in cottages and houses throughout the district (some going back over 100 years), but has also been dug from both peat and gravel during draining operations at Grizedale. There is thus a strong presumption that one is dealing with an unmixed, or at any rate dominant, stock of considerable antiquity. Although it could have been augmented from outside sources, the probabilities and weight of evidence so far are against this.'

The red deer now feed for preference on grass, either in the open or on the grassy floor of woods and plantations, and find in the oakwoods enough acorns to fatten on in autumn. Browsing on trees takes place in winter,

PLATE 15 *Above*, Wastwater, a stony-shored and unproductive lake, with Great Gable in the background. *Below*, Wastwater Screes: these shifting screes are colonised by isolated bushes and other plants but never develop a continuous plant cover.

PLATE 16 *Above*, Esthwaite Water: a shallow and productive lowland mere with reed-fringed shores. *Below*, Little Langdale Tarn: a small valley lake; Fellfoot Farm and Wrynose Pass in the background.

particular species being preferred, such as juniper on higher ground, and 'The next in order is lodge-pole pine, followed rather closely by Norway spruce, and then the larches and Scots pine. It is interesting to note that while planted larches can be rendered useless by browsing, the natural seedlings come up in clumps and there is nearly always an undamaged survivor in the centre to take the lead. Sitka spruce has normally proved immune to browsing, even when the grass around it is grazed bare. . . . In the hardwood areas at Grizedale the main buffer, which also gives physical protection to both planted trees and natural regeneration, is undoubtedly bramble. Unfortunately it was quite eliminated by sheep and it took between 8 and 12 years from the time the woods were closed against them after the war for the grass swards to be dispersed and the natural woodland flora to re-establish itself. In parts the process is not completed yet. During this period there was heavy browsing by deer on species which are now much less affected, such as oak and birch. . . . Broom, ivy, holly and yew are all sought out especially by the deer in winter, but none is present in sufficient quantity in the Grizedale woods for its influence to be measurable.' (Chard, 1966.)

The red deer of these fells do not normally herd, but for most of the year spread themselves out in very small parties unless they are much disturbed. Except during the rut, stags and hinds keep separate company, although their movements frequently overlap. The main concentrations of deer are near Graythwaite, on the Dale Park side, and on Claife Heights. Some of the stag groups have recently been found to cross Coniston Water and move west as far as Hardknott. During the 1939–45 War there were both deliberate attempts to reduce the deer stock and felling of timber and extension of sheep-grazing in the woods, which reduced the habitats available to deer. Since then the stock has been building up, and counts suggest a breeding success of 50 per cent – 'which if it were to continue, without adequate control or other mortality in the older age classes, would obviously soon lead to a population explosion. The main point, perhaps, is that it provides an explanation of how a relatively small stock of deer has been able to survive for so long in Furness Fells, with a minimum of protection beyond that afforded by its habitat.' (Chard, 1966.) The maturation of many of the Grizedale plantations, which have been opened out into the pole stage, has now increased the habitats suitable for the red deer.

The other herd of red deer in the Lake District is in Martindale, on the Dalemain estate, on ground which deer have occupied continuously since early medieval times when they were all over the Lake District. The Martindale herd has been managed as a sporting preserve and is the only deer forest of this kind in England. Martindale (Rampsgill) and the adjoining dale of Bannerdale are not open to free public access (see Wainwright, Vol. 2), for the deer are protected from disturbance. They are not fed in winter but range the heights in the same manner as the deer in Furness. Deer now present in Kentmere and on the west of Ullswater have probably spread from Martindale; there are some red deer also on the Thirlmere catchment area.

Roe deer (*Capreolus capreolus*) are said to be present at some time or other in nearly every wood in the Lake District, but in many woods they are seldom seen. In the Grizedale Forest roe invaded each area as soon as it was planted in the 1940s and 1950s, and increased in numbers as the woodland habitat was extended by the new plantations. When plantations close into thicket the numbers of roe decline. Interesting work on the relation of numbers of roe to their effect on coppice is going on at Roudsea Wood. The absence of bramble from the very beautiful hazel coppice at Roudsea is said to be the result of roe browsing. In commercial plantations it is necessary to exclude roe by deer-proof fencing at certain stages – otherwise their browsing destroys the young trees. One of the advantages of Sitka spruce is its immunity to this. The Forestry Commission's leaflet, *The Roe Deer*, describes the relationship between commercial forestry and the effects of this species.

The British red squirrel (*Sciurus vulgaris leucorus*) is a race found only in Britain, and the woods of Furness and the adjoining parts of South Westmorland are one of the places where it has remained most frequent. It does also occur in Cumberland; on Great Mell Fell this species goes up to 1,500 feet. To many people this graceful little animal is one of their happiest memories of the Lake District woods. During the war its numbers were reduced, partly as a result of tree felling and possibly also by disease, but it is now appearing again in increasing numbers. It seems to have a long history in the Lake District, for it is depicted on a Runic stone from Bewcastle in Cumberland, and appears on some thirteenth century glass at Bowness in Westmorland. There is, of course, no proof that either of these was drawn from nature locally, but Squirrel Nutkin, most famous of Lake District squirrels, certainly was, and he was no 'offcome' for he sailed across Derwentwater on a raft. Products of the native forest, acorns, hazel-nuts, birch seeds and autumn fungi of the woods (e.g. species of *Boletus*) are all favourite foods, but so also are seeds from pine cones and the sappy inner bark of young conifer trees in the new plantations. In past centuries, wild cats and perhaps pine martens must have taken toll of the red squirrels, but now they have few enemies except stoats and possibly kestrels. 'It is likely that the species suffers more losses through hard winters, disease and the destruction of its habitat, than from any other cause.' (M. Shorten, *Squirrels*, in this series.)

Of the smaller carnivores the fox and badger are common in these woods, otters live around the lake margins and along the rivers, and pine martens have reappeared in Grizedale Forest, where they are, of course, no longer persecuted as vermin. Stoats and weasels are common, as in most natural or semi-natural country. Anyone who doubts the frequency with which badgers are now found in the Furness woods can read the observations of a local family, who experienced closer than usual contact with their badger neighbours when they reared and then set free an abandoned badger cub (Shepherd, 1964).

Of the woodland birds, the pied flycatcher (*Muscicapa hypoleuca*) is one of the most characteristic of southern Lakeland. It is common between late April and July, and is known to have increased over the last 50 years. The woods of the Coniston and Windermere areas, the Rydal and Grasmere valleys, and those round Ullswater and Derwentwater, are all places where it is frequently seen. These attractive small birds, the cock so strikingly pied, appear to compete with tits, starlings and redstarts for natural nesting sites, and in recent years have been encouraged by a rather widespread provision of nesting boxes on trees, in plantations, woods and gardens. The spotted flycatcher (*Muscicapa striata*) is widespread, and common in open woodland up to 750 feet. Willow warblers (*Phylloscopus trochilus*) and wood warblers (*Phylloscopus sibilatrix*) and chiffchaffs (*Phylloscopus collybita*) are frequent in nearly all wooded areas during the same April to July period, the wood warbler ranging up to nearly 1,000 feet, where suitable trees and bushes remain. The redstart (*Phoenicurus phoenicurus*) is another characteristic and typical bird of the wooded valleys, from April to September, nesting up to the tree limit in holes in walls and hollow trees, and seen in isolated rowans in the upper gills; lower down the valleys it characteristically breeds in holes in stonework, round farms and old buildings.

Tits, robins, chaffinches, wood pigeons, blackbirds and thrushes, jays and magpies are common in these woods, as in most others. The jay (*Garrulus glandarius*) has been local at times, but there are plenty now in the Furness woods. The green woodpecker (*Picus viridis*) has shown some interesting fluctuations, being rare seventy years ago, then generally increasing and breeding up to about 900 feet, often in old ash trees, but of late years becoming less frequent in many places. Tree creepers (*Certhia familiaris*) are characteristic and fairly common, but nuthatches (*Sitta europaea*) are rather scarce.

Woodcock (*Scolopax rusticola*) nest in nearly all types of woodland, as well as on open ground among scattered junipers above the woods. They are frequent in the woods of the limestone scars of South Westmorland. It is about a hundred years since woodcock began to nest in Lakeland; before that they had been winter migrants, frequently snared in the eighteenth century on the moors above Grizedale and Esthwaite in sprints or springes laid between tufts of heather.

Of other woodland birds there are three, tree-creepers, coal-tits (*Parus ater*) and goldcrests (*Regulus regulus*), which are thought to have been inhabitants of the pine and birch forests of the early post-glacial period, and then to have become adapted to life in the mixed oakwoods which succeeded them. These three birds are now common and flourishing in the new coniferous plantations. Other birds of these coniferous woods are the crossbill (*Loxia curvirostra*) and the hawfinch (*Coccothraustes coccothraustes*), which has increased in the present century.

Comment will be made in Chapter 10 on the changes observed in the habits of foxes since the almost complete disappearance of gamekeepers from Lake District woods. Another predator once persecuted but now left in peace is the sparrow-hawk (*Accipiter nisus*), which is present, though not seen so often as the buzzards and kestrels.

In woods enclosed efficiently to exclude grazing deer or sheep, the ground flora, particularly grasses, grows long and rank. This is often followed by a marked increase in mice and voles (which prevent natural regeneration of trees by eating all the seeds) and this in turn has led in some places to an increase in the local owl population. The short-eared owl (*Asio flammeus*) is often found under these conditions.

When rough moorland which has formerly been managed as grouse moor is planted with conifers, as on the ridges of Furness Fells, game birds no longer preserved, such as red grouse and black game, are now found in plantations.

CHAPTER 9

THE HABITATS: THE MOUNTAINS

. . . our ascent to Scaw Fell Pike. There, not a blade of grass was to be seen – hardly a cushion of moss, and that was parched and brown; and only growing rarely between the huge blocks and stones which cover the summit, covered with never-dying lichens, which the clouds and dews nourish, and adorn with colours of the most vivid and exquisite beauty, and endless in variety.

Dorothy Wordsworth's Journal:
Excursion up Scaw Fell Pike, 17 October, 1818

ON the summit ridges and the mountain tops, where conditions are very like those on the summit of Great Dun Fell described in Chapter 6, we find communities of plants which must resemble those which have continued to occupy these sites, above the highest trees, ever since the last glacial episode. Some of these montane vegetation types now extend downwards to lower altitudes, but in general they remain distinct from the typical moorland and hill grassland vegetation which has replaced the upper forests since these were destroyed. In this chapter we will consider the 'natural' vegetation of the summits – the mountain habitats – and in the next, the moorland vegetation of the fell country. The animal life of the two habitats, mountains and moorlands respectively, has many resemblances and overlaps. Conditions which govern the character and distribution of the montane vegetation of the summits are primarily the shortness of the growing season and the extreme exposure to wind.

William Wordsworth noted the undistinguished appearance of the high-level vegetation of his native mountains, and in his *Guide* he contrasted this appearance with that of the high meadows of the Alps. 'Among the luxuriant flowers there met with, groves . . . of Monkshood are frequently seen; the plant of a deep rich blue, and as tall as in our gardens; and this at an elevation where, in Cumberland, Icelandic moss would only be found, or the stony summits be utterly bare.' Today we can find several reasons for this, but the mountain flora of the Lake District is indeed poor in comparison either with that of the Alps, or with that of the more favoured parts of the Scottish Highlands, such as Ben Lawers. There is no rock type in the Lake District sufficiently rich in lime and other bases to resist the leaching effects of the mountain rainfall of more than 150 inches a year, so that on the whole the vegetation is poor and acid, with few species of great rarity or striking beauty. There are certain small areas, however, where the substratum is unusually base-rich for one reason or another, where a rather rich alpine vegetation is to be found. Most of these richer sites are places where faults in either Skiddaw Slate or, more especially, Borrowdale Volcanic rocks, have been secondarily penetrated by material richer in bases, particularly in calcium, than the parent rock itself. Often these veins and fault-fractures contain material softer than the main rock, so that erosion has produced little gullies with crumbling sides in steep rock faces. Where this unusually lime-rich bedrock occurs on steep crags inaccessible to grazing sheep, the most interesting mountain plants of the Lake District are found. These habitats, though found in both Skiddaw Slate and Borrowdale Volcanic country, are practically absent from the acid rocks of the western intrusions, the Eskdale Granite and Ennerdale Granophyre. Among the botanically well-known areas are the eastern face of Helvellyn above Red Tarn, the crags above Blea Water in Mardale, Piers Gill on Lingmell, and the great northern gully of Glaramara. In all these places the Borrowdale Volcanics are unusually rich in bases, especially lime, chiefly in the form of calcite. Other habitats for rare plants are found among the steep and crumbling gullies on Wastwater Screes, where in deep ravines which consist of rapidly eroded fault zones in an altered, reddish volcanic rock, the rare shrubby cinquefoil (*Potentilla fruticosa*) and other interesting mountain plants are found. The other Lake District rarity, the red alpine catchfly (*Lychnis alpina*) of Hobcarton Crag, is found where quartz veins unusually rich in pyrites run through metamorphosed Skiddaw Slate. The steep and crumbling crags which protect these rare plants from grazing Herdwick sheep have also protected them from collectors, except of the most athletic kind, and long may they continue to do so. On most of the larger crags, ledges inaccessible even to the agile Herdwick sheep can be found, with good neutral humus accumulated on them, bearing a rich vegetation of luxuriant tall flowering herbs, including plants found elsewhere as woodland herbs, or in damp meadows and roadside verges. The best of these flowery ledges, such as examples on the eastern cliffs of Helvellyn and on Blea Water Crags, in the words of Dr Ratcliffe, 'give some indication of the vegetation natural to these moist, base-rich soils before the advent of hill farming.' The general poverty of the local montane flora is therefore a combination of a base-status lowered by leaching (except where this is counteracted by local enrichment of the rock) with a grazing intensity which has amounted to over-grazing in much of the district. Those rare and interesting mountain plants which do occur in the Lake District are discussed quite fully in Dr Ratcliffe's 1960 paper on *The Mountain Flora of Lakeland*, to which the interested reader is referred.

One of the most outstanding characteristics of the high montane habitat is the instability of the substratum. Apart from solid rock, most of the ground available for plant colonisation is mountain-top detritus on the summits of peaks and ridges, and block scree or gravel slides on the flanks. This, of course, is because the intensity of frost erosion at altitudes above about 2,500 feet is continually shattering the exposed rocks, and the results of alternate freezing and thawing through the long period of winter conditions produce solifluction movements which transport both fine material and sizeable stones down slopes. This results in the various forms of patterned ground which have been considered in Chapter 3. Because of this inherent instability and the prevailing steep topography of the mountain zone above 2,500 feet, there is a constant process of renewal of the substratum, and much of the high montane vegetation represents fairly early stages in colonisation. Both mountain-top detritus and block scree are usually first colonised by the woolly hair moss (*Rhacomitrium lanuginosum*) but after this the resemblance ceases. On mountain-top detritus most of the early stages in colonisation include only mosses and lichens, whereas on the screes flowering plants and ferns soon become established in the shelter of the larger and more stable blocks. Many screes, of course, including parts of the famous Wastwater Screes, are always so unstable that colonisation even by mosses and lichens never progresses very far. Much of the scree in the montane zone above 2,500 feet is of this unstable type, as is the very coarsest 'mountain-top detritus' on the highest slopes of such peaks as Scafell Pike.

RHACOMITRIUM HEATH

The stony wastes on most summits are usually in the first instance colonised by *Rhacomitrium lanuginosum*, and on some mountain summits, particularly those of Skiddaw Slate, notably on Grasmoor and parts of Skiddaw, and Sail above Sail Beck, this is the dominant vegetation. Death and decay of the moss carpet gradually lead to the accumulation of humus and the beginning of soil development, and later to the appearance of certain flowering plants. Those on Grasmoor include the bilberry and cowberry (*Vaccinium vitis-idaea*), the crowberry (*Empetrum nigrum*) and the viviparous fescue. Club-mosses are also frequent (*Lycopodium selago* and *Lycopodium alpinum*), as are lichens, which include *Cornicularia aculeata*, *Cetraria islandica*, *Sphaerophorus fragilis* and *Cladonia* spp. Other plants found consistently and frequently in the established *Rhacomitrium* heath are the mountain sedge (*Carex bigelowii*), the bent (*Agrostis tenuis*) and the heath bedstraw (*Galium saxatile*). On Skiddaw there are patches of a rather different mountain vegetation – a lichen-rich dwarf *Calluna* heath. Least willow (*Salix herbacea*) can be found on several summits, in very exposed and wind-swept situations, for example on Fairfield and on Helvellyn, and on Sharp Edge of Saddleback. (Plate 2, p. 33.)

SUB-ALPINE GRASSLAND

This, which seems to represent a natural development from the *Rhacomitrium* heath, is found on many summits including that of Helvellyn, particularly on Borrowdale Volcanic rocks, but also on some Skiddaw Slate summits such as Sharp Edge. Most species of flowering plants found in the moss heath are present, and an accumulation of humus has usually covered the underlying stones. In the continuous carpet of vegetation *Festuca vivipara* is often dominant, with silver hair-grass (*Deschampsia flexuosa*) where acid humus has accumulated, bilberry, cowberry and all the plants which have been listed for the *Rhacomitrium* heath. But these natural developments in soil and vegetation are slow, and normally they are much retarded by the continual 'frost-heaving', and often by the instability of the surface due to its slope and to solifluction effects. So long as the winter frosts are continually lifting up the soil surface, puffing up the soil and extruding stones, so long will the formation of a continuous turf of a few species be impossible, and a more varied flora will persist, marked especially by an abundance of *Rhacomitrium*. The least willow, which is found both on Skiddaw Slate and on Borrowdale Volcanic mountains, grows only in places where the ground is kept open by these processes of frost-heaving, but the mountain sedge is able to grow successfully in continuous stabilised grass heath.

The rather uninteresting grasslands on many of the summits are poor in plant species, and are derived from these normal conditions. The principal factor in this development appears to be sheep-grazing, which not only destroys the more interesting herbaceous plants other than grasses, but also, because of the close treading of the sheep, leads to trampling and 'puddling' of the surface, so that the beneficial effects of frost-heaving on soil aeration are quickly lost. *Rhacomitrium* is particularly sensitive to trampling and soon disappears on heavily sheep-grazed summits. Many places on the high Skiddaw ridge show this very clearly.

The nature of the vegetation on each mountain-top at any time therefore depends on the relationship between all these factors – instability of the substratum, wind-erosion of developing carpets of woolly hair moss, and the intensity of the sheep-grazing which develops on sub-alpine grassland. Coarse and unstable mountain-top detritus like that of Scafell Pike remains very sparsely colonised by any plant; as Dorothy Wordsworth noted, 'not a blade of grass was to be seen' – only the lichens, including *Umbilicaria cylindrica*. In situations exposed to wind and solifluction, mechanical disruption of the *Rhacomitrium* heath or sparse sub-alpine grassland may occur at any time, and a new succession be initiated. On the summit of Grasmoor conditions are such that the succession never proceeds further than *Rhacomitrium* heath. On the other hand, many

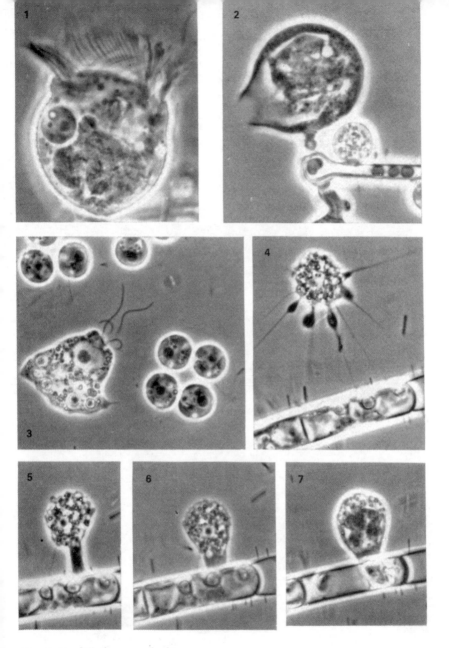

PLATE 17 Windermere plankton:
1. Living *vorticella* with a young spherical parasite body inside. × 1600.
2. Dead *vorticella* containing an empty sporangium of a parasite whose bi-flagellate zoospores have escaped via the opening in the wall. The *vorticella* is attached to a cell of *Asterionella* which itself is parasitised by a chytrid a sporangium of which (out of focus) can be seen immediately below the *vorticella*. × 1600.
3. A Protozoan advancing towards four cells of the alga *Paulschultia*. × 1080.
4. – 7. A series of photographs to show the withdrawl of the content from the cell of an alga by *Vampyrella*. × 1200.

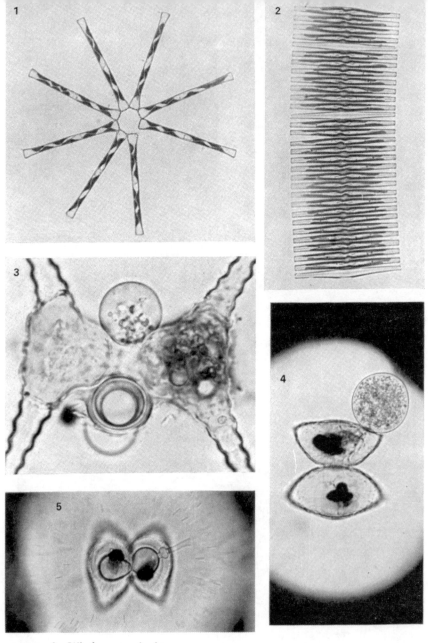

PLATE 18 Windermere plankton:

1. Asterionella. × 480.
2. Fragilaria. × 480.
3. A desmid *Staurastrum* parasitised by a chytrid. *Above*, a young sporangium; *Below*, a resting spore. × 1200.
4. Another species of *Staurastrum* bearing externally a large chytrid sporangium. Inside the alga is a branched system of rhizoids. × 615.
5. *Staurastrum* containing empty sporangia of the bi-flagellate fungus *Myzocytium*. × 615.

4 and 5 mounted in Indian ink to show envelope of mucilage around the desmid.

summit ridges which show markedly active solifluction effects of the polygon or stone stripe character do not develop *Rhacomitrium* heath at all. On Broad End on Skiddaw at 2,700 feet, *Rhacomitrium* heath has developed on patterned ground in which the polygons appear to be fossil – that is, under present climatic conditions, no further movement of the stones is taking place. Actively moving 'striped scree' at about the same altitude is colonised only by *Festuca vivipara*. On many of the more popular summits, such as Coniston Old Man and Helvellyn, which are visited nearly every day in the year and are thronged with people in summer, erosion by human trampling is becoming one of the important factors determining the vegetation. *Juncus squarrosus*, the heath rush, which is commonly associated with mat-grass on the poorer grasslands of the lower fells (Chapter 10), has spread on to peaty ground as a result of human interference and land use in former centuries. On the broad ridge of High Street, where horse-racing took place in the eighteenth century, the great spreads of heath rush in the summit grassland form a rare example of anthropogenic vegetation on the top of a mountain. (Plate 26, p. 241.)

BLOCK SCREES ON THE FLANKS OF SUMMITS AND RIDGES

The large stones and rocks of which this type of scree is composed offer a good deal of shelter, so that flowering plants and ferns establish themselves at an early stage. The most famous scree pioneer of the Lake District is the Parsley Fern (*Cryptogramma crispa*), which is found in this habitat at every altitude from the shore of Wastwater to the fell summits, and on the artificial screes provided by quarry wastes, as well as on natural scree of all types from blocky to rather earthy. This is one of the mountain plants found in leached and acid habitats, and not usually in the lime-rich situations. With it are often found the Mountain Fern (*Thelypteris limbosperma*) and that most beautiful and typical of Lakeland mountain plants, the alpine lady's mantle (*Alchemilla alpina*). Stabilised scree well colonised by *Cryptogramma crispa* and *Alchemilla alpina* provides the mountain vegetation most truly characteristic of the Lake District, for in no other British mountains do these plants flourish so abundantly. (Plate 21, p. 192.)

Factors influencing the distribution of *Alchemilla alpina* have been discussed by Dr Ratcliffe (1960). He points out that though it is plentiful on the more basic rocks where a rich assemblage of other species can be found, it is also found on relatively base-deficient soils. 'A plant of wide tolerances, it is surprisingly little affected by sheep-grazing. Whilst growing in the utmost profusion on many of the high crags, it is no less abundant on some grassy slopes and soily screes, often at much lower levels.' In discussing its distribution on the Skiddaw Slates (e.g. on Dove Crags, Grasmoor, where it is abundant) and on the Borrowdale Volcanic fells, Dr Ratcliffe reaches the conclusion that though this plant is tolerant of base-poor soils with a comparatively low nutrient level, it needs something better than the poorest of Lakeland soils. hence its absence from much of the Skiddaw Slate and from the acid western intrusions of Eskdale and Ennerdale. It also avoids soils where an accumulation of acid humus (mor) has taken place. Dr Ratcliffe gives as an example the slopes of Eel Crags above the Newlands valley, where the junction between the outcrops of Skiddaw Slates and Borrowdale Volcanics runs up the fell-side with the volcanic rocks above the slate. *Alchemilla alpina* here grows abundantly on the Borrowdale Volcanics, but is only found on the slates in places where some drainage is received from the volcanic rocks higher up the slope. 'Again, Robinson above Buttermere is a Skiddaw Slate hill but has some rather calcareous patches of this rock in one place. *A. alpina* is abundant on these lime-bearing outcrops, but is quite absent from the acidic rocks which form the bulk of the mountain.'

The high-level or sub-alpine grasslands which merge into the more open vegetation of scree and gravel-slide (where physical instability prevents the development of a complete vegetation cover, and at the same time this factor combined with various degrees of wind exposure or solifluction prevents the formation of a continuous moss carpet) probably represent the only wholly natural form of grassland in the Lake District. At lower levels the sub-alpine grasslands merge into the extensive *Festuca–Agrostis* grasslands which cover much of the lower mountain slopes. These will be described in the next chapter, and the evidence that they are biotic communities, derived from former woodland or scrub, will be given in Chapter 13. Montane heath communities, on dry rocky ground or scree which has become more or less stabilised, are less rich in species in the Lake District than on the Scottish mountains. *Calluna* (up to 2,400 feet) and *Erica cinerea* (up to 2,200 feet) are replaced as dominants at higher altitudes by *Empetrum nigrum*, *Vaccinium myrtillus* and *Vaccinium vitis-idaea*. *Empetrum hermaphroditum* is a much rarer member of this latter community, usually above 2,000 feet but found at about 1,200 feet on screes in Riggindale. Bearberry (*Arctostaphylos uva-ursi*) which is so common in the Scottish Highlands, has only scattered localities in the Lake District. One of the best-known is at sub-montane altitudes on the western face of Grasmoor – a broken rocky wall of crumbling Skiddaw Slate which is well known to climbers and scramblers for its luxuriant vegetation (see A. H. Griffin, *The Roof of England*). (Plate 11, p. 112.)

THE MONTANE FLORA OF FLUSHED HABITATS

There are many places on a mountain that support flush vegetation, simply because there are many channels for the constant downward movement of soil and of drainage water from above. The most easily defined habitats are those which surround emerging springs, those that lie above the crumbling sides of little watercourses, or that occupy ledges or rock-faces which receive soil or downward-draining water. These are all lines of active erosion or deposition, exposing new soils or accumulating material from above. Nearly all the more interesting mountain plants in the Lake District are found in these flushed habitats, rather than on the predominantly leached summits and ridges and their flanks.

Bryophyte flushes surround emerging springs, and generally have characteristic marginal silver-green carpets of the moss *Philonotis fontana*, while immersed in the water there are likely to be reddish-black beds of the liverwort *Scapania*. Other mosses often present include the striking pale green *Dicranella palustris*, and *Brachythecium rivulare*. The flowering plants are usually somewhat scattered, not crowded as on ledges, and gravel with or without mosses commonly occupies the intervening spaces. The flowering plants usually occur on the mixture of humus and sandy silt which has accumulated in pockets among the bryophyte flora. The flora of wet flushes is likely to include certain species present at almost all levels, with others which are commoner in the montane region above 2,000 feet.

A species list from a bryophyte spring high on Brown Cove on Helvellyn is given by Dr Ratcliffe in *The Mountain Flora of Lakeland* (1960).

Agrostis canina	f.	Philonotis fontana	a.
Brachythecium rivulare	a.	Poa annua	o.
Bryum weigelii	o.	P. trivialis	f.
Cardamine pratensis	f.	Pohlia wahlenbergii var. glacialis	o.
Cerastium holosteoides	f.	Rumex acetosa	f.
Chrysosplenium oppositifolium	l.d.	Sagina procumbens	o.
Cochlearia alpina	a.	Saxifraga hypnoides	a.
Deschampsia cespitosa	f.	S. stellaris	a.
Dicranella palustris	f.	Scapania undulata	a.
Epilobium alsinifolium	f.	Solenostoma cordifolium	f.
Festuca rubra	f.	Stellaria alsine	a.
Mnium punctatum	f.		

o = occasional f = frequent a = abundant l = local l.d. = locally dominant

This is a typical bryophyte flush such as can be found in great numbers on all the Lakeland mountains – the water in the springs being of average composition for the region and not particularly base-rich.

More calcareous flushes where the water is derived from calcite-rich beds and veins in the Borrowdale Volcanics have a greater variety of species of flowering plants, including, for example, the flea sedge, *Carex pulicaris*, and the purple saxifrage (*Saxifraga oppositifolia*). Some strongly calcareous flushes, including an example from High White Stones quoted by Dr Ratcliffe, contain characteristic mosses, including the golden *Cratoneuron commutatum*, as well as *Ctenidium molluscum* and *Meesia uliginosa*.

Damp ledges, on steeper slopes and rocky crags, carry a vegetation which can be extremely variable but which usually follows a logical pattern. Almost all the montane flush species may at first be present, and the yellow mountain saxifrage (*S. aizoides*), roseroot (*Sedum rosea*) and the mountain sorrel (*Oxyria digyna*) are usually prominent on all crags where the rock is at least moderately base-rich; that is, on nearly all the Borrowdale Volcanics. The sea-campion (*Silene maritima*) is not infrequent, a somewhat unexpected plant to find at high altitudes. More local in their distribution are the mountain species of *Poa* (*P. alpina*, *P. glauca*), the alpine hawkweed (*Hieracium holosericeum*), the alpine meadow-rue (*Thalictrum alpinum*) and alpine saw-wort (*Saussurea alpina*). After an initial stage of colonisation by plants such as these, humus accumulates, and larger plants, found commonly in damp flushes at lower altitudes, tend to crowd out the more strictly montane species; examples of these are the globeflower (*Trollius europaeus*), mountain cranesbill (*Geranium sylvaticum*), water avens (*Geum rivale*), meadowsweet (*Filipendula ulmaria*) and the great woodrush (*Luzula sylvatica*). After heavy rain the whole system on such a ledge may collapse, and then the process starts again, but often humus accumulation continues for long enough to allow the upper layers to become more and more base-deficient. The vegetation then comes to include a considerable proportion of heath and bog plants growing in the poorer surface layers of humus, as well as the true flush species rooted in the lower layers of the accumulated soil, and those nearest the rock. When this happens the vegetation becomes shrubby, with bilberry and crowberry. As boggy conditions develop, species of *Sphagnum* appear. The heathy and boggy ledges are commoner on buttresses than in gullies and on those rocks which are poorer in lime.

Dr Ratcliffe (1960) gives the following species list for the north-east and east facing cliffs of Helvellyn at 2,600 to 2,800 feet. It 'gives some idea of the vegetation on the bigger ledges with a well-developed layer of mull-humus soil. It is a composite list, though a few ledges have most of the species named.'

Alchemilla alpina	f.	*Geum rivale*	a.
A. glabra	a.	*Heracleum sphondylium*	f.
Anemone nemorosa	f.	*Lathyrus montanus*	o.
Angelica sylvestris	f.	*Luzula sylvatica*	a.
Cochlearia alpina	f.	*Oxyria digyna*	f.
Crepis paludosa	a.	*Ranunculus acris*	f.
Deschampsia cespitosa	a.	*Rhinanthus minor*	o.
Festuca rubra	a.	*Rubus saxatilis*	o.
Festuca vivipara	a.	*Rumex acetosa*	f.
Filipendula ulmaria	a.	*Saussurea alpina*	f.
Galium boreale	l.	*Saxifraga hypnoides*	a.
Geranium sylvaticum	f.	*Sedum rosea*	a.

Solidago virgaurea	a.	*Mnium hornum*	a.
Succisa pratensis	f.	*M. punctatum*	f.
Taraxacum officinale	f.	*M. undulatum*	a.
Thalictrum minus	f.	*Philonotis fontana*	f.
Trollius europaeus	l.	*Plagiothecium denticulatum*	f.
Valeriana officinalis	o.	*Polytrichum alpinum*	f.
Atrichum undulatum	o.	*Pseudoscleropodium purum*	o.
Brachythecium rutabulum	f.	*Rhacomitrium lanuginosum*	a.
Breutelia chrysocoma	f.	*Rhytidiadelphus loreus*	a.
Campylium protensum	o.	*R. squarrosus*	a.
Ctenidium molluscum	a.	*Sphagnum plumulosum*	f.
Dicranum majus	f.	*S. subsecundum* var. *auriculatum*	f.
D. scoparium	a.	*Thuidium tamariscinum*	a.
Drepanocladus uncinatus	o.	*Lophocolea bidentata*	a.
Eurhynchium praelongum	f.	*Tritomaria quinquedentata*	f.
Hylocomium splendens	a.	*Plagiochila asplenioides*	o.
Hypnum cupressiforme	a.		

'Similar ledges elsewhere on the fell have *Chamaenerion* (*Epilobium*) *angustifolium* (rosebay) and *Silene dioica*. Elsewhere in Lakeland, rarer members of such a community include *Potentilla fruticosa, Cirsium hetero-phyllum, Vicia sylvatica, Aquilegia vulgaris* and *Rosa pimpinellifolia*, whilst at lower levels *Vicia sepium, Trifolium medium, Centaurea nigra* and *Epilobium montanum* are added to the list. In the Highlands, *Salix lapponum* often grows in tall herb communities, but the survivors on Helvellyn occupy rather bare rocks.' (Ratcliffe, 1960.)

Dry flushes, on dry ledges and crumbling unstable cliffs, where the bedrock provides an adequate supply of lime and other bases, provide a habitat for some of the rarest and most interesting of the mountain plants of the district. These species seem to be restricted to newly exposed and open sites, partly because the freshly crumbled and unleached rock supplies the necessary mineral nutrients, and partly because these species cannot tolerate much competition and so do not do well in a continuous community. Dry habitats on the crags of the Helvellyn ridge are the localities for many of these interesting plants, including the mountain avens (*Dryas octopetala*), *Saxifraga oppositifolia*, moss campion (*Silene acaulis*), *Minuartia verna, Potentilla crantzii, Cerastium alpinum, Saxifraga nivalis, Veronica serpyllifolia* ssp. *humifusa, Draba incana, Antennaria dioica, Carex atrata* and *Polygonum viviparum*, as well as the two mountain and maritime species, *Armeria maritima* and *Plantago maritima*. Crags on other mountains including Scafell will be found to have some of these species. A characteristic community including *Minuartia verna, Alchemilla wichurae*, and *Thalictrum minus* can be found in base-rich gullies in andesite on Tarn Crag, Grisedale. *Lychnis alpina* is found in a dry-flush habitat on Hob-carton Crag, but on acidic and not basic soil.

Other interesting mountain plants of basic soils and rocks include the holly fern (*Polystichum lonchitis*) on shady flushed ledges and in crevices, *Epilobium alsinifolium* and *Juncus triglumis* on rock ledges and by rill sides, and *Ajuga pyramidalis* on a single ledge in the High Street range. *Sedum villosum* grows in calcareous flushes in the Helvellyn range. Only one colony of *Woodsia ilvensis* is known to survive in the district; this plant 'seems to favour an uncommon habitat, namely dry basic and very rotten rocks' (Ratcliffe, 1960). *Saxifraga stellaris* (star saxifrage) is one of the most familiar of the attractive mountain plants, for it grows in a wider range of habitats and is more tolerant of base-poor soils than are the other saxifrages. It is therefore more likely to be encountered by the ordinary walker in the hills who is not intentionally searching for lime-rich localities. It is 'one of the few mountain species to occur plentifully on the Skiddaw Slate. Moist rocks, stream-sides, small rills, flushes and springs are its chief habitats, but it grows sparingly on exposed, rather dry, summits and screes. Fine robust clumps occur in many damp shaded rock crevices, and it is sometimes associated with others of its genus on the more basic rocks.' (Ratcliffe, 1960).

Though snow patches may linger on the east-facing crags of the Lake District into May, and in the highest coves of Helvellyn into June, there is no specialised 'snow-patch' vegetation in the Lake District mountains, as there is in the highest parts of Scotland. '. . . apart from one or two rare mosses, such as *Dicranum starkei*, species associated with late snow lie are absent', according to Dr Ratcliffe. Higher average temperatures and a lighter and more irregular snowfall than those of the Scottish mountains are doubtless the reason for this difference.

THE FAUNA OF THE MOUNTAIN HABITATS

The truly montane vegetation of the summits and ridges which have always been above the forest limit marks the boundaries for the fauna of the montane habitat. But apart from one bird, the dotterel, of the heights and summit ridges, the only alpine community which has been recorded in detail is the invertebrate fauna of flushes and water drips, the damp and mossy steep rocks and small waterfalls which form such a characteristic habitat on the high crags and just below the actual summits.

In this community certain predatory beetles are often noteworthy. Presumably they live on the larvae of small flies in the damp moss. In Cumberland the beetle *Dianous coerulescens* is almost universally present in this habitat. Here also are found daddy-long-legs species, including *Tipula cheethami*, which is especially noticeable because its pupal skins remain sticking to the moss. The bulk of the population in the damp moss, however, is usually composed of midges (chironomids). Around the spring-heads are also other Diptera, particularly the tipulids *Trichyphona claripennis*, *T. unicolor* and *Dicranota guerini*.

At all altitudes peat erodes to form basins in which water accumulates, and, in these pools, water-beetles and water-bugs are often numerous. Above about 1,600 feet two common members of the latter group are *Callicorixa wollastoni* and *Sigara nigrolineata*. *C. wollastoni* is confined to high ground as far as is known. In Britain it occurs in all the upland regions on the west, as far south as Dartmoor. It appears to be a northern species, recorded in Scandinavia but not in the Alps, or the Pyrenees. *S. nigrolineata*, in contrast, is abundant at low altitudes also, and is frequently taken in ponds liable to dry up. Found in greater abundance in the Pennines, where some peat pools are larger, but taken only occasionally in the Lake District are *Glaenocorisa propinqua* and *Arctocorisa carinata*. Both are mountain species known also from Scandinavia, the Alps and the Pyrenees. *A. carinata* has also been recorded from the Caspian region. Neither species is wholly confined to high altitude or latitude and it is unlikely that their range is limited by temperature. Possibly in more temperate waters they cannot compete with other species.

The water-strider, *Gerris costae*, occurs on the surface of high peat pools. The water-bugs are commonly found in broad pools with extensive areas of open bottom, the beetles in narrower pools with a growth of *Sphagnum* round the margins. Over twenty species have been recorded in high pools and high tarns and three, *Agabus congener*, *A. arcticus* and *Hydroporus morio* have not been taken in any other type of water body.

Running-water species found at high altitudes are discussed in Chapter 5, on streams. Little is known about the other inhabitants of peat pools.

The mountain spiders mostly belong to the group of small dark-coloured forms known as the Linyphiidae, which includes many types generally found in Arctic regions. One of these, *Eboria caliginosa*, is recorded only from Scafell Pike and one locality in Yorkshire. Among the most noticeable of the other mountain invertebrates are two species of daddy-long-legs commonly found on mountain-top detritus, *Tipula macrocera* and *T. excisa*. Generally the larger Diptera seem to be the most frequent insects at higher altitudes, and their larvae are certainly characteristic inhabitants of high-level soils.

The only British alpine butterfly, the mountain ringlet (*Erebia epiphron*) is found in the Lake District mountains (its only English locality) above 1,800 feet. '. . . it flies abundantly in restricted areas, from which stragglers range widely over the neighbourhood. Such colonies tend to shift their quarters every few years.' (Ford, 1945.) The larvae feed on grass.

The dotterel (*Eudromias morinellus*), a bird of the *Rhacomitrium* heath and high stony plateaux, feeds on small flies, spiders, beetles, and insect larvae. It nests on stone-littered ground, usually above 2,400 feet, rarely, erratically, and possibly not at present, in the Lake District. On spring and autumn passage it is occasionally recorded, as, for instance, at 2,000 feet on Black Combe in October, 1930, and more frequently during its spring passage in May. 'The breeding places of the very few pairs that stay to nest in Cumberland and Westmorland are on stone-littered ground, mostly above 2,400 feet, on certain of the higher fells, and some times actually on the summit plateaux. In part, the elusiveness of the dotterel is accounted for by the fact that any given haunt is not necessarily resorted to annually, and may not be occupied for several seasons. It is sufficient to add that, in one haunt or another, the dotterel continues as a nesting species, although a scarce one. Incubated eggs have been found before the end of May, and the breeding grounds appear to be deserted normally in August.' (*The Birds of Lakeland,* 1943.)

Among the predatory birds, the raven (*Corvus corax*) and the peregrine (*Falco peregrinus*) inhabit the same type of mountain country, and both nest on crags – often upon the same crag. Both birds have more nesting *sites* than settled pairs, which makes counting nests difficult. There is plenty of evidence for the raven having formerly occupied a much wider range of country and nested in trees, but the British peregrine is not known ever to have nested in trees, and at no time in the last few centuries does it seem to have been either more numerous or more widely distributed than it was before the recent decline attributed to pesticides.

The raven breeds in all the high fell groups of the district, and about fifty crags between 1,250 and 2,000 feet are known to be commonly used as nesting sites; the usual breeding population has been estimated at about forty pairs. Many non-breeding individuals are commonly seen, and at all times of year there are usually some ravens to be seen among the high fells. This bird is not often seen far away from the fells. The nests, substantial wool-lined structures on cliff ledges or recesses, are often beneath overhangs and frequently on inaccessible parts of the crags. On the whole, both ravens and peregrines choose only high crags as nesting sites where roads or habitations are near, but in wilder places they will nest on crags less than fifty feet high. The raven is a virtually omnivorous feeder, and appears to eat much sheep carrion when this is available. An analysis of the diet of the raven, determined by Ernest Blezard from castings accumulated at inland haunts in northern England and southern Scotland, gave: sheep (as wool) 16, rabbit 6, field vole 2, water vole 1, red grouse 1, eggs of domestic fowl and mallard 1 each, dor beetles 4, grass and moss 8, gravel and grit 6. From this it can be seen that the food of this bird is not provided in any great measure by the mountain habitats, except in the form of sheep carrion. Presumably it is the inviolable nature of the crag nesting sites which makes the raven today a characteristic bird of the mountain habitats.

The peregrine is a bird of the remote crags of the central Lake District fells, and about 20 pairs at any one time seem to represent the breeding population. Most eyries, like the raven nests, are found at altitudes of 1,500 to 2,000 feet, on similar crags but usually on flat, often grassy,

PLATE 19 *Above*, Keskadale Oaks: a high-level sessile oakwood of unknown history. *Below*, Juniper in Glenridding: high-level juniper scrub has replaced many former woods of oak and other deciduous trees.

PLATE 20   *Lycopodium selago* (Fir Clubmoss) and *Lycopodium alpinum* (Alpine Clubmoss).

ledges. Peregrines hunt the common birds of their surroundings, and have often been seen to kill at some distance from the nest. The domestic pigeon is a favourite prey, also the fieldfare in winter, and red grouse, blackbirds and starlings, together with birds of the high fells in summer in smaller numbers, such as ring ouzels and meadow pipits. Like the raven, the peregrine must often travel considerable distances from its nest in its search for prey, and does not depend on food available in its nesting habitat. In winter the peregrines may leave the fells for the lowlands and coasts.

In the choice of nesting sites by both birds, Dr Ratcliffe believes that the altitudinal breeding limit of 2,500 feet, which is never exceeded in spite of the existence of many suitable crag ledges at higher altitudes, is primarily climatic, in that neither ravens nor peregrines tolerate the low temperatures and often rather prolonged snow cover above 2,500 feet. They are therefore birds of the sub-montane rather than the montane zone. Dr Ratcliffe believes that where the golden eagle breeds, as in the northern Scottish Highlands, it may compete successfully for nesting sites with ravens and peregrines, the density of which is low in eagle country.

The golden eagle (*Aquila chrysaëtus*) was extinguished as a breeding species in the Lake District by the end of the eighteenth century, by the relentless persecution of sheep-farmers, to whom it was a major pest. It has been recorded regularly as a visitor over the last twenty years, and it is once more attempting to breed. It is now very strongly protected by law, with a fine of £25 or a month's imprisonment for any attempt on its life; at the same time the R.S.P.B. has inaugurated a reward scheme to encourage farmers and gamekeepers on whose land it may attempt to nest, to give every assistance and protection. The eagle can be distinguished from the common native buzzard by its much greater size, its longer and less rounded wings, its superior powers of soaring, and, of course, by the mewing cry of the buzzards. In its diet the eagle combines the tastes of ravens and peregrines, catching grouse, duck and gulls as well as feeding on carrion, especially sheep, and on live lambs where available. The Rosthwaite farmers of 200 years ago, hardy cragsmen who destroyed the eggs and eyries of the eagles which tried to nest in Borrowdale, reckoned that each eyrie cost one lamb a day. The standard payment by the parish at that time was a shilling for each eagle destroyed. It is said that the last native eagles of the Lake District bred on the crags of Burtness Combe above Buttermere.

Of the other mountain birds, carrion crows nest up to 1,800 feet, kestrels up to 1,700 feet, and merlins up to 1,700 feet, so these are birds of the moorland fells rather than the montane habitats. The meadow pipit (*Anthus pratensis*) nests from sea level up to 2,900 feet in the central fells; the wren (*Troglodytes troglodytes*), not a bird one thinks of as a mountain bird, is the only small bird commonly found all the year round up to c.

2,000 feet, and breeds up to 1,700 feet, often in craggy situations; and the wheatear, one of the commonest summer residents, breeds up to 3,000 feet. Like the dipper (*Cinclus cinclus*), which follows the becks up to about 2,700 feet, though it does not usually nest above 1,500 feet, and that attractive summer visitor the ring ouzel (*Turdus torquatus*), and the golden plovers, these are primarily birds of the moorland habitat which from time to time move upward into the mountains.

CHAPTER 10

THE HABITATS: THE FELLS AND DALES

'The general surface of the mountains is turf, rendered rich and green by the moisture of the climate.'
William Wordsworth: *Guide to the Lakes*

'The stag's-horn is very beautiful and fresh, springing upon the fells.'
Dorothy Wordsworth: *Grasmere Journal,* 4 May, 1802

DURING the first half of the post-glacial period, from about 8000 B.C. until about 3000 B.C., the forests of the Lake District must have covered fells and dales alike. The stages by which the primeval forest has been transformed into the landscape of today will be considered in later chapters, after the human history of the district has been outlined, but at this stage of our survey of the landscape it is appropriate to deal with the vegetation types and plant and animal communities of the bare fells below the montane zone and of the dale pastures and meadows, remembering that these are biotic communities originally derived from forest.

The unenclosed fells and the high intakes above the valley meadows are either rather acid grasslands, heather or bilberry moors, or boggy moors locally known as mosses which have cotton-sedge and bog-moss as well as heather. Broadly speaking, the differentiation into these vegetation types has depended partly on the composition of the rock and drift from which the soils have been derived, but also very considerably on the local relief and its effect on soil drainage. Superimposed on this basic differentiation has been the effect of land use by prehistoric and later men over the 5,000 years since 3000 B.C.

The deeper well-drained soils of average composition on the older rocks have remained as free-draining brown earths, on which the original forest has been replaced by good grasslands of the fescue type. These are now in general either heavily infested with bracken, up to about 1,000 feet, or are degenerating under over-grazing by sheep into poor mat-grass (*Nardus stricta*) pasture. Wherever free soil drainage has been impeded, either by the relief, as in basins and flat saddles, or by the presence of relatively impermeable clayey drift, the processes described in Chapter 7 have tended to lead to an accumulation of acid humus at the surface, and to leaching of the mineral layer below by humic acids, so that a peaty and base-poor soil has developed. Such soils naturally carry the heath rush (*Juncus squarrosus*) with *Nardus*, and are very widespread in the middle zone, between about 1,000 feet and 2,000 to 2,500 feet. In drier areas there is much wavy hair-grass in this vegetation. In stony places this vegetation type grades into the communities of stabilised screes (Chapter 9). The three common club-mosses, stag's-horn, fir-tree and alpine (respectively *Lycopodium clavatum*, *L. selago* and *L. alpinum*) are found in these mountain grasslands; the alpine club-moss does not generally descend below 700 feet, and is commoner at higher altitudes, but the other two species come down to lower altitudes in some places.

Heather moors dominated by *Calluna vulgaris* are less common in the Lake District than in Scotland. There is some evidence that they have been more widespread in the past, and that sheep-farming in the Lake District has tended to produce 'sheep-walk' on nearly all soils which will support it: the evidence from Skiddaw Forest will be given on page 181. Heather moor is now more frequent on the northern fells of Skiddaw Slates than on the Borrowdale Volcanic rocks and this can be correlated with the generally poorer soils found on the Skiddaw Slates and the drift derived from them, but in places there is good grassland on the Skiddaw Slates with, for example, ox-eye daisy (*Chrysanthemum leucanthemum*), a herb of better grasslands. (Plate 4, p. 49.)

On the generally better (more lime-rich) soils of the Borrowdales, grassland predominates. Both heather moors and bilberry (*Vaccinium*) 'edges' such as that of Catbells are characteristically found on soils where a layer of mor humus or peat has accumulated over a somewhat leached mineral soil – the incompletely developed podsolic profile so common in the Lake District – or on ranker soils where the organic soil lies immediately above stones or solid rock. On both the Skiddaw Slate mountains of the north and the ridges of Silurian slates or grits of the south, there is a general tendency for heather moor, with or without bilberry, to replace grassland on shallow stony soils, particularly on steep well-drained slopes and on summit ridges above about 900 feet.

Among the rarer plants of intermediate altitudes are the two interesting plants of Langdale – the interrupted club-moss (*Lycopodium annotinum*) on the Langdale side of Bowfell, and the lichen *Umbilicaria crustulosa* on Raven Crag between the Old Dungeon Ghyll hotel and Mill Gill. This is one of the two currently recorded British localities for this plant.

GRASSLANDS OF THE FELLS

The Fescue Grasslands

These, which are typical British upland grasslands, are found in all parts of the district and provide the pasture of the Herdwicks and other mountain sheep. Under certain conditions they change and become dominated by *Nardus* or bracken. In their normal state the fescue grasslands are dominated by *Festuca ovina* and the bents (*Agrostis tenuis, A. canina* and *A. stolonifera*). Besides the dominant grasses, there are present with great constancy such species as the tormentil and heath bedstraw, and often also the sweet-scented vernal grass (*Anthoxanthum odoratum*) and dog's tail (*Cynosurus cristatus*). Almost equally constant is the moss *Rhytidiadelphus squarrosus*, and frequent are *Pleurozium schreberi* and *Hypnum cupressiforme*. The grass sward is very complete, covering 65 to 75 per cent of the whole ground, so that associates are not very numerous, though they may actually include many species. Of these, some are rather uniformly scattered, like the sheep's sorrel (*Rumex acetosella*), milkwort (*Polygala vulgaris*) and speedwell (*Veronica officinalis*). Other plants, such as the white clover (*Trifolium repens*) are, like the fescue itself when very abundant, useful as indicating a larger lime supply in the soil, although it still remains lime-deficient in general. The presence of some other species indicates acid humus – these include wavy hair-grass and bilberry. Lastly, there are plants associated with former cultivation or treatment. These, though most common at the lower levels (say below 1,000 feet) occur also at surprisingly high ones on occasion. They include ribwort plantain (*Plantago lanceolata*), creeping buttercup (*Ranunculus repens*), cat's ear (*Hypochaeris radicata*) and self-heal (*Prunella vulgaris*).

This is the hill grassland of the mountain sheep-walk, derived by grazing from the former cover of native woodlands, and passing upwards into sub-montane grasslands which contain in places rarer species, such as the mountain pansy (*Viola lutea*). The composition of a grassland is always much affected by the amount of grazing it receives and the season at which it is grazed. On the one hand, grazing causes a certain amount of stimulation, both by treading, which increases the tillering of the grasses, and through the marked manurial effects of the animal droppings. On the other hand, grazing is always selective, in that some species are eaten while others are not. As a general rule, grasses are least affected by grazing, but plants with exposed growing points such as herbs, heather and bilberry, are much damaged. Further, selective grazing means that species which are least palatable tend to persist at the expense of the more palatable.

Thus heavy grazing of *Festuca-Agrostis* grassland by sheep seems to lead first to the spread of the bents and then to the extension of *Nardus stricta*, a species which is scarcely, if ever, eaten. One of the commonest signs in the Lake District of over-grazed upland pasture is thus an abundance of this grass and of its associate the heath rush (*Juncus squarrosus*). Though the latter affords a welcome 'bite' for sheep in seasons of scarcity, there is extremely little nourishment in *Nardus*, and the sheep do not graze it (see *Mountains and Moorlands*, Chapter 6). Over-grazed pasture is now extremely widespread on the Lake District fells, both on the highest intakes and on the unenclosed fell commons above them.

Bracken

As a general rule, the surviving *Festuca-Agrostis* grasslands cover the brown-earth and creep-soils of the steeper upland slopes. Where these soils are deep enough, more than nine inches or a foot in depth, they are likely to have on them also the bracken. Consequently there is a continual tendency for bracken to spread into the best pasture on the good, deep well-drained soils. The tall and frequent fronds then overshade the grasses in summer, and smother them in winter and spring beneath a litter of dead leaves, through which grasses cannot penetrate. Thus by the elimination of grass, the grazing value of bracken-covered slopes quickly becomes negligible.

There is no doubt that bracken has spread enormously over the hill pastures in the last hundred years or so, particularly where pockets of glacial drift provide a deeper soil. The spread of bracken has been hastened by two things: a general decline in numbers of cattle and replacement by sheep on the hill grazings during this period, and the great increase in the cost of labour. Cattle eat a certain amount of young bracken (though older bracken can be poisonous to them) and, moreover, they break down and trample more than they eat. Thus the plant normally fails to establish itself in cattle grazings. Also cattle as they were once kept on the hills required bracken for winter bedding, and regular cutting of bracken for this purpose checked the spread of established patches. On land other than cattle grazings, bracken maintains itself, once established, and spreads by means of branched and cable-like underground stems, in which considerable reserves of food are stored. In order to eliminate an established colony, the underground stems must either be removed or else their food reserves used up. The latter is rather simple if sufficient labour and time are available. The fronds are cut off in early summer as soon as they expand, and the process repeated later in the year whenever new growth develops. Thus the food reserves are used up in producing new growth, and no new stores can be laid down if the leaves are cut off as soon as they develop. Three or four mowings usually suffice to eliminate the plant, but they involve time-consuming hand labour. This has led to attempts to devise mechanical ways of uprooting the underground stems. Some farmers have successfully eliminated bracken from part of their grazings by cutting or uprooting, but both the high cost of labour, and the difficulty of using any machine on rocky land where the bracken grows in pockets of soil between rock outcrops, have limited bracken control in the Lake District. There is no doubt that many walled intakes which were valuable pasture when they were enclosed between one and two hundred years ago, are now completely covered with bracken and useless for any form of production except afforestation; young trees planted in such land will shade out and destroy the bracken when well-grown.

The bracken-infested pastures are the lower grasslands, in general below about 1,000 feet. The upper limit of the bracken is usually set by the effects of frosts on the new fronds in early summer, and is lower on slopes facing north or east than on south-facing fell-sides. The future of these ruined grasslands depends on what form of land use is adopted. Sir George Stapledon in *The Land Now and Tomorrow*, has pointed out that at altitudes below about 1,000 feet, bracken is a sign of improvable land, for its presence indicates deep, well-drained soils. We shall see in Chapter 15 how the spread of bracken in the Lake District has accompanied the decline in numbers of small farms. When families had to find subsistence on very small holdings of land, they worked long hours and every square yard of good soil must have been valued, so bracken was kept in check by cutting. Both amalgamation of small farms into larger ones, and the retreat from the highest farms which set in about 1870, have materially reduced the labour available to cut bracken on the hill grasslands, and this has reinforced the effects of the change from hill cattle to more sheep. It would probably be only under quite exceptional circumstances that the capital investment in paid labour necessary to destroy existing bracken by cutting would ever now be made. As yet no selective weed-killer has proved capable of destroying bracken efficiently, but trials of a promising one are now in progress.

Meanwhile as an element in the scenery of the Lake District the bracken is undoubtedly popular with many of those who contribute as visitors to the economy of numerous hill farms. For eight months of the year it flames on the fell-sides as warm colour in a cool northern land. For six weeks in early summer its fresh young green shoots up through the russet carpet like shot silk. A great many people would be sorry to see the beauty of these useless fell-sides replaced by neatly fenced productive grassland, or by larch plantations – the 'vegetable manufacturies' which Wordsworth so much disliked. In the absence of any human interference, by cutting, or by planting and tending of trees, the bracken will remain as the climax vegetation of these ruined grasslands, for natural regeneration of trees does not take place under the deep summer shade of a continuous layer of bracken fronds. Of course there is in the Lake District much rocky land where the bracken layer is not continuous, because the areas of deep soil are interrupted by rock outcrops. On these, if the sheep were to be excluded, it would be expected that some regeneration of birch and possibly of oak might take place (see page 154), on thinner soils where the bracken is not continuous.

Nardus grassland

On the grassy mountains of the central Lake District three broad zones can be distinguished: the lowest one in which bracken is now abundant, a middle one above about 1,000 feet in which *Nardus stricta* is prominent, and then the montane zone above about 2,000 feet. There is, in short, a zone in which *Nardus* is most characteristic, and this corresponds roughly with the region of high rainfall and thoroughly leached soils. Apart from the heath rush, this type of grassland contains few constant associates in addition to the *Nardus*. In the drier parts the wavy hair-grass largely replaces the heath rush. Otherwise the most usual associates are bilberry and, though somewhat more scattered, the heath bedstraw and tormentil.

In the Lake District *Nardus* is common on the gentler and more stable slopes below rocky knolls or ancient screes, and also on hummocky clayey drift of the most recent glacial episode. Because it indicates areas which are less thoroughly drained than most of the mountain grasslands, the bleached and whitish *Nardus* vegetation is generally a very useful aid in estimating slope from a distance during the winter months. But it is also indicative of differences in the character of the underlying drift, since it marks out areas where relatively poor drainage results from impermeable clayey drift, as distinct from coarser drift of gravel or sand. This difference can be seen unusually clearly in Brown Cove on Helvellyn, where a well-drained fan of coarse drift and long-stabilised scree supports a green oasis of good fescue grassland among the surrounding *Nardus*; every sheep in Brown Cove is usually to be found on this fan between the two becks, illustrating well how over-grazing of the best pastures goes on even though the density of sheep over the total acreage of the grassland would seem to be a reasonable one.

Like its frequent associate the heath rush, *Nardus* is not often common on deep undisturbed peat, and in general both plants seem to do better with some contact with mineral soil, even if this is a very poor one. On the whole, however, the soils under *Nardus* grassland are almost always to some extent peaty, though the organic layer is shallow; they are base-deficient and acid, always oxidising in summer, and though often somewhat damper, strongly resemble those found beneath a heather-moor. On the other hand, though, *Nardus* grassland also occurs on poor and well-washed sandy drift and alluvia beside mountain streams.

The manner in which *Nardus* spreads into formerly better grasslands as a result of over-grazing has been described. It has, however, no capacity for withstanding shade and so does not colonise woodlands. Nor can it compete with large grasses like *Molinia*. Almost always the extension of the *Nardus* grasslands has been by colonisation of poor ground or by succeeding old and grazed-down *Festuca* grasslands. It is a form of vegetation typical of sites which were cleared of woodland at an early stage in prehistory and which have since been grazed and leached to a moorland state. The acid moorlands round Devoke Water, rich in Bronze Age cairns and settlements of Romano-British type, form a good example, and so do parts of the Coniston fells which are also rich in such remains, like Torver High Common. (Plate 1b, p. 32.)

In wetter situations where the mineral soil is near the surface, the community of *Nardus* and *Juncus squarrosus* is invaded by the taller rushes, such as *Juncus effusus* and *J. acutiflorus* (see the foreground in Plate 1b, p. 32). Wet rushy moorland of this type may also contain the two species of cotton-sedge, *Eriophorum angustifolium* and *E. vaginatum*, and various species of *Carex*, with *Sphagnum* species where the water-table reaches the surface. This mixed type of vegetation is found all over the district at the transition from wet grassland to bog communities. Great spreads of rushy moorland are found round the northern skirts of the Skiddaw Fells, on the wide sweep of country between Matterdale Common and the Greta valley east of Threlkeld, and around Black Combe in the south-west on places like Corney Fell – all in the middle zone between about 800 and 1,500 feet.

CALLUNA MOORS

Land use and vegetational change in Skiddaw Forest

Skiddaw Forest is the name given to the moorland basin whence drain the headstreams of the River Caldew. Flanked to the west by Skiddaw itself, to the east by the Blencathra mass and to the north by lesser, rounded fells (Great Calva and Knott), it is a terrain of smooth sided fells and boggy flats more reminiscent of the Pennines than the rugged centre of Lakeland. While doubtless a true forest of olden time (cf. Fig. 14, p. 128), it is now a virtually treeless landscape, with only scattered rowans and birches along a few deep-cut side glens, and the term forest has applied latterly more in the sense of a sporting preserve (see Chapter 15). Dwindling fragments of juniper scrub survive farther down the Caldew, on Carrock Fell and Bowscale Fell, but deforestation in this area has in general been followed by a dominance of dwarf shrub (especially *Calluna*) heaths, acidic grasslands and bracken. The actual distribution of these derived vegetation types does, however, interestingly reflect the actual pattern of subsequent land use in the area.

The ground to the west of the Caldew, and including most of the Skiddaw Forest basin, was developed during the nineteenth century as grouse-moor, and managed intensively as such until the break-up of the Leconfield estate in the 1950s. The land east of the Caldew, that is, Blencathra, Bowscale Fell and their spurs, was not part of this grouse moor and has had a much longer history of management as sheep walk. On grouse moor, management aims at maintaining extensive stands of heather of different age classes, involving a rotational system of burning, and sheep numbers are deliberately kept down. On sheep walks, burning tends to be more indiscriminate, and sheep stocks are usually as high as the ground can carry. In Skiddaw Forest, the result has been to produce a contrast between heather clad fells on the western, grouse moor section, and grass covered hillsides on the eastern, sheep walk parts. A sharp boundary between the two vegetation types follows the sinuous course of the Caldew and then runs along the property march fence where this crosses the col to the head of the Glenderaterra draining south from Skiddaw Forest.

The contrast in vegetation types is not related to soil differences, for in Skiddaw Forest the parent rock is acidic Skiddaw Slate on both sides of the Caldew (though there are igneous intrusions farther down its course), and the range of soil types is the same on the heather ground as on the grasslands. All these soils are essentially base-deficient and podsolic, but vary from skeletal brown earths on steep, well drained ground, to peaty and gley podsols with mor humus horizons in wetter situations, and these finally give way to blanket peat where the ground is more completely waterlogged.

Within the recollection of older observers (W. H. Pearsall, E. Blezard), there was formerly at least some heather ground on the Blencathra side of the Caldew, but this has been entirely lost. On dry ground here the grassland is mainly of fescue-bent with variable amounts of bracken, but where it is damp, mat grass and heath rush take over. The peaty plateaux of Mungrisdale Common and Bannerdale top have shallow blanket bog dominated by cotton-sedge (*Eriophorum vaginatum*). The implication is that these monocotyledonous plant communities have been derived from other types in which dwarf ericaceous shrubs were once dominant or abundant, but have been reduced or eradicated by indiscriminate moor burning and heavy grazing. In other words, the sheep walk vegetation has been produced from that of the grouse moors.

This idea is supported by observations made by the writer (D. A. R.) within the grouse-moor section of Skiddaw Forest, where changes of this kind have begun to appear in recent years and show every indication of continuing and extending in the future. In 1945, there were continuous sweeps of dense dry heather moor from base to summit on Great Calva and Coomb Height, over a vertical height of a thousand feet. On the peatier flats, both in the forest floor and on the watersheds of these hills, the cotton grass bogs had a co-dominance of heather. Locally there were patches of bilberry, but bracken was sparse or absent. In 1952, the delightful little glen of Burdle Gill draining from Knott was largely heather clad from top to bottom and on both sides. From about this time, however, regular management of the Skiddaw Forest grouse moor appeared to cease, and there has evidently been an increase in the stocking density of sheep.

The actual changes are now visible. In several places where the regenerating heather was heavily grazed after being burned, or simply allowed to grow long and 'leggy' without being burned, there has been an increase in bilberry, grasses and bracken. Locally, much of the heather has a moribund look with the contorted, stunted appearance characteristically produced by heavy grazing. Some former dense stands of heather in Burdle Gill are now largely bilberry communities. With continuation of heavy grazing and burning the bilberry becomes invaded and eventually suppressed by grasses or bracken, and dwarf shrub heath is lost. In places there is a change directly from heather moor to grassland or bracken, and where burning has been severe on steep ground there has been some soil erosion and incipient scree formation locally. Once deterioration has begun, other adverse influences, for example severe frost, will hasten the disappearance of heather, as has happened on Great Cockup immediately north of Skiddaw. While good areas of heather still remain, if the former grouse moor continues to be managed as sheep walk, it is probably only a question of time before ericaceous vegetation disappears, and the two sides of the Caldew assume a virtual identity of appearance. Apart from loss of soil and spread of bracken, the changes are not necessarily deleterious from a grazier's point of view, but they are much to the disadvantage of the naturalist. The dwarf shrub heaths of the grouse moor support a richer fauna than do the sheep walk grasslands, and the forms which disappear range from birds such as the merlin (*Falco columbarius*) to insects such as the oak eggar moth (*Lasiocampa callunae*). Floristic impoverishment is an obvious effect, and disappearance of heather and bilberry moor causes a very real loss of aesthetic value to the fell lover.

It would be rash to assume that dwarf shrub heaths generally replaced forest throughout the Lake District. Grassland may have followed directly after woodland clearance where sheep grazing was heavy (see Chapter 13). Nevertheless there is a good deal of observational evidence to suggest that heather moor was once much more widespread in Lakeland as a whole, and that long continued exploitation for sheep has gradually reduced and is still reducing, its extent in favour of acidic grassland. The regression of dwarf shrub heath is by no means confined to Skiddaw Forest, and may be seen in many other places, including another former grouse moor, Fauld's Brow, above Caldbeck. Heather communities have survived best on the poorer rocks, such as Skiddaw Slate, where high sheep stocking rates could not be maintained; or on boggy moorlands such as those between Derwentwater and Thirlmere. In places, dwarf gorse (*Ulex gallii*) is another shrub which has suffered the same kind of reduction or eradication as heather. The other common dwarf shrubs of Lakeland, bilberry, cowberry (*Vaccinium vitis-idaea*) and crowberry (*Empetrum nigrum*) are all more resistant to fire and grazing than heather, but will in turn succumb and be replaced by grasses when these land-use influences become too severe.

The southern moorlands

In the south of the Lake District the Bannisdale Slates, which include flags and grits, often yield an undulating surface of which the ridges and knolls, particularly above about 900 feet, bear *Calluna* and bell heather (*Erica cinerea*), while grasslands, usually with bracken, occupy the hollows. Juniper is abundant in this area, and on the flatter-topped hills between the valleys of the Duddon and the Leven an interesting damp *Calluna–Juniperus* heath may be developed. Some of this moorland was once managed as grouse-moor, and burning has reduced the proportion of juniper. Bilberry and crowberry are more abundant than *Calluna* in some places on these moors; as Dr Ratcliffe has pointed out, these shrubs are more resistant to fire than is *Calluna*, and the heavy and frequent burning of areas such as Kirkby Moor in the interests of grouse has been a major factor in determining the present vegetation.

MOSSES OF THE FELLS

The boggy moors or mosses are those particularly ill-drained parts where *Calluna* is accompanied by the cotton-sedges (*Eriophorum* spp.) and bog-moss (*Sphagnum* spp.). Valley bogs or 'mosses' are found on deep peat in basins, usually over the sites of former lakes and alder fens, and in these the water-table is very near the surface. Much more extensive are the hill mosses which cover areas of gently sloping or nearly flat ground in many parts of the district, particularly above about 1,250 feet. These are the nearest approach in the Lake District to 'blanket-bog', but because slopes are so steep over much of the district, the areas of continuous blanket peat are not very great. This peat is localised to the flatter summit ridges such as High Street, certain areas of low relief in the western fells between the feet of Wastwater and Ennerdale Water, Matterdale Common and parts of Skiddaw Forest in the north, and the eastern fells round the heads of Mosedale, Bannisdale and Longsleddale (see Fig. 14, p. 128).

Many of the mosses are periodically flushed with drainage water from higher slopes; only on summit plateaux does the peat and peat-forming vegetation conform to the definition of true ombrogenous bog (Chapter 7). Much of the peat now shows traces of vigorous erosion and dissection into peat hags, but there are also both wide areas of wet and intact peat surfaces, and places where 'healing' is going on – that is, the growth of living *Sphagnum* is choking channels in the peat and reversing the dissecting effects of surface drainage. The wetter mosses carry communities of *Eriophorum* and *Sphagnum*; 'White Moss' is a common place-name for the cotton-sedge mosses. The drier peat of the dissected mosses has communities of *Calluna* and *Eriophorum*, with more or less *Sphagnum* according to the present wetness of the peat surface. All the mosses, except the wet valley bogs, where the water-table is at the surface, have been greatly modified by attempts to improve them as pasture by deepening drainage channels and by periodic burning of the vegetation. Even though the original replacement of forest at these higher altitudes by bog was the result of natural processes, the present state of the mosses has been greatly influenced by land use.

Peat formation on the uplands began in hollows and gradually extended to mantle considerable areas where the relief is subdued and rainfall high. Erosion and dissection of the peat by drainage channels, as well as draining and burning, have all tended to change the bog vegetation from a continuous *Sphagnum* cover to one dominated by cotton-sedges with varying proportions of *Calluna*. It is only those bog surfaces which are least changed that are now almost completely covered by bog-mosses. *Sphagnum papillosum* is a common species, and through this *Sphagnum* carpet on such bogs project scattered shoots of many grassy or sedgy plants which often include, in addition to the cotton-sedges, the deer-sedge (*Trichophorum cespitosum*), and almost always the beautiful bog-asphodel (*Narthecium ossifragum*). Along with these are short and slender shoots of *Calluna* and cross-leaved heath (rarely much exceeding 6 inches in height) with certain small liverworts, and the sundew (*Drosera rotundifolia*) up to an altitude of about 1,800 feet. Other plants found in such a bog community include the cranberry (*Vaccinium oxycoccus*), which is common, bog rosemary (*Andromeda polifolia*) and two rarities, the great sundew (*Drosera anglica*) and the bog orchid (*Hammarbya paludosa*). Bogs of this general type can be found on particularly wet areas of the fells, such as Armboth Fell between Watendlath and Thirlmere (see page 127). On many areas of upland bog, however, a continuous *Sphagnum* carpet is found only round springs and in basins where the ground water is at the surface. On sloping ground and flat plateaux, the spreads of upland peat are generally drier, with cotton-sedge (*Eriophorum angustifolium*), *Calluna*, and sometimes deer-sedge and the purple moor-grass as the peat-forming plants. Where the peat on slopes is flushed with drainage water from above, carrying some silt, the vegetation of the present surface of even quite deep peat can be dominated by *Juncus squarrosus*, a plant which increases on blanket-bog if grazing by sheep is heavy. In such situations the wavy hair-grass can also be abundant. The cloudberry (*Rubus chamaemorus*), which is common in the cotton-sedge bogs of the neighbouring Pennines, is in the Lake District found only locally in a few places, most of them in the eastern fells.

It seems probable that under present climatic conditions true blanket-peat, depending on rainwater only for water and dissolved salts, can form only in the wettest parts of the uplands of northern England. Much of the wet peat of the Lakeland fells either occupies the sites of former shallow lakes, such as the great bogs in Upper Eskdale and Wythburn above the falls, or is accumulating round springs. The deep wet peat round spring bogs, made up of particular species of *Sphagnum* such as *S. recurvum*, constitutes one of the worst of hazards to the unwary walker; frequently the water and peat of spring bogs like this are red with bacterially precipitated ferric oxide (bog iron-ore) as well as deep, but fortunately the bright green colour of the bog-mosses of these springs is usually conspicuous.

One of the commonest habitats on the Lakeland fells is the small area of flush bog or marsh so frequently found beside the small feeders of the becks, at any altitude up to 2,500 feet but commoner below 2,000 feet, with butterwort (*Pinguicula vulgaris*) and grass of Parnassus (*Parnassia palustris*). In these wet places the moss carpet is often of *Sphagnum rubellum*, *Polytrichum commune*, and *Aulocomnium palustre*, with sundew and the bog pimpernel (*Anagallis tenella*) abundant. Purging flax (*Linum catharticum*) is another characteristic species, usually on the drier fringes, together with the grass *Briza media*. *Erica tetralix*, *Narthecium ossifragum*, *Prunella vulgaris*, *Pedicularis palustris* and *Ranunculus flammula* flower freely in such wet places which are transitional between bog and marsh, together with most of the species of grasses and rushes already mentioned, and three common sedges – *Carex echinata*, *C. panicea*, and *C. binervis*. Rarer sedges found in wet *Sphagnum* bogs are *Carex paupercula*, *C. limosa* and *C. pauciflora*, the two latter being found in the bogs on Watendlath Fell.

ANIMALS AND BIRDS OF THE FELL COUNTRY

The mammals and birds of the biotic grasslands up to 2,000 feet, and the high peatlands, represent in some ways a transition between the remaining woodland communities and those of the summits. The red deer are, of course, descendants of forest animals. Hill foxes, stoats and the very rare pine marten are the predators of the fells, together with the peregrines of the crags and the buzzards and merlin which belong to the broken lower fells rather than to the mountain-tops. The invertebrate fauna of the acid grasslands and peaty moorlands is poor when compared with that of richer grasslands or woodlands; earthworms are scarce or absent, ants few, and snails largely replaced by slugs. *Arion ater*, the common slug, is usually the most frequently seen invertebrate. Certain moths are often noticeable, particularly forms feeding on the mat-grass or moor-grass (*Molinia*). The fox-moth (*Macrothylacia rubi*), one of the commonest moorland species, feeds on mat-grass, and so does the antler-moth (*Cerapteryx gramineus*) which at times occurs in great numbers. Another fairly characteristic species is the small rush-moth (*Coleophora caespititiella*) which, up to an altitude of c. 1,800 feet, lives as a larva on the fruits of the heath-rush. The most characteristic birds of the country so far discussed in this chapter are the meadow pipit (*Anthus pratensis*), the cuckoo (*Cuculus canorus*), which so often parasitises it and haunts the highest scattered trees, the wheatears (*Oenanthe oenanthe*) and curlews (*Numenius arquata*) and golden plovers (*Charadrius apricarius*), the sandpipers (*Tringa hypoleucos*) nesting by the mountain tarns, the scavenging carrion crow (*Corvus corone*), and the buzzards (*Buteo buteo*) soaring above the high woods and lower crags. On heather moors nest the merlin (*Falco columbarius*), another enemy of the meadow pipits, and in places the red grouse (*Lagopus scoticus*) and black grouse (*Lyrurus tetrix*).

The hill foxes provide one of the most securely rooted of native sports. The large dark grey foxes which used to be found on higher ground and were up to 15 lb in weight were possibly of the sub-species *Vulpes vulpes vulpes*, rather than the sub-species *crucigera* which includes the present reddish foxes, but this question needs critical examination. Lake District hill foxes range over the high grasslands up to the summits, and it is fairly common to find their tracks in these places in the snow in winter. The fell earths are made in broken rocks and cairns (borrans) or in cracks in rock faces. Lake District foxes are not, of course, preserved, but are hunted in earnest with foot packs of hounds, and Lakeland terriers, as a necessary protection to hill sheep-farming. There are now six packs of hounds, hunting about three days a week from October until April and killing perhaps 350 foxes a year, but there is no perceptible diminution in fox numbers.

To talk to experienced regular followers of the fell packs is to realise that there has been a big change in foxes and their habits over the last fifty years. Over this period there has been a steep decline in the extent to which the woods have been policed by gamekeepers, as wages have risen and land use in the woods has changed from game preservation to forestry. Most of the foxes now found by the hunts are of the reddish colour, smaller size and shorter legs of the sub-species *crucigera*, which lives in the woods when not persecuted by keepers, rather than on the fells. The old type of long-legged hill fox which was hunted by John Peel and his contemporaries is now rarely found; some say that there has not been one for thirty years, and all agree that the long runs of up to six hours of which these foxes were capable are now almost unknown. There has been over the same period of about 30 to 50 years a change of ground by the foxes, and it is suggested that this may be due to the way in which the number of walkers in the fells has increased at the same time that the number of gamekeepers in the woods has declined. All through the nineteenth century current opinion held the view that it was dangerous to walk the high fells without a guide, such as the one who conducted the Wordsworths up Scafell Pike in 1818, and so parties of walkers were few. Fifty years ago ordinary walkers were finding their way on to the fells in increasing numbers, and the last professional guide for walkers in Langdale retired in 1927. Since then there has been a steady increase in numbers of people on the fells, up to the present estimate of 600 people on Helvellyn every day in summer. The valley and hill woods, no longer patrolled by gamekeepers, have become a more peaceful place for foxes than the fells, and now the hunts can count on putting up foxes on most of the fell breasts where the woods thin out into juniper and bracken as they rise from the dales. Before this change in habitat, the fox was much more of a fell animal and was rarely met with in the woods.

Now there are fox earths in every woodland area of any size, in old rabbit holes and badger setts, and in covered drains where these have been laid in the woods, and frequently in the drains of the bordering fields. The mixed diet of foxes can be found in both fell and woodland habitats, and foxes travel the fells continually, but nowadays they are commonly found lying up in the woods or the brackeny intakes, whereas fifty years ago they spent more of their lives on the higher fells. Individual foxes seem to vary very much in the degree to which they worry lambs in spring; hunt followers say that the worst lamb-worriers are usually either unmated females or the fathers of litters whose vixen mother has been killed.

The pine marten (*Mustela martes*) was plentiful enough to be hunted regularly in the eighteenth and nineteenth centuries, but is now very rare. Though by nature a forest animal it had been driven, by the destruction of the forests and by persecution, to the rough broken ground of the craggy fells. Stirring accounts of hunting of the 'Mart' can be found in, for instance, Macpherson's *Vertebrate Fauna of Lakeland* (1892). At the end of the nineteenth century there were marts over much of the high fell country at the head of the major dales, but they were thought to be most numerous in Eskdale and Wasdale. The name Sweetmart was used to distinguish them from the Foumart or polecat (*Mustela putorius*). This, though once common, is now generally agreed to be extinct, the last certain record having been for Ullswater in 1922. The polecat was an animal of the dales and the lowland mosses rather than of the higher fells. Stoats (*Mustela erminea*) and weasels (*Mustela nivalis*) are still common everywhere.

The buzzard, which is commoner than the peregrine and perhaps in some ways a more characteristically Lakeland bird than the raven, nests on both high crags frequented by peregrines and ravens, and on smaller crags, as well as in trees of several kinds in the hill woods. The hunting or soaring buzzard, with its broad wings and tail is often seen in spring and summer above the rocky broken ground where the upper woods give way to the little crags of the lower fells. Some buzzards stay on the higher ground all winter, but many come down to winter in the valley woods or on the coast. Sheep carrion is one of the main foods of the buzzard, and the suspicion that young fell lambs were attacked by it led to local persecution, so that parish records in the seventeenth and eighteenth centuries contain entries of payments for killing buzzards as well as eagles. Rabbits, another major source of food when available, have, of course, fluctuated in numbers in recent years. Alternative foods of the buzzard have been found to be smaller birds – young of the meadow pipit, curlew and red grouse, in one nest, a young crow in another, together with remains of voles, mice, rats and leverets.

Between the years 1924 and 1940, regular observations by Miss M. Garnett in the Kentmere and Troutbeck valleys showed the existence of eight nesting sites of buzzards in Kentmere and four in Troutbeck. In any particular year, not more than three sites in Kentmere and two in Troutbeck were used, suggesting the presence of this number of pairs in each dale. Some nests were found in trees – holly, birch and oak – but most were on crag ledges. Many nestings were unsuccessful, the eggs or young disappearing. The common habit of buzzards of laying fresh green leafy branches on to the structure of a nest they intend to use that year was repeatedly observed.

The carrion crow is common on the fells despite a certain amount of persecution, and breeds up to 1,800 feet, usually either in rocks or thorn bushes; it also has urban nesting sites in Carlisle and Barrow. Communal roosting flocks are common. Apart from carrion its diet is a mixed one, including beetles and grubs. In spring when the sheep are lambing on the lower fells, the traces of this bird's work can be found in eyeless Herdwick lambs which have been attacked shortly after their birth. At this time the carrion crows busily cover the ground feeding on the after-births of the ewes.

The two small birds most commonly seen on the fells in summer are wheatears and meadow pipits; both nest up to nearly 3,000 feet. They form the favourite prey of merlin, which are commoner on the heather country of the eastern fells than on the steep rocks and grasslands of the central mountains. The merlin nests in Kentmere between 1924 and 1955 were most often found in heather, but occasionally in trees, where they used old nests of other species, such as those of carrion crows in alders beside the becks and that of a magpie in a thorn. There was a certain amount of evidence to indicate that the presence of a good stock of small birds increased the likelihood of merlin nesting in any particular locality; it has been suggested that if merlin successfully raise a brood at the same site for several years in succession, the local population of small birds such as the meadow pipit becomes reduced below the level at which merlin will nest.

Curlews appear on the inland nesting grounds in late February and early March, and some of the breeding birds may winter locally. The nests are found on moors up to 2,600 feet. The Ring Ouzel (*Turdus torquatus*) also begins to arrive at the end of February, but may exceptionally winter in the fells. It often nests above 1,750 feet, and may go up to 2,500 feet, but not in large numbers. The crags where it is found are often bilberry-covered, and after nesting is over the birds join up in parties which can be found feeding on bilberries and rowan berries. Stonechats (*Saxicola torquata*) which were noted by Dorothy Wordsworth are sparse and local inland now, though common nesters on the coast. In the mountains they breed up to 1,600 feet and have been increasing in numbers since 1941. Whinchats (*Saxicola rubetra*) have fluctuated in numbers through the first part of this century; they nest in the fells up to 1,300 feet.

The kestrel (*Falco tinnunculus*) is the commonest bird of prey in the fells and dales, breeding on crags up to 1,700 feet but equally often seen among lowland hedgerows and woods.

A bird more characteristic of the eastern moorlands is the golden plover, which nests commonly in the neighbouring Pennines but only sparingly now in the central Lake District. Formerly, nesting sites of the golden plover were more abundant in the Lake District and at lower altitudes than the present distribution, which is at about 1,000 feet or higher. Former lower nesting sites were found, for instance, on Birker Moor between the Duddon and Esk, where the golden plover used to nest on peaty ground, but now these birds are more often seen in spring and summer on the eastern fells and in Skiddaw Forest, where their present nesting sites are found. In snowy winter weather golden plover are likely to come down to the western coastal fields. Also characteristic of the eastern fells are the autumn flocks of fieldfares (*Turdus pilaris*), feeding up to 2,000 feet on fruits and seeds of plants which include rowan and the field woodrush (*Luzula campestris*).

THE DALES – MEADOWS, MOSSES AND MIRES

Meadows

The characteristic pattern of a valley landscape is shown by the fields of Wasdale Head and those of Seathwaite in Borrowdale. The stone walls which enclose the dale meadows are here of great antiquity, probably following the lines of fields cleared and partly drained by the earliest settlers. Originally the flat floors of these U-shaped troughs must have been swampy alder and willow woods, passing into birch and oak in the drier places. If settlement were to cease at any time, the field drains to become blocked, and liming, mowing and grazing to end, these flat valley meadows would soon revert to moss and alder carr. Extreme contrasts in present vegetation can be seen on the two sides of the walls of the limits of these dale settlements, both on the sides of the valleys and at the dale heads. Mickleden, one arm of the head of Great Langdale, shows signs of a considerable settlement in the past, so that we cannot say that the present limits of the farmed land represent any natural boundary

– they are the present limit of economic agriculture. But the complete contrast in vegetation between the last green meadows of Stool End and Middlefell Place, and the rough undrained stony and swampy pasture of the dale bottom above the last field wall, is very striking, and must have been noted by thousands of fell walkers on the circling mountains. This difference is entirely the result of land use, and the green meadows owe their colour to draining, liming and fertilising.

The valley meadows of the Lake District cannot rival the flowery profusion of those on more calcareous soils, such as Birkdale in Upper Teesdale. Furthermore, recent improvement in agricultural techniques, stimulated by the drive to increase production on marginal land during the Second World War, has tended to produce a standard mixture of hay grasses in meadows which only thirty years ago were characteristically dominated by the great burnet (*Sanguisorba officinalis*) and, in damper places, the bistort or easter ledges (*Polygonum bistorta*) – two plants which found a place in local cookery as Burnip Wine and Easter Ledge Pudding. Burnet meadows have been ploughed and re-seeded, and easter ledges destroyed by selective sprays. Many damp meadows which used to flower with the alpine beauty of the globe-flower (*Trollius europaeus*) have been turned into more productive but less attractive hayfields. The traditionally late hay-time, the result of the long cool spring (Chapter 6) and the need to use valley meadows for the late mountain lambing, was associated with a species-rich meadow community. Now that the advantages (with respect to the grasses) of an earlier haytime are understood, and seeded grasses such as rye (*Lolium*) and timothy (*Phleum*) have become widely used, the meadows of the old Lake District of Dorothy Wordsworth have largely disappeared. But places still survive where meadows are bright with wood cranesbill (*Geranium sylvaticum*) and on the limestone the glorious deep blue of its relation, the meadow cranesbill (*G. pratense*). Meadows which are not heavily grazed sometimes have a rich and beautiful carpet of plants which normally grow in woodlands, but flourish in the open in this humid climate – like the windflower meadows in Great Langdale, and the daffodils in the fields of Broughton Mills in the Lickle valley. The meadows of Cockley Beck at the head of Dunnerdale are probably typical of most of the valleys, under present grassland management but without any alien introductions.

There are several interesting and characteristic plants of the dales: the sweet cicely (*Myrrhis odorata*) is always associated with old farms or former settlements, and recalls the days before cultivation of turnips as winter feed (see Chapter 15) when the great autumn slaughter of cattle was followed by the enforced use of increasingly unpalatable dried meat, so that strong-flavoured herbs were cultivated. The Welsh poppy (*Meconopsis cambrica*) is so closely tied to settlements that it must be a recent garden escape everywhere. The alien purplish-pink balsam

Impatiens glandulifera is naturalised in many places near rivers; the rarer native yellow balsam (*Impatiens noli-tangere*) is still to be found 'by the side of Winandermere not far from Ambleside' where it was recorded by Lawson in the seventeenth century.

Another interesting plant of lowland situations near Ambleside is the beautiful mealy primrose (*Primula farinosa*), which is common on the southern limestone (especially lovely on shell marl round the small Lonsdale Haweswater near Leighton Moss), and in places on the slopes of the eastern valleys such as those of the High Street range, but rare and local west of Kirkstone Pass. This is a plant of base-rich soils, but its distribution must depend on other factors which are as yet quite incompletely understood.

Mosses and Mires

The raised bogs of the estuaries round Morecambe Bay were formerly great domes of peat with an impassably wet surface, which for centuries blocked communications by coastal routes round the Bay, and caused the traffic between Furness and the rest of Lancashire to use the tidal route across the sands from Hest Bank to Kents Bank and Ulverston. These great bogs were built up on ill-drained clay flats laid down by the sea at the time of the mid-post-glacial marine transgression; after the sea receded the surface of the clay was colonised first by brackish swamps and then by reed-fen, which as it built up became more acid and passed into *Sphagnum* peat. Two processes have tended to change the state of the peat and the vegetation of these mosses within the last century, and particularly within the last fifty years. Peat cutting round the drier margins of the bogs led to draining and drying of the remaining masses of peat, and from some of the smaller mosses practically the whole of the peat has been removed by cutting for fuel. Secondly, consistent improvement in methods of draining the agricultural land around the mosses has lowered the water-table in the peat and changed the surface to dry rather than wet peat, with a corresponding change in the vegetation. Many of the mosses have been colonised by seed from pines and birches and now carry woodland rather than bog vegetation. The dry peat round the margins of these raised bogs forms a habitat where it is possible that the native Scots pine may have survived from the time when it was widespread (page 154). Rusland Moss, on the site of a former lake, is now almost completely wooded, and Deer Dike Moss to the east of Roudsea Wood is being rapidly colonised by pine and birch, though parts of its surface are still wet bog with a community of *Eriophorum vaginatum, Erica tetralix,Sphagnum* spp. and bog rosemary. Somewhat wetter bogs where draining and drying are not yet apparent are found at Holker Moss on the Leven estuary and Heathwaite Moss on the Duddon. Foulshaw, formerly the greatest and

PLATE 21   Four characteristic plants of Lake District fells: *Above left, Pinguicula vulgaris* (Butterwort).   *Above right, Saxifraga aizoides* (Yellow mountain saxifrage). *Below left, Alchemilla alpina* (Alpine lady's mantle).   *Below right, Parnassia palustris* (Grass of Parnassus).

PLATE 22 Four characteristic Lake District birds: *Above left*, Buzzard (*Buteo buteo*) bringing rabbit to tree nest. *Above right*, Pied Flycatcher (*Muscicapa hypoleuca*) – cock and hen. *Below left*, Dipper (*Cinclus cinclus*) in a characteristic pose. *Below right*, Merlin (*Falco columbarius*) at its nest among heather.

most impassable of the mosses, has changed very much as a result of recent agricultural drainage of the surrounding land.

Meathop Moss. Meathop Moss, near Grange-over-Sands, has been a Nature Reserve since 1920 and was administered by the Society for the Promotion of Nature Reserves until it was taken over by the Lake District Naturalists' Trust a few years ago. From 1920 until the Second World War the surface of the moss was very wet with a vegetation of cotton-sedge (*Eriophorum vaginatum*) and *Sphagnum* spp., together with abundant bog rosemary and cranberry. In the middle of the moss was a colony of lesser black-backed gulls (*Larus fuscus*) and the insect life was very rich and included the large heath butterfly (*Coenonympha tullia* race *philoxenus*). During the war the gullery ceased to exist because of the collection of eggs for food, and since the war more intensive drainage of the surrounding agricultural land has tended towards progressive lowering of the water-table, just as on Foulshaw Moss. Pines and birches have colonised the drying peat surface, and the whole nature of the habitat seems to be changing irreversibly towards something nearer to the present state of Rusland Moss. Parties of Conservation Corps workers, under the auspices of the Council for Nature, have cleared the tree seedlings and young trees from certain areas, and the large heath butterfly and some of the other interesting insects – for example *Crambus pascuellus*, *Perconia strigillaria* and *Selidosema brunnearia* – are still to be found. It is difficult for conservationists to devise means of counteracting the general lowering of the water-table in the peat, and the whole nature of the habitat on Meathop seems to be changing irreversibly towards something nearer to the present state of Rusland Moss.

Leighton Moss. This site on the southern edge of the Lake District, a few miles north of Carnforth, shows the entire dependence of the moss habitat on the type of drainage practised locally. It occupies a shallow valley between low ridges of Carboniferous limestone, and now forms the most extensive area of reed fen in northern England. It seems almost certain that at one time there was deep peat on Leighton Moss, for the eighteenth-century blast-furnace at Leighton used peat as well as charcoal. By the end of the nineteenth century all peat had been removed, except for small areas of marginal fen, and the valley floor was cultivated as highly fertile arable land whose productivity justified the cost of drainage by means of pumping water into a dike and then out to sea, first by a windmill and then by a steam engine. In 1918 this drainage scheme was abandoned, and in the next ten years the moss reverted to wet swamp and open water, into which the reed mace (*Typha latifolia*) and *Phragmites australis* spread from the areas of marginal fen which had remained. Willows then spread into the reed swamp and a carr stage was initiated. At first the area was used for wild-fowling, mostly mallard, but it gradually became colonised by a variety of interesting birds, which by the late 1940s included nesting

L.D.—N

bitterns (*Botaurus stellaris*). In 1964 Leighton Moss became a reserve of the Royal Society for the Protection of Birds, and in 1969 eight pairs of bitterns nested there.

Duck, mainly mallard, teal (*Anas crecca*) and wigeon (*Anas penelope*) but including shovelers (*Spatula clypeata*) and pochard (*Aythya ferina*) tended to decrease as the spread of almost pure *Phragmites* beds restricted the growth of their food plants. Management of the reserve is aimed at preserving the habitat for ducks by judicious cutting of the reeds in selected areas; on the other hand it is the extensive reed beds which have provided the habitat for the bittern, and which have been visited in winter by the bearded tit (*Panurus biarmicus*), a bird which is usually found only in the reed beds of East Anglia. There was an apparently natural succession from an early stage in the flooding of the agricultural land, when the food plants of the ducks, such as bur-reed, crowfoots, pondweed and water plantain, were abundant and a rich aquatic vegetation prevailed, to a later stage when *Phragmites* replaced the previous vegetation. A new mere has been excavated recently from an area of reed bed, and this disturbance of the peat has apparently renewed the plant succession in this area.

Other birds of Leighton Moss include the reed warbler (*Acrocephalus scirpaceus*), which was unknown before the flooding but now nests there in numbers up to 400 pairs, the water rail (*Rallus aquaticus*) which breeds abundantly in the reed beds, and the grasshopper warbler (*Locustella naevia*) which nests in the clumps of *Carex paniculata* and disappears from the habitat when these areas are colonised by willow carr. Sedge warblers (*Acrocephalus schoenobaenus*) are common, and so are snipe (*Capella gallinago*). Herons and kingfishers haunt the moss, herons feeding on the abundant eels which are also the food of the bittern. In May and June non-breeding ospreys (*Pandion haliaëtus*) visit the moss and feed on rudd. Marsh harriers (*Circus aeruginosus*) are regularly seen passing through. The reserve management is attempting to extend the habitats favourable for waders by creating more shallow marginal water and muddy flats free of reeds; green sandpipers (*Tringa ochropus*) and spotted redshank (*Tringa erythropus*) are among the waders seen in summer.

The geese which roosted here before 1939, mainly greylag (*Anser anser*) and pink-footed (*Anser brachyrhynchus*) are now very rarely seen, and encroachment by the reeds and consequent change in the habitat is thought to be the reason.

Blelham Bog. This small National Nature Reserve beside Blelham Tarn illustrates another type of lowland bog, a lacustrine bog developed over the lake sediments of two small kettleholes which changed from open water in the early post-glacial period to fen, carr and then bog (Oldfield, 1970). In the western kettlehole there is evidence for a direct transition from lake mud to a peat consisting mainly of *Sphagnum* remains, which records the development of a 'schwingmoor' at an early stage in the succession there. When the site was acquired by the Nature Conservancy in 1954, the vegetation of the western kettlehole was a wet birch–alder–willow carr, and that of the eastern one was an acid *Sphagnum–Molinia–Myrica* bog. It seemed possible at the time that these represented two stages in the hydroseral development from carr to ombrogenous bog. 'However, the exclusion of stock from the site since 1956 set in train a series of rapid vegetational changes which were difficult to interpret entirely in the light of the above hypothesis and accordingly a vegetation survey was carried out in 1959 which led in turn to the present investigation begun in 1961.' (Oldfield, 1970.)

Professor Oldfield's conclusion from this investigation is that over both kettleholes raised-bog peat formed on top of mid-post-glacial carr peat, and that there is then a hiatus in the profiles which indicates extensive cutting of this peat; this is supported by early nineteenth-century maps and conveyances which record turbary rights on the bog. Above the cut surface, Professor Oldfield has traced in the most recent peat layer the detailed history of vegetation development since c. 1830, and found evidence for the effects of flushing of the cut peat surface by drainage water when drains were laid in the higher marginal land (cf. page 261). Other changes in the vegetation can be attributed to the construction of the present causeway and diversion of the bordering stream (Fish Pond Beck), together with the effects of lowering the level of Blelham Tarn by deepening and straightening the outflow stream. Professor Oldfield has found evidence which dates these changes to the period 1848–88. Grazing has also influenced the vegetation pattern. The present vegetation of the area enclosed since 1956 shows recent changes consequent on the cessation of grazing. The reserve includes a rich variety of habitats, with plant communities characteristic of damp woodland, carr, fen, bog and swamps.

CHAPTER II

PREHISTORIC ARCHAEOLOGY

Let the Moon hear, emerging from a cloud,
When, how, and wherefore, rose on British ground
That wondrous Monument, whose mystic round
Forth shadows, some have deemed, to mortal sight
The Inviolable God that tames the proud.
William Wordsworth: *Guide to the Lakes*
(on seeing the stone circle Long Meg and her Daughters)

IN 1933 Professor R. G. Collingwood published his *Introduction to the Prehistory of Cumberland, Westmorland and Lancashire north of the Sands*, which has formed the basis of later research in the area. Owing to great advances of knowledge, notably since the last World War, the conclusions he reached are now largely out of date and the present interpretation will be summarised in this chapter. Fresh radiocarbon dates continue to modify accepted typological dating in all the prehistoric periods so that any written account may well be out of date before it is published.

It is not known when man first set foot in the Lake District and, until he became literate, something of his life, economic organisation and technical advance can be learnt only from the few material things which have survived. No Palaeolithic tools have been found here and the extent of the glaciation in this area makes their discovery unlikely, though Late-Glacial Creswellian artefacts have been found as far north as the Victoria Cave, Settle. The archaeological record begins with traces of the hunter–fisher economy of the Mesolithic which followed the final retreat of the ice and the growth of forests at the end of the Quaternary Ice Age. Microlithic flints used for barbs of harpoons and arrow-tips, scrapers and knives for flaying animals caught in traps or killed in the chase, have been found at a number of coastal sites from St Bees in Cumberland to Walney Island in Furness and also in the park at Levens Hall, Westmorland, during excavations there in 1968. All have been unstratified, chiefly in sand dunes, or in soils which have not preserved the perishable bone, antler, or wooden hafts in which some of these flints would have been set for use. The supply of flint was limited to pebbles collected from the beach, or from the drift, their small size largely governing the size of the tools which could be made. Occasionally fine-grained tuffs of the Borrowdale Volcanic Series were used as an alternative material. Less dense forest growth along the coastal strip made easier the establishment of campsites at a time before man was equipped to make serious inroads on the virgin woodland. The proximity to the sea would also have provided an additional source of food – shell fish, salt water fish and wild fowl. The first microlith recorded was from Trough Head, Walney Island and a microlithic flint industry was later found at Sandy Gap* on the same island, but the first large assemblage of Mesolithic flint tools was found at Drigg in the sandhills north of Ravenglass. More recently a similar flint industry has been found associated with the twenty-five foot raised beach at Eskmeals. These artefacts can be compared with tools and flakes of Sauveterrean affinity found stratified in a mud at Stump Cross, Grassington, Yorkshire, from which a radiocarbon date of 4555 ± 130 B.C. has been obtained. Microlithic flint tools were found in the Kirkhead Cave, Allithwaite in 1968–9 below a deposit of cave earth, resting on laminated clay and it is hoped that a close date can be determined.

Finds high in the Pennines suggest that Mesolithic hunters followed the upper margins of the forest, probably during the summer months, and it is likely that forays after game penetrated the central hills of the Lake District. None of the characteristic equipment of the period has so far been found there, but a single flint core-trimming flake, produced by a technique in use at this time, was found during cable laying in Borrans Road, Ambleside, in 1968 and may indicate that the lakes were not unknown to men of this period. An alteration in tree pollen content noted by Dr Donald Walker at Ehenside Tarn, Beckermet, at about 4000 B.C. could have been caused by men clearing trees and undergrowth round their camps. The date accords well with a recent assessment of South-West Scottish coastal Mesolithic which is thought to have flourished between 5000 and 3000 B.C.

With the advent of the first farmers of the Neolithic period in the centuries before 3000 B.C. man made undeniable impact on the vegetation of the district as demonstrated in recent pollen analytical work (see Chapter 13). Finds are mainly on the lighter soils more suitable for primitive agriculture – on limestone with its high fertility; on sandstone formations; on glacial sands and gravels and on alluvial spreads by lakes and rivers. Altitude, rainfall and forest growth are likely to have limited settlement, particularly in the central hills, which would have provided a source of raw materials and a centre for hunting. The polished stone axe was the all-important heavy tool of the period, not only needed for clearing forest to increase grazing for domesticated animals, but also when hafted as a mattock, or hoe, for breaking up the ground in some areas for cereal cultivation. What little is known of the material equipment of the time comes from a few settlements and burials, from the stone axe factories and from numerous stray finds of polished and roughed-out stone axes.

No house plans have yet been recovered here, but, for instance at

* The parish name follows that of most sites mentioned in Chapters 11, 12 and 14.

Knockadoon by Lough Gur in Ireland and Llandegai in Caernarvonshire, rectangular timber buildings were in use at this time. Ehenside
Tarn, Beckermet, in the New Red Sandstone area of west Cumberland,
was drained a hundred years ago revealing a number of ancient hearths
round its shores. These yielded polished and roughed-out stone axes, axe
rubbing and grinding stones, a saucer quern for grinding grain, pottery
and wooden equipment, including a bowl, two fish spears, clubs, the haft
of a stone axe and a paddle, thought to belong to a dug-out canoe said to
have been found nearby. The pottery is handmade and of two varieties –
carinated bowls of lustrous black ware, more akin to Grimston ware of
Yorkshire than to Lyle's Hill ware of Northern Ireland, and coarser sherds
decorated with bird-bone impressions, similar to the Peterborough style
of later Neolithic times, which came from an isolated hearth. These could
represent different phases of the occupation as suggested by radiocarbon
dates obtained from wooden objects from the site, the earliest of which is
3014 ± 300 B.C. and the latest 1570 ± 150 B.C. Other sherds of Grimston
ware have been found at Trough Head, Walney Island, a site which has
also yielded pottery of Peterborough type.

Leaf-shaped and *petit-tranchet* derivative arrowheads and other flint
tools found in the sandhills at Eskmeals and Drigg should fall within the
thousand years and more during which the Neolithic economy is now
believed to have been practised. Pollen diagrams from Ehenside Tarn,
Beckermet and Barfield Tarn (south of Bootle) confirm the intensity and
continuity of occupation of the Cumberland coastal strip, which prevented
the regeneration of woodland after its initial clearance. Flints and pottery
from the sand dunes at North End, Walney Island, have affinities with
contemporary material from Glenluce on the north side of the Solway and,
indeed, there appears to have been considerable contact between the
lands bordering the northern part of the Irish Sea at this time. Contents
of the middens associated with the flint and stone industry show a mixed
diet of shell fish and meat, bones of ox, pig, sheep or goat, and deer
having been identified. Many stone axes and saddle querns have been
rescued from quarrying operations in the limestone hills at Stone Close,
Stainton in Furness, proving the existence of a settlement there, while
stone axes from High Haume, Dalton and Skelmore Heads, Urswick, also
in Furness, and at Winder Moor, Flookburgh in the Cartmel peninsula,
show that these areas, too, were settled in Neolithic times. Habitation
sites in the limestone districts around Shap, Crosby Ravensworth and
Crosby Garrett in Westmorland have yet to be found, or near Penrith in
Cumberland, but the distribution of surface finds of stone axes and the
presence of burials mentioned below, show that they must have existed
there. Keswick, with its wide gravel spreads between Derwentwater and
Bassenthwaite Lake, provided the best centre within Lakeland for Neolithic farming communities and many roughed-out and polished stone

axes have been found in that area, notably at Mossgarth, Portinscale. A few finds near Troutbeck Bridge on Windermere, at Hawkshead, Nibthwaite at the foot of Coniston Water and in the area between Gosforth and Wastwater, show some penetration of the hillier ground beyond the main areas of settlement.

The scarcity of flint in the Lake District demanded an alternative material for fashioning the essential stone axes and adzes. Museums and private collections in the area possess an abundance of surface finds of these tools, in finished and unfinished condition, chiefly made from a fine-grained, greenish grey tuff of the Borrowdale Volcanic Series. In the 1920s Professor D. M. S. Watson collected a number of rough-outs and flakes from an erosion channel in the peat on Mart Crag Moor, near the top of Stake Pass, Great Langdale. These were later classified as Group VI in a petrological survey of stone axes, showing that axes made from this rock originated in the Lake District. It was not until 1947 that Mr Brian Bunch, when on a climbing holiday at Dungeon Ghyll, discovered extensive workings on Pike of Stickle and the screes below it. Specimens from the site proved to be identical with the earlier find from the valley. Loose scree was mainly used, though there is some evidence for limited quarrying and breaking up of boulders. Since that date work by Mr R. G. Plint and others has extended our knowledge of the workings in Great Langdale itself and, more recently, other factory sites have been found on Scafell, Scafell Pike and Glaramara where similar tuffs crop out. Many rough-outs are of large size, ready to make up into the thin-butted, narrow axes, often with faceted sides, known as the Cumbrian type. These are common in the Lake Counties and occur at Ehenside Tarn, where petrological examination showed them to be made of Group VI rock. Present knowledge suggests that the grinding and polishing processes were not carried out at the working sites, some of which on Scafell Pike are well over 2,500 feet, but that roughouts were trimmed with granite hammer-stones to minimum bulk and carried to more permanent settlements for finishing. The larger tree-felling axe blades were made from blocks of stone (core tools), but adzes and the lighter forms of axes were fashioned from flakes, as were the smaller tools such as knives and scrapers. It is fascinating to imagine the ringing of stone on stone high up on the Langdales and Scafell Pike during seasonal activity at the factories four to five thousand years ago. Some of the early prospecting and working may have been carried out by men accompanied by their flocks and herds, the pollen evidence for which will be discussed in Chapter 13. Charcoal found in the sediment of a former tarn in Langdale Combe could mean that fire was used to assist clearance, or may have been derived from camp fires.

Petrological identification of stone axes has shown that tools from the Lake District were widely traded in England and Scotland, also by water transport to the Isle of Man and, to a lesser extent to Ireland. A few axes with roughened butts, characteristic of the Ronaldsway Culture of the Isle of Man, and porcellanite axes from Tievebulliagh Hill, Antrim, have been found in our area, for instance at Seascale and Walney Island, while the half dozen flint axes recorded in the Lake Counties also came by trade, or were brought by original settlers from Yorkshire. Whether the exchange was by direct economic trading, or in the form of kinship gifts can never be known, nor can it ever be discovered in detail for what these attractive implements were exchanged. In southern Scotland a few hoards of Antrim flint suggest that flint was sometimes imported and it is likely that similar contact existed with the chalk-bearing districts of East Yorkshire. When the Great Langdale factories were discovered twenty years ago, it was thought that the export phase did not develop until about 2000 B.C., but recent radiocarbon dates have shown that trade was active by the Middle Neolithic of southern England, that is by about 2500 B.C. The first radiocarbon date relating to axe manufacture in Great Langdale has recently been given as 2730 B.C., which confirms the supposition that production for local use started sooner.

Little modern excavation has been done on burial sites of the period and megalithic tombs, common in most areas bordering the western seaways, are rare in the Lake District. Last century Canon Greenwell partially excavated the great long-cairn known as Raiset Pike, Crosby Garrett, close to Sunbiggin Tarn which lies in an area of glacial sand and gravel overlying Carboniferous limestone. This cairn is oriented south-east to north-west, is 179 feet long, 62 feet wide at the south-east and 36 feet at the opposite end. At least six partly burnt bodies were found in a trench which abutted a sandstone monolith within the cairn. To the west of this stone many unburnt bones of adults and children were found, but no pottery or other artefacts. Cremation long-barrows are known from east Yorkshire where recently radiocarbon dates of 3010±150 B.C. and 2950±150 B.C. have been obtained from timbers in a barrow of this type at Willerby Wold, and may give some indication of date. Canon Greenwell also excavated two large barrows on Crosby Garrett Fell in which grave-goods and methods of interment again have similarities with the Neolithic round-barrows of East Yorkshire. Possible long-barrows north of Hackthorpe and at Mossthorn, Newton Reigny, west of Penrith, have not been scientifically excavated, but a finely made beaker, now in the Carlisle Museum, probably came from one of the latter. In west Cumberland, Sampson's Bratful, a long cairn on Stockdale Moor, should belong to this period, as should a long mound recently excavated at Skelmore Heads, north of Urswick in Furness, which had been previously disturbed and skeletons and pottery removed from between two upright stones.

Mayburgh, an impressive ritual monument of single-entrance 'henge' type lies west of Eamont Bridge, the encircling bank of water-worn cobbles still rising in places to a height of 15 feet above the central area. A single monolith now stands there, but William Stukeley recorded in the eighteenth century that there were three others near it and, in addition, two pairs of standing stones in the entrance. A broken stone axe was found in the entrance in 1879. Recently a Group VI (Great Langdale) axe was found in the entrance of a 'henge' of this type at Llandegai, Caernarvonshire. Close to Mayburgh is King Arthur's Round Table, a double entrance 'henge' which has been much damaged by road works. Professor Bersu's excavations there in 1939 showed that there had been a cremation burial in the central area but there were no dateable finds. Many such monuments are now thought to have been built in later Neolithic times.

Towards the end of the Neolithic period new settlers, known to archaeologists as the Beaker people, reached Britain from the North European Plain and the Low Countries in the centuries around 2000 B.C., while a few early arrivals may have come direct from Iberia, or Maritime France. Single, as opposed to collective, burial and a new range of equipment distinguishes these people from the indigenous late Neolithic elements in this country, their culture remaining in use until at least 1500 B.C., overlapping with, and largely contributing to, the Food-Vessel culture of the Early Bronze Age. Finds suggest that some Beaker people spread across the Pennines from Yorkshire and Northumberland into the Eden valley early in the second millennium B.C., while others, who decorated their pottery with parallel rows of twisted cord, settled in the coastal area. The corded pottery has been found at the sandhills settlement at North End, Walney Island; in a barrow on Sizergh Fell, Levens and in a partly excavated cairn at Mecklin Park, Santon Bridge in west Cumberland. Burials in the Eden valley are associated with pottery in the northern devolved insular style, decorated before firing with a rectangular-toothed comb stamp, or with incised lines. At Clifton two sandstone cists were found in a ploughed-down barrow east of the river Lowther; one contained the crouched skeleton of a woman, a beaker, and a bone pin and the other a much decayed skeleton and two beakers. Nearby at Moorhouse Farm, Brougham, a similar sandstone cist was ploughed up and found to contain a crouched skeleton and two pottery vessels, one a late type of beaker, the other, now lost, is said to have been a food-vessel. Farther up the Eden sherds of Beaker pottery are recorded from cairns at Crosby Garrett and Crosby Fell (probably Crosby Ravensworth Fell).

The Beaker people here seem to have been herdsmen and hunters and, indeed, the scarcity of grain storage pits in the Highland Zone of Britain in Neolithic and Beaker times suggests that the oceanic conditions there limited the extent to which cereals could be grown and obviated the necessity to store. Grain impressions have not so far been identified on any

Beaker pottery here, though such are common in East Anglia. No finds of the period have come from the central hills and no metal objects have been found in any Beaker graves here; nor is there any certain evidence that these people prospected for copper and gold ores in the Lake District. A few surface finds of simple, perforated stone battle-axes, contemporary with late Beaker pottery, have been recorded from Dunmallet, near Pooley Bridge; Stanger End, Embleton; Row Farm, Waberthwaite and Vickerstown, Walney Island, a distribution consistent with other finds of Beaker equipment and burials.

Finely made tanged and barbed flint arrowheads of ogival form, associated elsewhere with Beaker burials of late date, have been found at the sandhills sites at Walney, Eskmeals and Drigg and two long barbed arrowheads have been recorded from Great Langdale itself. Contemporary with these are jet buttons with V-perforations which occur at several sites in the Lake Counties, but only at Moor Divock, Askham, Westmorland, within the area considered in this book.

It is possible that some of the great stone circles can be attributed to the Beaker people. At Shap, a double stone avenue ended in a small circle of free-standing stones, now partially destroyed by the mainline railway. At Castlerigg, near Keswick, is the most spectacularly sited stone circle in the Lake District, which also has the unusual feature of a rectangular setting of stones within the circle on its eastern side. In plan it resembles a degenerate passage-grave and it may be that some of the stone circles here are derived from the passage-graves of the Boyne culture of Ireland. Rock-engravings, often described as cup-and-ring marks, also link the Lake District with Ireland and have been found on cap-stones of cists, on stones encircling cairns, and on monoliths, including Long Meg at the circle of that name near Little Salkeld, east of the river Eden. Another well preserved circle at Swinside, a mile and three-quarters west of Duddon Bridge, yielded no trace of burials, or other finds when excavations were carried out there in 1901. These monuments appear to have been of social and ceremonial significance, but the many theories about the beliefs of the time, and the astronomical purpose and mathematical construction of the stone circles, are hard to prove.

The gradual replacement of stone by bronze implements began in northern England about the seventeenth century B.C., where the chief culture of the Early Bronze Age is called the Food-Vessel culture. No settlements of the period have yet been found with the exception of surface finds at Trough Head, Walney Island and the probable exception of the sandhills sites already mentioned at Drigg, Eskmeals and North End, Walney. However, it is known that some cereals were cultivated. Impressions of grains of hulled barley were identified on a food-vessel of Yorkshire type, found at Plumpton, near Penrith. It is assumed that digging sticks, mattocks, hoes, or ards (a form of crook plough) were used to break up the ground at this time before the development of a more advanced traction plough. The culture is mainly known from burials in the lower Eden valley, outside the scope of this study, which point to a closer connection with the counties east of the Pennines than with Ireland. Inhumation was in general use, but cremation also occurs. A small stone circle known as Standing Stones, Moor Divock, in the limestone uplands near Askham, Westmorland, was excavated by Canon Greenwell more than a hundred years ago. In the centre was a shallow pit containing a cremation and a food-vessel of Yorkshire type, richly decorated with impressions of twisted cord arranged in a herring-bone pattern. A burial cairn at Mecklin Park, Santon Bridge yielded food-vessel sherds, tanged and barbed flint arrowheads, a flint knife, a necklace of jet beads and a circular stone bearing a rudely incised human face. Nearby, at Ravenglass, a small food-vessel with thumb-nail decoration has some affinity with the Sandhills wares of Northern Ireland, while further down the coast at Roose, near Barrow-in-Furness, a small ridged cup found in a barrow again resembles Irish pottery styles.

It is uncertain when the polished stone axe went out of use, though none have been found here in burials or at settlements of purely Bronze Age date. Perforated stone battle-axes and adzes and, later, the larger, clumsier stone axe-hammers, were among the equipment of the period. The Lake District seems to have been chiefly supplied with metal tools from the flourishing bronze industry of Ireland in the Early Bronze Age and there is no evidence that metal working was carried out locally at this time. Among the bronze tools are flat and hammer-flanged axes, cast in open stone moulds, found at Castle Sowerby, Skelton and Greystoke near Penrith and at Gleaston and Roose in Furness; halberd blades are recorded from Maryport and Haberwain Rigg, near Crosby Ravensworth and a bronze awl accompanied an inhumation burial in a barrow on Birkrigg, near Ulverston. This distribution suggests that there was continued occupation of the Neolithic settlement areas and little penetration into the hills. Trade came by sea from Ireland and then by coastal movement southward to Furness and the head of Morecambe Bay, and also inland up the Eden valley to cross the Pennines by routes over the limestone hills which were already familiar to the makers of stone axes and to the Beaker people.

Until recent years cremation burials contained in Collared and Encrusted Urns, Enlarged Food-Vessels, or associated with 'pygmy' cups, were firmly attributed to the Middle Bronze Age. Fresh study of accompanying grave goods has shown that these forms had developed before 1400 B.C., the approximate date at which this phase started. Some archaeologists would assign all such pottery to the Early period, but the wider distribution of cremation burials associated with these vessels corresponds with the enlarged area of settlement indicated here by the distribution of

Middle Bronze Age metalwork (see Fig. 16, p. 207). Settlements are not yet known and without their discovery and excavation a very imperfect picture exists of the economy and life of the period. In southern Britain the circular timber-framed house had become predominant by this time. When one considers how quickly the charcoal burner's huts and 'pit-steads' of medieval to modern times have been hidden by undergrowth, it is small wonder that the flimsier wooden huts of the earlier prehistoric period are so difficult to detect. Indeed, later agricultural activity may have destroyed them altogether and the waller found ready to hand material in the numerous cairns and later stone-hutted enclosures. A few caves in the limestone area of Cartmel and Furness, such as Kirkhead, Allithwaite and Capeshead, Holker, are known to have been occupied during the Bronze Age – Kirkhead is a particularly impressive, high vaulted, commodious cavern.

Grain impressions of naked barley have been found on an early Collared Urn from Papcastle, confirming the continuity of some cereal cultivation. On present dating this urn should have been deposited by the fifteenth century B.C. Grain rubbers and saddle querns from Eskmeals, Stone Close, Stainton in Furness and other sites, may also belong to this time, though this type of quern continued in use until the rotary 'beehive' form was introduced late in the Pre-Roman Iron Age. Concentrations of cairns point to the areas favoured for settlement and sometimes indicate field clearance, rather than burial places. These are particularly abundant around Caldbeck and Hesket Newmarket; in Ennerdale Forest and on Stockdale Moor between 750 and 1,000 feet and on the lower hills east of the river Calder in the parish of Ponsonby. Two collared urns have survived from Lord Muncaster's diggings in cairns at Barnscar, on Birkby Fell, west of Devoke Water and Dr Donald Walker's work has shown that a woodland flora, with increased grasses, but few weeds of cultivation, existed there at the time when some of the cairns were built. Further cairnfields are at Waberthwaite, Bootle Fell and Thwaites Fell between 500 and 1,000 feet, while east of the Duddon many cairns can be seen below Heathwaite settlement, Woodland. Some of these pre-date that farmstead, which does not closely resemble other prehistoric settlements in this district. On Bleaberry Haws and Banniside Moor below Coniston Old Man, further cairns and circles confirm a movement into the higher hills, probably during a drier phase of the Sub-Boreal period. In Westmorland the best known groups of cairns and burial circles are in the limestone uplands at Moor Divock, Askham, also around Shap, Crosby Ravensworth and Crosby Garrett to the west of the Lyvennet and the Eden. The present barren nature of the ground has preserved these traces of prehistoric activity from later agricultural development.

Many burial cairns in the hills have been dug into without record, but a few reports exist which show a variety of monuments and a diversity of burial practices. At Hawkshead Hall Park a fine plano-convex flint knife was found with a cremation in a cairn which had larger stones near its circumference. It would be interesting to know what ceremonies attended the building of a cairn on the top of Boat How in Ennerdale Forest at a height of 1,337 feet, or on Lank Rigg in the same area above 1,600 feet. What beliefs impelled men to build barrows near the summits of Great and Little Mell Fell, Watermillock at this time? Some stone circles surround burial cairns and an especially impressive group is on Brat's Hill, south-west of Burnmoor Tarn above Eskdale. The largest circle here surrounds five cairns, which, when opened last century, were found to contain stone cists in which cremations, antlers of deer and bones of other animals had been placed. At Leacet Wood, Brougham, five collared urns and two other pottery vessels were found buried at the foot of the stones encircling a small cairn, and a similar arrangement was found at one of the circles at Lacra, near Millom. The 'Druid's Circle' on Birkrigg, south of Ulverston, contained a number of cremations, one of which had been placed in a collared urn of early form, while at Aughertree, Ireby, twelve collared urns were found ranged in a circle within the cairn. Occasionally urns of this kind are found with no trace of a covering mound, as at Ireleth Mill and Stainton in Furness, where a small bronze razor was found with the cremated bones. Yet another form of cremation cemetery is encircled with a bank of earth and stones, as, for instance, on Banniside Moor, Coniston, where W. G. Collingwood carried out excavations in 1909. It stands at a height of 810 feet, a bank ten feet wide enclosing an area 48 feet in diameter. Two urns and sherds of another vessel, two cremations without pottery, a clay bead, a flint scraper and flakes, were found in the central area. Of special interest was a fragment of woollen cloth found in one of the urns, woven with about thirty-three threads to an inch. This may have come from a cloth containing the cremated bones, or from the clothes of the dead person. Although no clothing of this period has survived in Britain, we know from the Danish oak-tree coffin burials that a wide range of men's and women's summer and winter wear existed by this time and that spinning and weaving were skilfully carried out. Radiocarbon dates from similar stone-ring cemeteries on Whitestanes Moor, Dumfriesshire, are given as 1360 ± 90 B.C. and 1490 ± 90 B.C., while, by present reckoning, monuments of this kind range from the sixteenth to the eleventh century B.C.

Bronze tools and weapons of the Middle Bronze Age are widely distributed in the Lake Counties, though not numerous (Fig. 16, p. 207), and suggest continuing contact with the bronze industry of Ireland and with that of north-eastern and southern England. Increased skill in casting brought a wider range of more efficient tools and weapons. New forms of flanged axes and a few palstaves replace the earlier types of axe and occur at such places as Santon Bridge; Stainton in Furness; Wraysholme Tower, Allithwaite; Crook; Ambleside and Penrith. Spear-heads with kite-shaped blades from Blindbothel, north of Loweswater and Whinfell Tarn, north-east of Kendal, are likely products of the Irish industry, while others with leaf-shaped blades and varying forms of attachment loops, from places such as Dalton in Furness, Ambleside, Keswick and Penrith, were probably cast in England, the type continuing in use into the Late Bronze Age. An engraved dagger from Helsington Moss, near Levens, compares closely with Irish weapons; and rapiers, longer, thrusting weapons, have been found at Page Bank, Rampside in Furness and St John's Vale, Keswick. Hoards of metalwork are rare, emphasising the value and comparative scarcity of bronze tools in this district, but a stone mould for casting looped and socketed spearheads, found at Croglin east of the river Eden, suggests that metalsmiths were working locally by this time. This is confirmed by the contents of an interesting hoard from Ambleside, found in the eighteenth century and now lost, which included two rapiers with cast bronze hilts of a type chiefly recorded in this country from Cumbria, but allied to weapons of north European origin, dating from the eleventh century B.C.

In the Lake District even less is known about settlements and burials of the Late Bronze Age, after 900 B.C. How long collared urns continued in use, or whether a mode of burial without pottery urns was adopted, has still to be discovered. Pottery styles current in southern England at this time were not in use here, and 'flat-rimmed' ware found in north-east England and south-east Scotland from about the seventh century B.C. has not been recorded here. The type of settlement and system of agriculture can only be inferred by comparison with other parts of Britain, where circular huts of timber construction, usually with a ring of posts to support the roof, have been excavated and it is thought that a light form of traction plough was in use by this time. Of special interest is a burial found in the limestone quarry at Butts Beck, Dalton in Furness, where a leaf-shaped bronze sword and spear-head were found associated with an inhumation. These probably date from the seventh or sixth century B.C. and show a contrast in burial rite with earlier Bronze Age practice. This may reflect contact with early Pre-Roman Iron Age burial customs, seen, for instance, in a seventh-century inhumation burial at Ebberston, Yorkshire, where a bronze sword and chape of Hallstatt type were found with a skeleton.

The new tools and weapons of the Late Bronze Age have also been found in the Lake District and date from the end of the tenth century B.C. to an uncertain date in the last half of the first millennium B.C. Styles point to continued contact with Ireland, particularly in the Cumberland coastal area where the socketed bronze axe has not so far been found. There is also some evidence that the intentional addition of lead to bronzes from the tenth century B.C. in southern England was not commonly

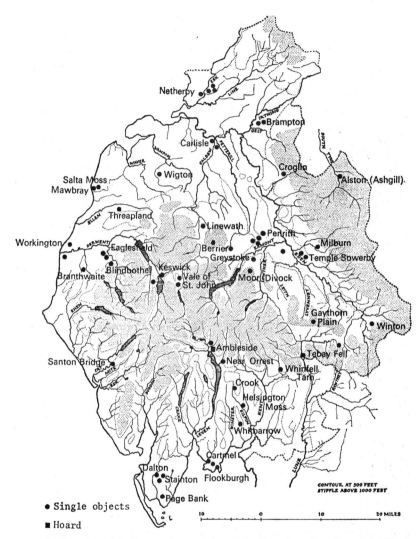

Netherby

●●Brampton

Carlisle

Wigton

Croglin

Alston (Ashgill)

Salta Moss
Mawbray

Threapland

Linewath

Workington

Eaglesfield

Berrier

Penrith

Milburn

Greystoke

Temple Sowerby

Branthwaite

Blindbothel

Keswick

Vale of
St. John

Moor Divock

Gaythorn
Plain

Winton

Santon Bridge

Ambleside

Near Orrest

Tebay Fell

Whinfell
Tarn

Crook

Helsington
Moss

Whitbarrow

Cartmel

Dalton

Stainton

Flookburgh

Page Bank

CONTOUR AT 500 FEET
STIPPLE ABOVE 1000 FEET

● Single objects

■ Hoard

10 ⊢⊢⊢⊢⊢ 0 ⊢⊢⊢⊢⊢ 10 ⊢⊢⊢⊢⊢ 20 MILES

FIG. 16. Sites of Middle Bronze Age metalwork findings. Based on Clough in CW2.
LXIX (1969).

practised in the north until about the eighth century B.C. Socketed bronze axes, more economical in metal than earlier forms, occur as stray finds in widely scattered areas, such as at Stone Close, Stainton in Furness; Low Fell, Little Langdale; Penrith and Rogersceugh near Shap. At Great Urswick in Furness a hoard of six of these axes was found in a crevice in the limestone south of Skelmore Heads, and a second hoard, now lost, came from Long Rigg Field, Little Urswick and is said to have contained axes, a spear-head and bronze rings. The distribution of finds of leaf-shaped spear-heads confirms most of the earlier settlement patterns, occurring, for example, at Dalton and Piel Castle in Furness; Whitbarrow and Troutbeck, both in Westmorland; and Penrith and Linewath Bridge, Caldbeck in Cumberland. The only leaf-shaped sword known from this area is that already mentioned from Butts Beck, Dalton.

Numerous stray finds of heavy, perforated stone axe-hammers are recorded but are difficult to date closely. They are particularly common in Furness and south-west Cumberland and occur not only in the areas of primary settlement but also on more acid soils, for instance up the Rusland valley and along the river Leven in Furness where no Neolithic polished stone axes have been found. Some of these are made of Coniston Grit which crops out in southern Lakeland (see geological map) and the proximity of rocks of this kind to the copper ores of Coniston makes one wonder whether these rich veins were discovered and worked by the end of the Bronze Age.

Climatic deterioration in the centuries around 800–500 B.C., bringing increased rainfall, is likely to have made this north-western region less attractive to new settlers, particularly for communities with a system of agriculture based more on cereal cultivation than on animal husbandry. Evidence of some forest regeneration in west Cumberland may reflect a reduction in population at this time (see Chapter 13), and we have already seen that no socketed bronze axes have been found there. New bronze and iron tools and weapons then appearing in southern and eastern England represent fresh contacts between continental Celtic peoples and Britain and their gradual assimilation by the indigenous Late Bronze Age population. These fresh influences begin to appear as early as the sixth, or even the seventh century B.C. and settlements as far north as Yorkshire have been identified, such as at Castle Hill, Scarborough, and Staple Howe, Knapton. A radiocarbon date in the fifth century B.C. has been obtained for one stage of the occupation at Staple Howe. Farther north, at Huckhoe in Northumberland, the palisade phase of the settlement has been dated to the sixth century. The culture represented at the Yorkshire sites is the Iron Age A of Hawkes's scheme for Britain and combines native Late Bronze Age with continental late Hallstatt (Iron Age) elements. It is uncertain when Celtic people penetrated into the north-west, for none of the early style pottery, iron, or bronze types have

PLATE 23   *Above*, Red Squirrel (*Sciurus vulgaris*), found in many Lake District woods.   *Below*, Spring in the Lake District: Dalesbred sheep and lambs and wild daffodils.

PLATE 24 *Above*, Haweswater from Bampton Common with Naddle Forest (*left*), an extensive area of semi-natural oak-ash woodland. The age and purpose of the prehistoric standing stones in the foreground are uncertain. *Below*, Castlerigg stone circle: a ceremonial stone circle on a ridge above Keswick.

been recorded except for a late Hallstatt bronze bracelet, supposed to have been found in Furness and now in Lancaster Museum. Lack of modern excavation and field work may account for the apparent absence of the first phase of the Pre-Roman Iron Age in the Lake District, which Professor C. F. C. Hawkes includes as the Cumbria region of his Pennine Province. Excavations at Skelmore Heads, near Urswick, suggest that the hill top was originally surrounded by a palisade and later defended by a rock-cut ditch on its north side. No closely dateable objects were found, but the structure has been compared with Huckhoe and could have an initial date as early as the sixth, or fifth century B.C.

Certainly many settlements marked on the Ordnance Maps as 'British Settlement' could have originated at this time, or even overlie earlier Bronze Age homesteads. In Northumberland Mr G. Jobey's work has shown that there the earlier Pre-Roman Iron Age huts were usually of timber, either with a ring of post-holes to carry roof supports, or with walls set in ring-grooves, the circular house plan continuing in use throughout the period; while the stone-walled hut circles and enclosures are often contemporary with the Roman Occupation, or continuing in use into the Dark Ages. Stone walled settlements containing one, or more, circular huts, are particularly abundant on the eastern fringe of the Lake District in the limestone hills at the head of the rivers Leith and Lyvennet, near Crosby Ravensworth, Crosby Garrett and Asby and are usually connected with small, rectangular fields of a kind known as 'Celtic' fields. Such settlements also occur in almost every valley running into the central hills of the Lake District (see Chapter 12). Among the dozen or so homesteads near Crosby Ravensworth, only Ewe Close has been partially excavated and fragments of rotary querns, Romano-British pottery, chiefly of second and third century date, and a little medieval pottery were found there. The existence of this settlement in pre-Roman times is inferred from the abrupt turn taken by the Roman road as it passes close by on its way north from the fort at Low Borrow Bridge in the Lune gorge, to Brougham, near Penrith. The absence of a Roman military post between these two forts has also been seen as an indication that the tribe living in the area may have remained friendly to Rome and continued to support the alliance, when Venutius, in opposition to his queen, Cartimandua, led the Brigantes in revolt in A.D. 69.

Air photography north of the central hills and south of the Solway has revealed a number of ditch-enclosed settlements. Among them is an oval, palisaded enclosure at Wolsty Hall, Silloth, sited on the gravels of the twenty-five foot beach, in which a circular wooden hut had four centrally placed roof supports, a style of building known at the Iron Age A farm at Little Woodbury, Wiltshire. A broken saddle quern had been used as a packing stone for the palisade and Hadrianic pottery occurred high in the silt of the ditch, suggesting an initial occupation before the Romans came.

In Furness, a walled oval enclosure called Urswick Stone Walls yielded an engraved piece of sheet bronze, thought to date from the second century B.C., and fragments of early types of rotary querns, similar to those found at Stone Close, Stainton, nearby. Part of a 'beehive' type rotary quern was found at the homestead at Threlkeld and points to settlement there by the first century. However, without detailed classification and excavation, knowledge of the farms of the final stage of the prehistoric sequence must remain obscure. Fine, wheel-made pottery was first made in this country by the Belgae, the last settlers in south-east Britain before the Roman conquest, but there is little evidence that their culture, Iron Age C, reached the north-west in any strength. A bronze cauldron of Santon type from Bewcastle is among the few indications of this contact.

Lakeland hill-forts are few in number and small in size and none have been excavated in recent years. On present reckoning those with multiple ramparts and ditches are later than those with single defences. The most impressive fort in this area is the five acre walled encampment on the summit of Carrock Fell, occupying a commanding position on the eastern edge of the Caldbeck Fells at a height of 2174 feet above sea level. No traces of huts are visible, but these are likely to have been circular, wooden buildings, their foundations hidden by heather and moorland grasses. The fort bears some resemblance to Garn Boduan and Tre'r Ceiri in Caernarvonshire, though there the huts had stone foundations. Professor R. G. Collingwood imagined that the defences had been slighted by the Romans late in the first century A.D. Numerous cairns on the lower slopes north of Carrock Fell may be contemporary with the fort and represent field clearance, or burials, but earlier settlement had existed along the river Caldew since Neolithic times. A multivallate fort on Warton Crag at the head of Morecambe Bay is also of Pre-Roman Iron Age type and a first-century bronze sword pommel of Brigantian style has been found nearby. Other probable forts of this period are Castlehead, or 'Atterpile', near Grange-over-Sands; Castlesteads, Natland; Castle Crag in Mardale and in the Cumberland Borrowdale, and the fort up Shoulthwaite Gill above Thirlmere. Castle Crag, Mardale, lies south-west of Haweswater at 1,250 feet and excavations there in 1922 showed evidence of circular floors inside the main rampart, and possible traces of others between two rock-cut ditches on the south side. No pottery or other objects were found and the work was done before excavators were trained to look out for post holes and other traces of timber houses.

Only one burial claims attention. Three crouched skeletons, one with a bronze, penannular bracelet on the right arm, were found in 1873 in a railway cutting near Crosby Garrett station. No barrow or cairn covered them. The bracelet can undoubtedly be compared with those found at the Pre-Roman Iron Age cemeteries at Arras, near Market Weighton, and Dane's Graves, Driffield, in East Yorkshire. The Yorkshire cemeteries have yielded personal ornaments and equipment belonging to Iron Age B of Hawkes's terminology, probably representing commercial La Tène contact with France, the fine metalwork being copied and adapted by the people already living here. The resulting mixed culture certainly spread across the Pennines into the Eden valley by the second, or first century B.C., if not earlier. The new settlers may have lived in some of the homesteads around Crosby Garrett, Waitby and Asby, bringing with them horses, carts and their trappings, which are among the possessions known from the East Yorkshire graves. It may even be permissible to envisage this intrusion as an offshoot from the tribe living in the Yorkshire wolds, later known as the Parisi, which itself became known in Roman times, as the Carvetii (see p. 212).

Excavation at settlements and fortified sites in the north suggests that herding of cattle, sheep and pigs, with the addition of pony breeding, was the main basis of the economy at this time and pollen analysis has shown little important increase of cereal cultivation before the second to fifth centuries A.D. It is uncertain whether the rich haematite ores of Furness, west Cumberland and other parts of the Lake District were worked by then, though two 'stone hatchets and a curious iron tool' were found last century in 'old men's workings' at Stainton in Furness. A few grooved stone wedges and mauls from the area could have survived from prehistoric mining activity. A small number of finds of fine bronze metalwork are recorded, including a pair of bronze, spoon-shaped objects of uncertain use, found near a spring to the east of Crosby Ravensworth. The style of engraving on their handles suggests a date of manufacture in the first century B.C. and it is possible that a sanctuary existed near the spring, for Celtic cults were often associated with wells, springs and rivers. Of similar date is a fine pair of bronze bracelets with 'buffer' ends, picked up on the west of Thirlmere, while a bronze bridle bit, with traces of red enamel decoration, came from the screes on the steep slopes of Place Fell, above Ullswater. This bit is late in the La Tène series and it is attractive to picture its owner riding his pony homeward in the safety of the hills, possibly to the settlement in Bannerdale, at about the time the Romans were thrusting northward to Carlisle. This piece, and the iron sword with engraved and enamelled bronze scabbard from Wythop Mill, Embleton, have affinities with the horse trappings and military equipment of the Brigantes, best known from the hoard of metalwork found near the great fortifications of Stanwick, near Darlington. They represent the accoutrements in use in the north when first Petillius Cerialis in A.D. 71 and, later, Agricola at the end of that decade, crushed the revolt of the Brigantes and marched forward into Scotland.

CHAPTER 12

THE ROMAN OCCUPATION

*For centuries, the Lakes have been a peaceful country: their modern glory,
the Lake Poets, were above all things the poets of peace and quietude. In
Roman times the region was a tangled chaos of hills in which wild
hill-men defied Rome and Roman ways. Rome could not leave them alone.*
Professor F. J. Haverfield, writing in 1913.
Trans C. W. A. A. Soc. (New Series) XIV (1914): 433

WITH the coming of the Romans, the light of history falls fitfully on
Britain and its inhabitants for the first time, while archaeological dis-
coveries include inscriptions which supplement the accounts of classical
historians and geographers. As with prehistory, so with the Roman
period, new excavations and fresh interpretation constantly change the
state of knowledge and we still have only a very imperfect picture of the
military occupation of the north, the civilian reaction thereto, or the
economic and political organisation of the time. It is known that Brigantia
was a client kingdom by A.D. 47 at the latest, her rulers submitting to
Roman power, giving tribute, troops and supplies in exchange for support
against external attack. Tacitus says that this was the most populous state
in Britain, while Ptolemy, writing in the second century, describes the
territory as being 'below the Selgovae and the Otadini, extending to both
seas'. The Lake District formed part of this territory and as shown in the
last chapter similarities of economy and equipment existed between the
Celtic peoples living east and west of the Pennines in the years immediately
before the Roman occupation. This occupation was predominantly
military in the north beginning after the suppression of the open revolt of
the Brigantes, led by their king Venutius, in A.D. 69. Later, when Britain
was divided into two provinces under Septimus Severus (A.D. 193–211)
the north fell within *Britannia Inferior* governed from York. So far as is
known at present, hostility between the Roman army and the local tribes
continued here well into the third century when there is some evidence
that local administration was carried out at civil settlements, or *vici*,
outside some of the forts, while *civitas* status, i.e. self-government of a
community not entitled to be full citizens of Rome, was granted to a sub-
tribe of the Brigantes living in the Eden valley called the Carvetii,
meaning 'The Stag People'. This, as already suggested on page 211, may
well have been a pre-Roman Celtic tribe whose domain became a *pagus*,
or canton, of Brigantia under Rome. In the later part of the occupation
the army and civilian population alike were confronted by a common

enemy from beyond the Wall and from across the sea, thus increasing comradely feeling.

The area covered by this book does not extend so far north as the great frontier work of Hadrian's Wall, which, by drawing an arbitrary line along the best route from the point of view of defence, may well have cut across tribal boundaries, particularly at its western end. Leading up to this frontier a network of roads and garrison forts was established, traces of which today bear witness to this episode of history. It is likely that Roman troops first came over Stainmore from their base at the Legionary Fortress at York during the years A.D. 71 to 74, when Petillius Cerialis crushed the revolt of the Brigantes.

Marching camps at Crackenthorpe, north-west of Appleby, and Plumpton Head, north of Penrith, may well relate to this campaign, when it is possible that a fort was also established at Carlisle. The road linking these places was either constructed then, or under Agricola a few years later when the route west of the Pennines was established. This main Roman road north from Chester on the west of the Pennines enters Westmorland up the Lune, keeping on the east side of the river until it crosses it to enter the fort at Low Borrow Bridge, near Tebay. Thence it continues northward over Crosby Ravensworth Fell, skirting the native settlement known as Ewe Close, near which sections cut across its line showed it to be twenty feet wide with the metalling bounded by stone kerbs. From Ewe Close the road makes for the crossing of the Eamont at Brougham, where, later, the fort of *Brocavum* was established, and onward to Old Penrith (*Voreda*) and to Carlisle, both possibly first built during Agricola's campaign. North of the Lake District hills roads linked Carlisle with Maryport (*Alauna*), from which port Agricola may have launched his attack on south-west Scotland, and later with Moresby (*Itunocelum*). Along this route forts at Old Carlisle, Caermote, north of Bassenthwaite and Papcastle, near Cockermouth, were possibly established in the first century. R. L. Bellhouse has also produced evidence for a direct road linking Old Carlisle with Maryport. Other roads branched off from Old Penrith and from Papcastle converging in the Keswick area, the only Roman fortifications known in this direction are three temporary camps at Troutbeck, Cumberland, shown up recently in air photographs by Dr St Joseph but first mentioned in West's *Guide to the Lakes* (1778). Evidence for another possible road from Old Penrith to Old Carlisle via Broadfield has been cited by Professor Eric Birley.

In southern Lakeland the roads and forts once thought to have been built by Agricola are not now believed to have been established before A.D. 90 at the earliest, the forts serving as a protection to the main supply road north up the Lune and as a means of controlling the recalcitrant hill men. Roads linking Watercrook (*Alione*) near Kendal with Burrow-in-Lonsdale, Low Borrow Bridge and Ambleside, have yet to be fully traced, but the spectacular road over High Street, between the forts of Ambleside and Brougham, which may have followed the line of an earlier track, has been sectioned north of Load Pot Hill and accepted as being of Roman construction. Westward from Ambleside Sir Ian Richmond traced in detail the route over Wrynose and Hardknott passes, its width of twenty feet emphasising its importance as a supply road. Indeed, it has been identified as the northern part of the Xth Iter of the Antonine Itinerary from Ravenglass, via Ambleside and Watercrook, to the south. The road link northward from Ravenglass (*Glannaventa*) seems to have been with Papcastle rather than with Moresby, skirting the hills of Ennerdale Forest and Loweswater Fells and cutting them off from the low ground of the Solway Plain, an area best suited for growing corn, so essential for the diet of the Roman army. No evidence has yet been found for a road running south from Ravenglass down the Cumberland coast towards Furness. The absence of forts and signal stations in Furness and Cartmel suggests that those areas were not occupied by the army and it is possible that the tribes there remained friendly to Rome, or that the area was sufficiently far away from the supply roads to need any garrisoning. That some degree of trade existed between the native population and the Romans is suggested by chance finds of Roman coins at such places as Ulverston, Urswick, Furness Abbey and Grange-over-Sands; and also by a hoard of six hundred coins, the latest minted in A.D. 250, found in a pot in Park Wood, Cartmel, about 1800. It is unlikely that all such finds could have strayed from later collections. Whether or not the oversands route to Lancaster was in use then cannot be known, but it has always beckoned adventurous wayfarers. Thus it can be seen that the central hills were ruthlessly enmeshed with a system of roads along which troops might swiftly move to crush any revolt and which effectively divided the main areas of settlement, making mass attacks on the forts more difficult. These roads were also essential for police duties and military administration (Fig. 17, p. 215).

The auxiliary forts themselves remain as testimony to their builders and all show the skill with which the military command selected their sites. An abundant water supply for both men and horses was essential, for some of the forts were garrisoned by infantry (*cohors*), others by cavalry (*ala*), or by a combination of the two (*cohors equitata*), and were designed to house five hundred men, or, in certain instances, a larger unit a thousand strong. Few Lake District forts have been thoroughly excavated and only an intermittent account of their history is yet known. Watercrook, lying in a loop of the Kent south of Kendal, used the river as a protection and controlled the ford across it. The site now shows up as a low platform, the ramparts and ditches being much reduced by ploughing and by stone robbing. Small scale excavations proved the existence of an early timber fort replaced by one of stone in the second

FIG. 17. Map of Roman forts and marching camps, Ewe Close and other native sites.

century, with a bath-house and unwalled civil settlement outside the fortifications. Buildings described in some detail by the Rev. Thomas Machell in 1692 are no longer visible, while the site of a tile or pottery kiln across the river to the south-west, is now hard to identifiy. Finds suggest that the fort was garrisoned from the late first, until the late fourth century. A similar length of occupation is indicated by finds from Low Borrow Bridge, now dwarfed by the vast roadworks connected with the M6, where formerly the Roman fort commanded the Lune gorge.

Borrans Field (*Galava*), at Ambleside, shows yet another position selected for a fort. No doubt the proximity to the lake shore and the protection afforded on the west by the junction of the rivers Rothay and Brathay were important factors in determining its position, while the rocky knoll to the north and the alluvial deposits on which it is sited provided the best drained position available. Extensive excavations here by Professor R. G. Collingwood between 1913 and 1920, showed that a timber-built fort had been replaced in the second century by a larger fort, built on an artificial gravel platform to raise the site higher above flood-level and overlying two-thirds of the earlier fort. This new fort had double ditches and clay rampart surmounted by a stone wall four feet thick, with four angle towers and with the main gate on the east side. The head-quarters building, commandant's house and granaries were also of stone, while the barrack blocks of timber probably followed the conventional layout of forts of the time but their outlines had been destroyed by later ploughing. The excavator saw evidence that some of these barrack buildings were destroyed by fire, possibly during attacks by local tribes-men. Indeed, a tombstone recently found outside the fort tells that Julius Romanus, record clerk, was killed in the fort by the enemy. Despite early local hostility a civil settlement grew up on the eastern side of the fort, leather working and other industrial activities being carried out there. Pottery finds suggest that the fort at Ambleside was manned until the final withdrawal of troops from the Wall in the decades following A.D. 383, when Magnus Maximus led part of the army of Britain to the Continent in his revolt against the Emperor Gratian.

We have already seen that a road continued westward along the Brathay leading ultimately to Ravenglass, with an intermediate fort built at Hardknott. Its wonderful position looking along Eskdale to Ravenglass and across the Irish Sea to the Isle of Man has often been emphasised and a fragmentary inscription led antiquaries to think that this fort had formed a link in the chain for an attack on Ireland planned by Agricola. However, it now appears that Hardknott was founded in Hadrian's reign, for a building inscription speaks of construction by the IVth Cohort of Dalmatians at a date between A.D. 117 and 138, and that the fort did not carry a regular garrison after the end of the second century. The bulk of the stone for the walls and principal buildings was won nearby, but the masonry of the gates was of red sandstone brought from the Gosforth district eleven miles away. Here, if anywhere, one is forced to admire the organisation which, nearly nineteen hundred years ago, could supply its troops with equipment, grain and all the necessities of life, which built them barracks and bath-houses and drilled them on a parade ground levelled out of the hillside above the fort, keeping them alert and ready to defend it and the road against an attack by hill tribesmen.

Of the supply port and fort at Ravenglass little is known; but Ravenglass, Lancaster on the Lune and Maryport at the mouth of the river Ellen would have provided good harbours at which the Roman fleet could help to supply the extended lines of communication. Ravenglass fort is much damaged by the railway on its western side and, more recently, by dense conifer plantations, but part of the bath-house outside the defences still stands to a height of twelve feet and has become known as Walls Castle. Here we can see the skilled Roman mason's work, which makes a striking contrast with the stone and timber hut construction in use at the native homesteads. There is no certain evidence when this fort was first built, but it is likely to be contemporary with Hardknott and Ambleside, continuing in use to the end of the fourth century. By this time a considerable civil settlement had grown up on its northern side, while tile and brick kilns at Muncaster show that building necessaries were manufactured locally where suitable clay was available. It is not thought that Ravenglass formed part of the Hadrianic fortifications guarding the south shore of the Solway, for this line of defence is now considered to have ended at the fort at Moresby, near Whitehaven, or at St Bees Head. As additional proof of this the fort at Ravenglass faces inland and not seaward as do the coastal defence forts farther north.

Only the extreme south-western end of the Hadrianic frontier defences of the Cumberland coast lies within the area covered by this book and includes the auxiliary forts at Maryport, Burrow Walls near Workington and Moresby, north of Whitehaven, together with the regularly spaced system of milefortlets and towers, extending from Bowness-on-Solway as far south as St Bees Head. All three forts face the Irish Sea, from which direction the main danger was expected. It is possible that an early fort existed on the high ground north of the river Ellen at Maryport before the construction of the second century frontier works. Its splendid position 170 feet above sea-level, large size – $5\frac{3}{4}$ acres – and relative freedom from later superimposed building, together with a fine series of inscribed and sculptured stones collected by the Senhouse family of Netherhall, give this fort exceptional interest. The red sandstone formation on which it stands provided excellent stone for building and for decorative mason's work. A very extensive civil settlement grew up on its north side in the third and fourth centuries, probably surrounded by a rampart, though this has not been proved by excavation and it is also uncertain when the fort itself ceased to be garrisoned. Burrow Walls (*Gabrosentum*) has comparatively recently been recognised from an air-photograph as a full sized fort and trial excavations there suggest occupation from Hadrianic times to the closing years of the fourth century. It is situated on the fields of Calva Farm north of the river Derwent at Workington and is partly destroyed on the west and north by the branch railway line to Seaton and Camerton. The site is now nearly a mile from the sea, but it stands south of the cliffs, known as Oyster Bank, which marked the limits of the land at the time when the 25-foot raised beach was formed, a line probably later followed by a loop of the river Derwent and now occupied by the Ling Beck. Despite the industrial spread at Lowca, Parton and Whitehaven the fort at Moresby (*Itunocelum*) still shows its strategic strength and intelligent siting as a look-out to the west. It stands just above the 100-foot contour, bounded on the north by a steep fall to the Lowca Beck and the boulder-clay cliffs of Lowca beyond, and on the west by the cliffs above the sea-shore and the rocks of the Coal Measures. When the new church was built at Moresby in 1822 a building inscription was found which showed that the first fort was built here by the XXth Legion under Hadrian in A.D. 128 at the earliest. The fortifications cover an area of 3½ acres and are linked to Carlisle and the Wall by the main road via Papcastle and Old Carlisle. The results of extensive excavations instigated by the Earl of Lonsdale in 1859–60 have never been published.

The pattern of milecastles and turrets for defence and observation established on Hadrian's Wall was continued by a system of milefortlets and towers from Bowness-on-Solway to the fort at Moresby, or even to St Bees Head. These coastal sites are still being investigated, but sufficient is now known to show that two detached signal-towers, at approximately 540 yard intervals, were built between each pair of fortlets. The garrison for such fortlets would have been a maximum of fifty men. The detached signal towers were stone-built, about 20 feet square externally, with walls 3 to 4 feet thick, stone-faced with a rubble core. Insufficient remains to determine the type of superstructure, but they are likely to have been two-storied buildings; the absence of roofing tiles, or slates, from these sites is taken to suggest that they had flat roofs. Iron spearheads found within several, such as at Cote How and Mawbray nearby and in the milefortlet at Cardurnock, shows that this was the principal weapon of the soldiers who patrolled the coastal defences, while pottery evidence points to the continued use of this system to the end of the second century, probable abandonment in the third and re-occupation of some of these strong points in later Roman times, possibly connected with the assaults on the Province of Britain by Picts, Scots and Saxons in A.D. 367–370. The road linking this coastal system is likely to be contemporary with its initial establishment under Hadrian in the years following A.D. 128, and we have already seen that the forts at Maryport and Moresby had direct links through Papcastle with Carlisle and the Wall.

North-west of the Lake District hills Papcastle (*Derventio*) lies on high ground north of the river Derwent, the approach from this side being flanked by buildings of a civil settlement. The fort was at an important road junction, and its continued garrisoning from Flavian times to the end of the fourth century bears witness to its responsibility to keep open the supply roads from Ravenglass, Moresby, Maryport and Carlisle, and to control any assaults from the hills south along the vale of Lorton, or even from the Keswick area, in which direction a possible Roman road strikes south-eastward over the Whinlatter Pass. Caermote, north of the foot of Bassenthwaite, is still virtually unexplored though it would seem that there was an early fort here with turf and timber ramparts, later superseded by a fortlet occupying its north-west corner. Caermote, too, could have served as a protection to the main road from attack from the south, though Sir Ian Richmond suggested that the later fortlet may have controlled lead mining activity in the Caldbeck Fells. Old Carlisle, south of Wigton, with its extensive *vicus*, has produced a considerable number of inscriptions, but it and the walled city of Carlisle are outside the scope of this study.

Old Penrith (*Voreda*) and Brougham complete the circle of forts around the hills. The former stands to the east of the river Petteril on the Penrith Sandstone and not only protected the main road north and south, but also served to control the district westward towards Blencathra and Skiddaw. Old Penrith may first have been established before Hadrianic times, though the present remains of the fort with sandstone masonry at the gateways is likely to be of third century date. Here, too, a considerable civil settlement, probably of *vicus* standing, grew up to the west and east of the fort and contained a number of substantial buildings now robbed of stone, and on the north an air-photograph shows a row of strip-houses at right-angles to the present road (A6). Seven miles south-east the fort at Brougham (*Brocavum*) lies south of the ford across the Eamont and again stands at an important road junction. Traces of civil settlement outside the east and west gates show up in air-photographs. On the east they extend along the road eventually leading to York, via Kirkby Thore and Stainmore, and it is on this side that an extensive cemetery almost half a mile from the fort has recently been excavated. Though its early history is uncertain, both fort and *vicus* were occupied in the second to fourth centuries to which the cemetery also belongs. The non-Roman names of some of the civilians, known from tombstones, suggest that there could have been a native element voluntarily living here in addition to retired soldiers, traders, camp followers and their families.

From surviving inscriptions it is known that the Lake District forts were manned by auxiliary units, both infantry and cavalry, drawn from many parts of the Roman Empire, while the crack troops of the imperial army were based at the legionary fortresses at York and Chester. It is strange to imagine soldiers from Thrace serving at Moresby, near White-haven, or at Burrow Walls, Workington; or to picture Spaniards and Dalmatians facing the western winds at Maryport; or a cohort of Dalma-tians guarding the pass at Hardknott in the second century. Small wonder that some of these men, with little or no hope of returning home, retired to the civil settlements outside the walls of the forts, married and brought up families there. The right of full citizenship accorded to these veteran soldiers made their position honourable in the *vici* and the possi-bility of acquiring land made such retirement not unattractive. Dedica-tions of altars show that, in addition to the worship of the Emperor, the official gods of the army were Jupiter (the guardian deity of the Roman State) and Mars (the god of war and of soldiers). In the north-west the auxiliaries worshipped the Celtic equivalent of Mars under the names of Cocidius and Belatucadrus. Of special interest is a group of seventeen second century altars found buried in pits north-east of the fort at Mary-port in 1870, probably close to the site of the original parade ground before the civil settlement developed in that direction. All except four are dedicated to *Iuppiter Optimus Maximus* and each gives the name of the regiment and its commandant. The other four show dedications to Mars and to Imperial Victory. They bear witness to the annual ceremonies which took place at the beginning of January when the commandant, on behalf of his troops, renewed vows for the welfare and safety of the State and for the Empire and Emperor. During these ceremonial parades the old altars were carefully buried and the new set up. Many other cults were practised and the auxiliary soldiers were permitted to worship the gods of their homeland outside the forts and their ancilliary parade-grounds. Christianity, which became the official religion of the Empire in the early fourth century and was widely sown in Britain fifty years sooner, has left few memorials here. A carved stone from Maryport and a ring from Brough-under-Stainmore, now lost, bore the Chi-ro monogram, and a tombstone from Brougham, dedicated to the memory of Tittus 'who lived thirty-two years or thereabouts', thought to be a Christian formula, are among the few indications that the Lake Counties had received the Christian faith. It is also from the surviving tombstones, with inscriptions in Latin, that we can learn at least the names and ages of some of the men, women and children who lived in the civil settlements and of the officers and soldiers who manned the forts. In this area such memorials are most numerous from Brougham, Old Penrith, Old Carlisle and Maryport.

There is little evidence that the native population adopted the ways of Rome, for the ideal of urban life did not appeal to the Celtic tribes. The religious beliefs current in pagan Celtic Britain have been studied in detail by Dr Anne Ross and it is clear that the bulk of our knowledge in the north-west comes from the Romano-British contexts around the forts and *vici* and not from the homesteads and hill-forts. No sanctuaries, or shrines, have been identified with certainty, but it appears that the cult of the severed head as a symbol of divinity and other-world power, and of the horned god, lived on here; while Romanised versions of the warrior god exist as Cocidius and Belatucadrus. Very little excavation, or classification has yet been done on the homesteads in the Lake District contemporary with the Roman occupation. It is possible that the varied plans which these show reflect tribal differences, or differences in the economy practised. However, as seen in the last chapter, the stone-walled settlements with circular stone-based huts, by analogy with investigations in Northumberland, largely date from this time though circular wooden houses continued to be built. Urswick Stone Walls and Stone Close, Stainton in Furness, both appear to have continued in use in the early centuries of this era. Early types of rotary querns, or hand-mills, found at both sites, point to cultivation of grain as well as stock rearing, while nearby an enclosure at Holme Bank, north of Scales, is another example of a small farm of this time. Settlements in High Furness are less easy to detect, since much of the ground is broken by rocky outcrops and remains uncultivated, the higher ground is covered with bracken, heather and rough grasses, and the lower slopes with the remnants of coppice woods. On the Hawk, above Broughton Mills, an oval enclosure with circular stone-based huts and a possible associated field, was found about ten years ago, sited on the narrow outcrop of Coniston Limestone, and an enclosure on the Torver Beck at the foot of Coniston Old Man, within a hundred yards of that formation, may well be contemporary. Early types of rotary querns are recorded from Satterthwaite and Nibthwaite while in Seathwaite and Dunnerdale cairns and enclosures above Stonestar and cairns on the southern slopes of Caw point to considerable settlement. On the Cumberland side of the Duddon, extensive field systems at Crosbythwaite, associated with at least one circular stone hut, are likely to date from Romano-British times.

To the north-east of Windermere is a settlement at Hugill, with an enclosing wall ten to fourteen feet thick and circular stone huts and irregular divisions, probably cattle pens, within it. Of similar character is a homestead at Millrigg, Kentmere, covering nearly three-quarters of an acre, where, in 1935 one of at least seven circular huts was excavated and a hearth and broken paste bracelet of second century date was found. Further south, on the limestone ridge between the Gilpin and the Kent, a small oval enclosure, now much robbed of stone, can still be seen on Sizergh Fell. It covers about half an acre, has an inturned entrance at the north end and an additional smaller enclosure on the south side, while its wall abutted on a burial cairn. An inhumation burial was found in this cairn, with personal ornaments, including a bronze penannular brooch of a kind favoured by the Celtic peoples in the early centuries A.D., a bronze ring and part of a glass melon bead of Roman type, likely to have been supplied by traders moving between the Roman forts in the second or third century. That native metalsmiths produced brooches, dress-fasteners and harness mounts in the Celtic idiom during the occupation is suggested by finds of second century date, chiefly from the forts of Brough-under-Stainmore, Kirkby Thore and Stanwix. Across the valley of the Kent from Sizergh Fell the hill-fort known as Castlesteads on the Helm at Natland is likely to have been rendered harmless when the Romans established their fort at Watercrook. Any trace of settlement in Kendal itself will have been destroyed by later building, but an early type of rotary quern, recently found in the town, suggests that native occupation did in fact exist there. Settlements in Longsleddale and Bannisdale and, north of Shap, at Towtop Kirk, Bampton, Skirsgill Hill, Askham and Yanwath point to a considerable population chiefly engaged in stock-rearing, but in some places, such as the limestone area of Skirsgill Hill, carrying out some arable farming. This group of farmsteads was separated from the numerous walled settlements around Crosby Ravensworth, Crosby Garrett and Waitby, by the Roman road from Low Borrow Bridge to Brougham.

Excavations at Ewe Close produced evidence that this farm continued to be used in Roman times, while the rectangular shape of some of the enclosures in this area is sometimes considered as showing Roman influence (page 209). However, this form of settlement could have resulted from a more ancient heritage when Celtic peoples moved westward across the Pennines from Yorkshire in the final centuries B.C. (see page 210). Rectangular buildings at Ewe Close and Cow Green, Crosby Ravensworth, and Severals, Crosby Garrett, have not received sufficient attention to prove that they are of Roman date and all such huts may well be later. Indeed, a little medieval pottery was found at Ewe Close as well as sherds of Romano-British date. More recent investigations at Waitby Intake (Monument 13 of the Royal Commission Report on Westmorland) have produced Romano-British pottery of the late fourth century found outside the northern enclosing wall. These settlements may have fallen within the administrative territory of the Carvetii. In any case the tribal capital at *Isurium Brigantum* (Aldborough) can have had little authority over this and other sub-tribes of the Brigantes in the Lake District. The enclosed nature of some of the small rectangular fields, and occasionally, as at Severals, Crosby Garrett, the presence of drove roads directing stock past the cultivated fields to the open fells, points to a mixed economy. Professor Stuart Piggott gave the name 'Stanwick' to the stock-rearing, pony-breeding way of life of the Brigantes in contrast to the predominantly arable farming of 'Woodbury' type, in general use farther south in the late Pre-Roman Iron Age, while Sir Mortimer Wheeler showed in his excavations at the Brigantian stronghold of Stanwick that ox, sheep, pig and horse were numerically important in that order. It is probable that the same animals were bred by the native population west of the Pennines.

Air photography has shown that a number of ditch-enclosed farms of varying plan were established near the Roman forts, their arable fields making use of the better agricultural land which lay around Brougham, Old Carlisle and Maryport. These are likely to date chiefly from the later part of the occupation when better relations existed between the troops and the local population, and when the growing of grain to supply the forts and civil settlements was probably encouraged. Naked and hulled barley were important crops in earlier prehistoric times and it is known that oats and wheat were also among the crops grown in the Pre-Roman Iron Age and during the occupation. Wheat from the granaries at Ambleside and Papcastle may well have been imported, but parched oats found in a clay-lined pit at Cockermouth could have been grown locally (see Chapter 13). Very little excavation has yet been done on these farms, but at Risehow, near Maryport, and at Jacob's Gill, Rosley, sections of their ditches produced third and fourth century Romano-British pottery. Risehow, with its long drove road leading into the enclosure, is of the 'banjo' pattern, known in Wessex to originate before the conquest, but to continue in use during Roman times. Perhaps the strongly defended enclosures at Aughertree, north of the Uldale Fells, which have a similar drove road, represent a hill version of this type of cattle compound.

West of Penrith the settlement at Threlkeld on the Skiddaw Slates with circular stone huts and enclosing walls has already been mentioned (p. 210) and a homestead on the more fertile limestone formation at Stonecarr, near Motherby, may also date from the early centuries of this era. The hill-fort on Carrock Fell may have been dismantled at the end of the first century, while Castle Crag in Borrowdale, from which Roman pottery has been collected, and other small fortified sites in the central hills, could have been sporadically occupied until more peaceful relations were established with the troops in the third century. In the heart of the hills at the head of Ullswater stone-walled circular-hutted homesteads at Hartsop near Brotherswater, at Deepdale, Glencoyndale and Bannerdale, point to a considerable settlement there. This suggests that the Romans built their road over High Street to prevent these people joining forces with tribesmen in Mardale, Bampton and Askham, to attack the fort at Brougham.

When we turn the corner southward from St Bees Head, evidence for settlement in the west Cumberland foothills continues. Cairns at Infell, Ponsonby, lie west of a sub-rectangular enclosure, while another stone enclosure is said to have been destroyed on the fields of Hurlbarrow farm a little to the south. Bolton Wood enclosure above Gosforth is circular in plan, not unlike the 'rounds' of Cornwall, while south of the Esk at Barnscar and at Brantrake Moss, settlements existed in the early centuries A.D. A penannular bronze brooch of this period came from a homestead up the Whitrow Beck at Waberthwaite and it is likely that similar farms still remain to be recorded, while others will have been destroyed by later farming and by walling. Agricultural activity reflected in the pollen diagrams from Brant Rake Moss and Devoke Water will be discussed in Chapter 13, and may first have been encouraged by the Roman authorities at Ravenglass.

In the absence of classification and excavation it is impossible to know how many of the native farms and forts were occupied at any one time and estimates of population can have little real foundation. Mr A H. A. Hogg has recently suggested that the native population in north-west Wales at this time was about 4,000, a ratio of 8 to 1 with the Roman garrison at Caernarvon (*Segontium*). On this basis, the larger area of the Lake District with four of the forts garrisoned, could have carried a population in the region of 16,000. Population estimates for A.D. 1500 give a total of between 70,000 and 80,000. In addition to supplying their own needs of iron tools, weapons and husbandry gear, of fuel, building materials, food and clothing, the inhabitants had to meet the demands of the occupying army which would also have taken heavy toll of manpower and of local resources. Horses for their cavalry; hides for jerkins, boots, sandals, saddlery and tents; grain and lard for their rations; stone and timber for building; wood for fuel, would all have been requisitioned, while mining for lead at Alston and possibly in the Caldbeck Fells, and for iron and copper (early workings have not yet been identified) would have come under imperial control. The drafting of men into the auxiliary forces, intermarriage between local women, soldiers and traders, and taxation in all its forms, would not have endeared the Roman administration to the inhabitants. Romanisation of the countryside, reflected in fine villas in the Vale of York, with outliers as far north as Durham and west as Gargrave in Craven, has no counterpart in the Lake District. Here the adoption of Roman building methods and refinements – temples, houses, baths and shops – are confined to the civil settlements outside the forts and to the town of Carlisle. But in return the Celtic population learnt the importance of unity against attack, the potential benefit of improved methods of agriculture, road construction, pottery-making and the use of currency for trading purposes. A few princely families, and those involved in commerce and administration, would have learnt the Latin language for official dealings, a tongue which was eventually to survive only as the language of the Church and, later, of the Law. Despite hardships endured during the early years of the occupation, and later from the onslaughts of Picts, Scots and Anglo-Saxons in the fourth and fifth centuries, it was the

Celtic peoples of the homesteads, settlements and small hill-forts who lived on in the Lake District after the Roman frontier had collapsed. The preservation of the institutions of chieftainship and tribal government, related by bards and handed down by oral tradition, enabled the people of the Highland Zone of Britain, including the Lake Counties, to feel less forlorn than did the inhabitants of the cities and villas of the Lowlands, when in A.D. 410 Honorius told the *civitates* of Britain to look to their own defence.

CHAPTER 13

THE CHANGING LANDSCAPE AND HABITATS THROUGH PREHISTORIC AND ROMAN TIMES

When the first settlers entered this region (says an animated writer)
they found it overspread with wood; forest trees, the fir, the oak, the ash,
and the birch had skirted the fells, tufted the hills, and shaded the valleys,
through centuries of silent solitude; the birds and beasts of prey reigned
over the meeker species; and the bellum inter omnia *maintained the*
balance of Nature in the empire of beasts.

William Wordsworth: *Guide to the Lakes*

In the last two chapters we have learned of the evidence on which is based our knowledge of local human history – evidence in the form of material relics of the native peoples, and a few written records left by the Roman occupiers. Another kind of illumination is shed on this long period of Lake District history by the study of records of the changing vegetation, which nature has provided in the accumulating sediments of all the numerous lakes and tarns of the district. It is now time to consider how results from the study of vegetation history may be integrated with the archaeological evidence to produce a picture of the changing landscape of the district from the time of the earliest human occupants. Only by considering the present habitats in the light of their early history is it possible to approach any understanding of the contemporary plant and animal communities.

It is possible to investigate the history of a vegetation by using the technique of pollen-analysis. This depends on the fact that pollen is produced by most flowering plants in quantities far in excess of requirements, and that, by a fortunate chance, the outer coat of a pollen grain is made of one of the most resistant of all plant products to anaerobic bacterial decay. Consequently the large quantities of pollen which are shed into the atmosphere by the local vegetation in any area, and fall as a 'pollen rain' on land and water, are preserved intact wherever the environment lacks oxygen, as in growing peat or the accumulating sediment of lakes. The proportions in which each type of pollen is found will reflect the relative abundance of each plant. Most pollen grains can be identified to family, genus or species level. By 'pollen-analysis', which is a research technique by which pollen grains from each successive horizon in a profile are concentrated and counted, it is possible to build up a picture of the changing vegetation of a piece of country so well supplied with suitable sediment profiles as the Lake District. Three factors have been involved in the vegetation changes; they are changing climate, changing soils, and the activities of man.

Apart from the long profiles such as those provided by lake sediments, further evidence about the past vegetation can be found in certain types of rather acid soil, where most pollen grains (though probably not all) are preserved from decay. In archaeological excavations in different parts of the world it has been possible to supplement what is learned about these men of the past from their material relics, by pollen analysis of acid organic soils or peats in which the relics were found, thus gaining a good idea of the type of vegetation (forest, fen, bog, grassland or heather moor) which surrounded the site, of the crops which were grown and the weeds which flourished. In this chapter, an attempt will be made to integrate what has been found out about the history of Lake District vegetation with the factual record of local human history, in order to trace in general terms the history of the landscape through the four thousand years between the first traces of prehistoric man and the departure of the Roman occupiers.

We have seen that the Mesolithic hunters, fishers and shell-fish gatherers, who have left traces of their presence on the western coasts of the Lake District, were not equipped to make much change to their environment except perhaps by fire. Unbroken deciduous forest covered the valleys and hills; only the mountain tops, above about 2,500 feet, rose above the blanket of trees. Though these people probably had no tools with which to cut down trees, any settlement or fishing and fowling site frequented by them would become some sort of clearing, because of the effect of their presence in preventing regeneration of trees. In such clearings certain plants, which do not grow under trees because they avoid shade, would be able to grow. It is a record of this type of modification of the primary forest which was found in the sediment profile of Ehenside Tarn by Dr Donald Walker (p. 197), and is found also in the sediments of Barfield Tarn, near Bootle, where it was dated to just after 3700 B.C.

When the first Neolithic farmers arrived in northern Europe, the continuous deciduous forests would offer no pasture for their flocks and herds except in the form of those deciduous leaves which possess nutritive value. Primitive tribes in remote parts of the world like the Himalayas can still be found using in this way the leaves of various trees, especially the elm, to feed stalled cattle. We shall see in Chapter 15 that there is a long tradition in the Lake District of using the leaves of various trees as fodder for sheep in winter, persisting into such recent times that a notable twentieth-century sheep-farmer, Mrs Beatrix Heelis (née Potter), would never cut down a holly tree, for hollies provided useful winter feed for sheep. Leaves of elm are the most nutritious of all for feeding stock, and it is now thought that elm leaves were used on a large scale by farmers of the first Neolithic culture to reach northern Europe, and that this was the cause of the sudden decrease in the proportion of elm pollen in the pollen rain at this time, at all sites including the Lake District. These farmers are thought to have gathered leafy branches of elm over a wide area of the forests round their settlements, whereupon the trees would produce few flowers and very little pollen. The horizon of the Elm Decline in Ireland is just before 3000 B.C., and in the Lake District it has been dated at three sites to the centuries between 3300 and 3000 B.C., while the earliest date from the Ehenside Tarn settlement (obtained from a wooden artefact) was 3014 B.C. This must have been the date of the first significant modification of the primeval forest – a process upon which we know that Wordsworth pondered, though he can never have imagined that it began at such an early date.

The Lake District is, of course, strongly associated with the manufacture of one of the first human tools designed to cut down trees. The characteristic polished Neolithic axe, made of flint or stone, has been shown by modern experiment to be an efficient implement for this purpose. The Lake District was the centre for production and distribution of the Cumbrian type of stone axe, and it is not surprising that profound changes in the local vegetation are recorded for the third millennium B.C., for the axe factories on Pike of Stickle and Scafell must have been in their highly productive phase by the middle of that millennium. A pollen diagram from Barfield Tarn on the Cumberland coast shows that by 3000 B.C. the oaks and elms round the tarn were being destroyed, and grassland with its associated herbs was spreading; a few grains of cereal pollen at the same horizon suggest the cultivation of small plots. The clearing process went on there until there can have been little woodland left, except for swampy carr of alder and birch, with an ever-increasing proportion of the pollen of cultivated cereals and associated weeds. A similar record was found, though it has not yet been dated, in the profile from Ehenside Tarn. At Barfield Tarn, changes in the type of sediment indicate very considerable soil erosion from the surrounding slopes as a result of this clearance and cultivation; this sort of result is familiar to us in the history of many parts of the world where the virgin forests were destroyed during the last century.

In a swampy hollow near the sea at Eskmeals, a farmer recently dug a drainage ditch and exposed in the side of it a layer of peaty soil in which pollen was well preserved. Analysis of this layer showed that the base of it, which contained 10 to 15 per cent of elm pollen, dated from before 3000 B.C., but that just above the base of the peaty layer, the Elm Decline of 3000 B.C. was recorded. Flints and pottery sherds of Neolithic type had been found on the fields round about, and then continuation of the ditch-digging towards the dry margin of the peaty hollow turned up a beautiful perfect rough-out of a Cumbrian axe. The rather dry marginal humus in which the axe was embedded contained the pollen of mainly herbaceous plants, indicating an origin later than the main clearance of the forest at the site, so it is not possible to say just where the axe was positioned in relation to the Elm Decline, except that it was above it and therefore more recent, but probably not far above it.

The picture which emerges from study of the vegetation history at these three sites, Ehenside, Barfield Tarn and Eskmeals, is one of primary utilisation of elm followed very rapidly by continued clearance of the coastal forest, from 3000 B.C. onwards, and rather dense settlement around small coastal tarns, with primitive cultivation of cereals of the type suggested by the pollen grains at Eskmeals and Barfield and the relics found at Ehenside (p. 198).

Neither material relics nor vegetation history can tell us, as yet, when or which people found and began to work the outcrops of the special tuff from which the axes were made, but from pollen analyses of the sediments of Blea Tarn between Great and Little Langdale, and Angle Tarn above Rossett Gill, it can be shown that the Elm Decline episode was well-developed in the Langdale Fells. The change in composition of the rain of pollen produced by the forest at this time – that is, the sudden diminution in the proportion of elm pollen – shows that the exploitation of the elms was very considerable in this area and other parts of the central mountain group, but was much less intense in the south-western fells round Burnmoor Tarn and the head of Wastwater. This is consistent with more intense utilisation of elms for fodder in areas where the desirable form of tuff crops out, but does not of itself, of course, prove any connection between the Elm Decline people and the discoverers of the raw material for the Cumbrian axe.

The effect of this primary attack on the primeval forest was to reduce, and in many places to suppress, the elm, and to allow the expansion of the ash tree into the somewhat thinned and lighter forest. From this lighter secondary forest, recognised in pollen spectra by scarcity or absence of elm and the presence of ash pollen, greater quantities of the pollen of woodland herbs such as the dog's mercury (*Mercurialis*) and of the woodland shrubs such as holly (*Ilex*) reached the accumulating sediments. Oak, birch and alder, with some hazel, remained the dominant trees of the forest. In the pollen diagram from Blea Tarn a more profound disturbance of the forest is found a little way above the Elm Decline; here an increase in the pollen of grasses and ribwort plantain (*Plantago lanceolata*) is first found at a horizon dated to *c.* 2800 B.C., and this evidence of real clearings in the forest persists until a level dated to about 2200 B.C. The dates are obtained from calculation of the rate of sedimentation, based on three radiocarbon dates. After this the forest closed in again, and secondary forest persisted round Blea Tarn for the rest of the prehistoric period.

Charcoal associated with axe chippings has now been dated to 2730 B.C. ±150.

The dating of this period of clearances in the upland forest round the head of Great Langdale is in very close agreement with the dates in the third millennium B.C. which have been suggested on archaeological evidence for the period of maximum activity of the stone axe factories, and this correlation, as has been pointed out in Chapter 11, does suggest that the men who worked the factories are likely to have pastured animals in forest clearings. At the same time, pollen evidence from Angle Tarn and from Langdale Combe indicates a progressive decline in the high-level forests from this time on, and the charcoal which Dr Walker found stratified into the old lake sediments in Langdale Combe suggests that fire was used in this attack on the upper margins of the forest.

Two permanent effects of these Neolithic inhabitants on the landscape of the Lake District can therefore be recognised. The rolling fields of the West Cumberland coastal plain were never again to be forested; the mixed pastoral and arable farming of this area is a form of land use of enormous antiquity. And the centuries during which the axe factories were in production must have seen great destruction of the high-level forests which, before that time, had cloaked the higher fells up to 1,500–2,500 feet. This destruction was greater in the area of the factories round Langdale and Scafell than in neighbouring parts of the fells where no workings are known, and in these latter parts the forest persisted for much longer. Where the forest on the high fells was cleared or burned by Neolithic men it did not regenerate, but soil erosion set in, and increasing soil acidity transformed the old forest soils into peat.

On the undisturbed fells and on steep slopes where soil fertility was maintained, a long period of fairly stable forest cover followed, while peat continued to accumulate in ill-drained hollows and on the flatter-topped ridges. By about 1950 B.C. birch forest at about 1,700 feet on the gently sloping land round Red Tarn, between Crinkle Crags, Pike o'Blisco and Wrynose top, was being entombed in peat; possibly there was a general acceleration of the rate of growth of peat at about this time.

The next dated change in the vegetation comes from Seathwaite Tarn, at the head of one of the major tributaries of the Duddon. It is part of a rather widespread phase of decline in upland forest and replacement by hill grassland and heather moor. The places where it has been found, which in addition to Seathwaite Tarn include Devoke Water, Burnmoor Tarn and Haweswater, are all near to existing remains of burials, cairns and circles, of which those which have been excavated have proved to be of Bronze Age type (see pages 203-5). The date for the end of this episode at Seathwaite Tarn is 1090 B.C. The sites where this clearance phase is clearly recorded in the pollen diagrams are in general between about 700 and 1,000 feet; it is not found in the profiles from Blea Tarn, or in the valley lakes, or Blelham Tarn or Loughrigg Tarn. The evidence from changing pollen assemblages suggests a pastoral form of land use in the uplands. The great expansion of grassland which went on could have been the result either of deliberate felling of trees, or of widespread failure of trees to regenerate because of heavy grazing and browsing of animals – sheep, cattle or pigs – among the trees. This form of land use has been shown to correspond in distribution with the burials of Bronze Age type, and is absent from the record in those areas where there are no remains of this type. At Devoke Water the record is very similar to that of this dated horizon at Seathwaite Tarn. The catchment area of Devoke Water is particularly rich in these burial cairns of Bronze Age type, and from the pollen diagrams it is clear that the first upland forest clearance in this area came at a time which is very probably the same as that of the burial cairns. Dr Donald Walker excavated a cairn at Barnscar, near Devoke Water, and found that in the acid soil below and inside the cairn there was a preponderance of tree pollen which indicated that when the cairn was constructed, forest was the dominant vegetation. Outside the cairn, however, all pollen in the peat and soil profiles contained an overwhelming preponderance of herbaceous plants – grasses, sedges and heather being most important. This indicates that the 'turf-line' preserved inside the cairn was a fossilised sample of the soil and vegetation at the time of construction of the cairn, and that the soil outside the cairn had received since the construction of the cairn the pollen rain from a very different sort of vegetation.

By this time, about 1000 B.C., the upland soils must have become increasingly acid, as a result of seven thousand years of continuous leaching since the end of the last glaciation. The soils of acid oakwoods, such as these must then have been, are particularly susceptible to irreversible changes if the forest cover is destroyed. Therefore, destruction of woods such as those which then existed round, for instance, Devoke Water and Burnmoor Tarn, as well as Seathwaite, either by felling, or by grazing so intensive that no seedling trees grew to maturity, would immediately accelerate the process of soil erosion and soil deterioration. As the soils degenerated, no regeneration of trees would take place even if the human settlers moved on, and many of the treeless grassy fell-sides of the Lake District, as well as patches of heather moor like those round Devoke Water and at Moor Divock near the foot of Haweswater, must have come into existence during this pastoral occupation of the second millennium B.C.

A different form of land use, also apparently of this same period, is recorded in the sediments of some of the valley lakes, such as Thirlmere and Rydal Water. Detailed analysis of these profiles has revealed a pattern of repeated short-term clearance episodes, each followed by regeneration of the secondary forest to its previous condition. Pollen grains resembling those of barley have been found associated with these episodes. From this evidence it would seem probable that shifting cultivation may have been practised at some places in the valleys during this time, but that in general the valley woods remained uncleared. The pasturing of flocks and herds went on at altitudes above about 700 feet, where the forest was lighter and easier to clear, and where predators such as the wolf were less of a menace than in the dense valley woods. As was pointed out in Chapter 11, there is some evidence in the form of slow growth of the peat bogs to suggest a drier, and possibly rather warmer climate than at present, during parts of the Bronze Age, and this would, of course, encourage settlement in the uplands.

At some time between 800 and 500 B.C. the climate seems to have deteriorated, becoming wetter and possibly colder. Foulshaw Moss and the other great raised bogs of the Morecambe Bay estuaries became wetter, and their surfaces began to grow rapidly. A 'corduroy' trackway made of logs, embedded in the peat several feet below the surface, was formerly known from Foulshaw Moss; it was illustrated in Tansley's books on British vegetation, but has now disappeared. Kate's Pad, a similar trackway on Pilling Moss south of Lancaster, has been dated by radiocarbon to c. 800 B.C. Similar trackways are known from this period from the Somerset raised bogs, some still bearing the imprint of the tools of the men of the Late Bronze Age who fashioned them to keep open communications across a bog surface which must have been rapidly becoming wetter. So rapidly did conditions worsen, however, that these trackways suffered very little wear from the passage of traffic, but were almost immediately engulfed by the growth of peat.

Though we have little direct evidence for climatic conditions on the uplands at this time, it does seem possible that the change in climate which so greatly accelerated the rate of growth of peat on the lowland mosses was accompanied by worsening conditions in the uplands, and that this change put an end to the Bronze Age occupation of what are now the wet and windswept moorlands round Burnmoor and Devoke Water, and the similar upland occupations recorded on Banniside and Little Arrow moors above Coniston. In the sediments of Devoke Water and Burnmoor Tarn there is recorded a period of partial regeneration of the forest, above the occupation of the second millennium B.C. This shows that though the Bronze Age farmers and their animals had converted much of the upland forests into heathery or grassy moorland, the forest had not been entirely destroyed even in those areas which have traces of considerable Bronze Age populations. Nor had the forest soils completely deteriorated, and tree seedlings must have grown up and restored the forests on parts of the western fells, at least, during parts of the last millennium B.C. There are as yet no radiocarbon dates available for the pollen record at Ehenside Tarn, but through the period which must correspond with this thousand years there is evidence in the Ehenside Tarn pollen diagram for continued occupation and cereal cultivation on the coastal plain.

There is therefore only scanty evidence from vegetation history as to conditions in the Lake District during the later Bronze Age and the beginning of the Pre-Roman Iron Age. At altitudes above about 1,500 feet, the inevitable deterioration of soils under the influence of factors discussed in Chapter 7 must have gone on, and this process would be accelerated by the supposed change to cooler and wetter conditions after about 500 B.C. On high-lying plateaux like the top of High Street, western fells like Lank Rigg, and Matterdale Common, peat was forming and swallowing up the forest wherever drainage was poor; by the time the Roman engineers began to make their great road along the High Street tops, the wet peaty soil must have led to drainage problems in places, but along this high ridge we know there can no longer have been any forest to clear, for the record of this period is found there in deep peat.

The upland pollen record does not suggest any great change in the way of life of the inhabitants of the 'British settlements' of stone huts (page 209) until the second or third century A.D., but in the pollen diagram from Ehenside Tarn Dr Walker detected a period of forest regeneration, indicating abandonment of cultivated land, which, from his calculated Scaleby Moss time-scale, began about A.D. 100. During the unsettled years when the local hill-men were gathering in their hill forts, on Carrock Fell and other strong points, the balance between forest and moorland does not seem to have changed much. By the time the Romans entered the Lake District as a military occupation one can therefore picture it as a region of thickly wooded valleys, with spreading oakwoods on the steep valley sides, and similar woods still cloaking the lower moorlands except where the Bronze Age cattle, sheep and pigs had been most active. When the Romans came to build their fort at Hardknott, probably in Hadrian's reign, they must have had to clear oakwoods for their site and parade-ground, and on both sides of their military road, except perhaps at the very summit of the pass. Though the surviving walls at Hardknott show construction entirely of stone, and the roofs are thought to have been of slate, excavation of some of the minor buildings within the wall of the fortress has shown that timber played a part in their construction, and wood for fuel would be needed in the bath-house. Nevertheless, there were still oakwoods remaining round Hardknott after the Roman soldiers ceased their permanent occupation of the fort in the late second century A.D. We know this because in a wet hollow on top of the ruins of one of these minor buildings – perhaps a store – peaty soil began to accumulate and continued to do so for a long time, incorporating the current pollen rain into its substance in ordered sequence. All round and above Hardknott, wherever the bracken grows today, the oakwoods were still there when the fort first fell into disuse.

But soon there came a change, one of the most profound changes ever to affect the Lake District landscape. The most widespread and permanently effective attack on the upland oak forests dates from the late second and third centuries A.D. Some stimulus caused the men of the upland settlements, the stone-hut villages and isolated farmsteads which have been described in the previous chapter (page 221) to clear vast acres of upland forest in the fells of the south-west, west, north and east. The record of this great transformation of the landscape, which must have taken place within a few generations, can be found in the sediments of a score of moorland tarns, among them Devoke Water, Burnmoor Tarn, Low Tarn above Wasdale, Overwater north of Skiddaw, Bowscale Tarn, Red Tarn high on Helvellyn, and in Haweswater and others of the large lakes. The destruction of the oakwoods on the fell-sides round Hardknott is recorded near the base of the growing peat, a few centimetres above the last ruins of the Roman buildings. In the little fields enclosed by low banks that we can still see, these British hill-men grew cereal crops which have left their pollen in the sediments of lakes and tarns, in that Hardknott peat, and in the mantle of blanket peat which had already muffled and entombed the forests above about 1,500 feet on the flatter fells such as High Street. From all these sources come analyses which record this period when cultivation of cereals must have penetrated farther and higher into the Lakeland hills than before or since. In the Hardknott peat and in the Devoke Water sediment it is possible to recognise the grains of rye pollen, a cereal which according to Helbaek (1953) the Romans introduced into northern England.

We do not know very much about the reasons for this tremendous improvement in agriculture and energetic expansion of farmers into the fell country. There is a certain amount of evidence for a better climate in Britain as a whole during the Late Romano-British centuries, and certainly by the fifth century A.D. the Morecambe Bay bogs were again growing very slowly, so that highly humified peat (dated to c. A.D. 436 at Helsington Moss) was forming. It also seems possible on historical grounds, as pointed out in the last chapter, that by later Romano-British times, relations had improved between the local Brigantes and their Roman occupiers, so it is reasonable to suppose that it became profitable to the local farmers to produce corn to sell to Roman buyers – whereas it is known from historical evidence that at the time of the Roman invasions the British hill-men had lived mainly on meat and milk.

The layer in the deposits of Devoke Water which spans this period when cereals must have been cultivated nearer to Devoke Water than before or since has been dated by radiocarbon to the years between about A.D. 200 and A.D. 580. The middle of the corresponding layer at Burnmoor Tarn gave a date of A.D. 390. As part of an attempt to find out more about the small native hill farms of this approximate date, certain settlements in the south-western fells have recently been surveyed. Traces of one such settlement remain at Brant Rake Moss, a sheltered little hollow in the heathery fells between Eskdale and Birker Moor. The banks outlining its little fields remain only in part, and no material relics of the people who lived here have been found. There are two oval enclosures which appear to have been used comparatively recently as sheep folds, and no circular stone-walled huts were visible among the bracken and heather of the hillside. A trench was dug across one of the field banks, and a plan made of its construction. The large stones which formed the foundation of the bank were firmly placed in and below a layer of black organic soil which had been the surface soil at the time of construction. This accumulation of dark organic matter (mor) shows that even by the time of construction of this field bank, the soil had become too acid and sour at this point to be worth cultivation; the areas of this kind of soil are now under heather and must have been the pasture fields of this settlement. But a few yards away where the slope is steeper and the drainage better, great patches of the fell-side are now covered with bracken growing in deep and fertile brown-earth soil. Undoubtedly these are the patches where the British farmers grew their crops. The neighbouring area of acid soil has, however, preserved most beautifully the pollen shed into the air at that time, so that it was possible, by pollen analysis of the soil around and below the foundation stones of the field bank, to determine the percentage composition of this pollen rain. These pollen spectra were then matched with those of a certain level in the long pollen diagram from Devoke Water, which lies just over that shoulder of Water Crag which shelters Brant Rake on the south-east. The horizon in the Devoke Water profile which matched the pollen spectra from the base of the Brant Rake Moss field bank was that lying between the two samples dated to A.D. 200 and A.D. 580 respectively. This established the date of the building of the field bank, and completed satisfactorily this small piece of detection. From the pollen record we know that these Brant Rake farmers, and others like them in many parts of the Lake District uplands, cut down woodland to make more grazing land, and cultivated rye, barley and possibly wheat in their little fields. The docks and mugwort which grew as weeds in those fields have left their pollen in the Devoke Water sediments.

The other thing which we can learn from study of the lake sediments in such areas is that the agricultural methods of these upland farmers brought about very severe soil erosion. Large quantities of the soil which they tilled are now forming part of the sediments of Devoke Water and similar tarns. Much more must have gone down to the sea in the waters of the Esk, the Duddon, and many other Lake District rivers. Characteristic soil profiles from these moorlands today present the appearance of having been truncated, and it appears from the sediment profiles that most of this erosion took place as a result of the intensified farming of this period. Settlements such as the one at Brant Rake would find their land became much less productive as time went on, and the end of this phase of arable farming in the uplands would certainly come about because of decreased soil fertility, which must have been a major reason for change in the settlement pattern.

At this time there is no evidence for any appreciable clearance of the valley woods. Both the oak or mixed woods on the sides of the main valleys, and the swampy alderwoods on the valley floors, must have remained little altered except in the immediate neighbourhood of Roman stations like Ambleside, and the scattered native settlements. The problem of draining the flat floors of the glacial troughs had not yet been tackled. Pollen in fen peat surrounding a Roman civil site which was investigated during building work east of the Ambleside fort (*Galava*) shows that swampy alderwoods came quite close to the outskirts of the fort at a time when Roman pottery, and leather shoes of Roman type, were being used.

CHAPTER 14

DARK AGE TO VIKING TIMES

If only we labour diligently and examine carefully, gather up facts as they present themselves, and place on record our experience as it grows; if only we speak that we know, and testify to that we have seen, bearing with each other and helping each other, we shall gradually unfold the pages from which may be read the history of our counties . . .
Canon James Simpson at the Inauguration Meeting of the Cumberland and Westmorland Antiquarian and Archaeological Society, 11 September, 1866. *Trans C.W.A.A. Soc.*, 1

By the middle of the fifth century the Roman Province of Britain was lost to the Empire. Excavations at forts and *vici* in the north of England have shown no sudden calamity, rather a gradual abandonment and decay after the troops and their dependents returned to the Continent. Many of the *vici* had already declined after the Pictish war of 367. The absence of contemporary records and the resurgence of the barbarian world has caused this period of history to be called the Dark Ages. North of Hadrian's Wall the Celtic tribes living south of the Forth/Clyde isthmus developed into the British kingdoms of Strathclyde and Manau Gododdin. In the Lake Counties the British kingdom which evolved during the fifth century was called Rheged, but the boundaries of its territory are not clearly known. It is possible that Rheged can be equated with the land of the *Carvetii* (p. 212), but it may also have held sway over much of the domain of the earlier Brigantian confederacy. From early Welsh sources and from place-names, Rheged appears to have held territory on both shores of the Solway, while west of the Pennines some authorities give the Ribble as its southern boundary. The inhabitants of this kingdom, together with those of Strathclyde and Manau Gododdin, were known to later Welsh tradition as 'The Men of the North'. The name Cumbria at first applied to the whole extended kingdom of Strathclyde and was not used until much later in the restricted sense of modern geographers. Cumbria, and Cumberland, are derived from the name *Cymry* – the compatriots – a term used by early Welsh writers to describe the Celtic peoples both of Strathclyde and of Wales.

The pedigree of the royal house of Rheged was recorded by Nennius in *Historia Britannorum* and traced this ancestry to men with Roman names, which suggests that the British kings were hereditary descendants of Celtic chieftains living during the Roman occupation. The outstanding king of Rheged was Urien, who besieged Anglian-held Lindisfarne in about 574 and joined with the king of Strathclyde, and with two other British princes, in an attack on the Anglian king, Hussa. Urien was eulogised by the Welsh bard, Taliesin, as a great warrior and was said to have lived at *Lywyfenedd*, identified by some scholars as the district near the River Lyvennet in Westmorland. It has also been suggested that the stone-walled settlement at Burwens, Crosby Ravensworth may have been Urien's home. However, other authorities think that he ruled from Carlisle, a very likely centre since that city was probably the capital of the *civitas* of the *Carvetii* from the late third century. After Urien's death at the end of the sixth century the kingdom of Rheged fades from the scene and the Lake Counties became part of Strathclyde, until the English from Northumbria conquered the district about the middle of the seventh century.

Virtually no research has yet been done to identify Dark Age sites in the Lake District, and scarcely any archaeological material has survived. Some of the forts and homesteads of earlier centuries certainly continued in use, while the traditional circular house plan remained predominant. It may well be that Castle Howe, Peel Wyke, at the foot of Bassenthwaite, Dunmallet at the foot of Ullswater and Castlehead, or 'Atterpile Castle' near Grange-over-Sands, were among the fortified sites held at this time. On analogy with excavations such as those at Tre'r Ceiri in Caernarvonshire, Huckhoe in Northumberland, or Crock Cleuch in Roxburghshire, some stone-walled forts and farms established in Romano-British times were still occupied down to the sixth or seventh century. This may well be true for settlements like those at Waitby and Crosby Ravensworth where fourth century pottery has been found. Stock rearing, together with horse, sheep and pig breeding, remained the dominant land-use of the Celtic peoples as is clear from early Welsh and Irish sources.

Dr Douglas Simpson has argued persuasively that a sub-Roman community survived in the vicinity of the fort at Brougham until Anglian times and that the traditional link of the parish church, formerly known as 'Ninekirks', with the British saint, Ninian, at the close of the Roman occupation, may have some authentic foundation. The work of the Celtic Church in Cumberland through St Kentigern could be a true record of a mission undertaken at the command of the king of Strathclyde after his victory at *Arfderydd*, identified as Arthuret, north of Carlisle, in 573. Crosthwaite, near Keswick, is the traditional site at which St Kentigern set up his preaching cross, while among the churches close to the Lake District hills which were later dedicated to him are Caldbeck, Castle Sowerby and Mungrisdale. No early Christian inscriptions in the Latin language and Roman lettering, or in Primitive Irish, written in the Ogam alphabet, have been found in the Lake Counties. Indeed, the absence of the latter confirms the successful defence of the Solway and the

Cumberland coast against raiders, or settlers, from Ireland in the centuries after the Romans withdrew.

In the absence of written history and the scarcity of archaeological information, place-names give some clue to the successive peoples who have lived here since the Roman period. This evidence must be used with great caution, for, as W. G. Collingwood once wrote to a fellow antiquary, 'It is always valuable to collect the old forms, and, indeed, it is unsafe to guess at modern names without knowing their history.' The English Place-Name Society has recently published its volumes for both Cumberland and Westmorland, while Lakeland Lancashire was included in Professor E. Ekwall's survey for Lancashire, published in 1922. These volumes emphasise the rarity of early sources for many Lake District names and the consequent difficulty in deducing their derivation. Only one pre-Conquest document, Gospatric's writ, of mid eleventh century date survives for Cumberland (and that in a late copy), while Domesday Book, completed in 1086, includes only the south-western tip of Cumberland, the districts of Furness and Cartmel, and the lower Kent and Lune valleys. In the succeeding centuries the surviving cartularies of various monastic foundations provide one of the most valuable sources. The dearth of early forms of names applies in particular to the central hills. Here British names are infrequently recorded, Anglian names are few in number, but those of Scandinavian origin are abundant. However, these last need not be early on account of the dominant survival of the Scandinavian element in medieval language and in modern dialect. Professor Kenneth Jackson has suggested that the late forms of some of the British place-names may mean that Cumbric continued to be spoken in the northern part of this district until Strathclyde was finally merged in the Kingdom of Scotland early in the eleventh century.

Many British names will have been replaced by Anglian and Norse forms, but those surviving relate chiefly to rivers, a few to hills and others to topographical features. These are more abundant in the foothills which have been attractive to pastoral peoples since prehistoric times, rather than in the high fells. Eden, Lune, Kent, Crake, Esk, Calder, Derwent and Ellen are among the river names of British origin; Blencathra, Carrock- and Mell- among those of hills, while words corresponding to Modern Welsh *glyn* (valley), *pen* (head), *blaen* (top), *tor* (peak) and *caer* (fortress) appear in names such as Glencoyne, Penruddock, Blennerhasset, Torpenhow and Caermote. None of the place-names relating to the Middle English Arthurian Legend, which associates Arthur's court with 'Merrie Carlisle', are of early date and there is no evidence that the misty, historical King Arthur of late fifth or early sixth century ever lived so far north.

The Anglian realms of Bernicia, centred on Bamburgh, and Deira, based on York, were united into the kingdom of Northumbria in the reign of Æthelfrith 593–617. It was under him and his successors that the main English expansion and conquest took place in the north. From place-name evidence some authorities think that the movement into Cumberland began in his reign and accelerated after he defeated the Welsh at Chester about 613. However, the absence of pagan cemeteries west of the Pennines suggests that any large scale movement of Anglian people in this direction did not occur until after Northumbria was converted to Christianity in the decades following 627. Two possible pagan Anglian burials of seventh century date were excavated by Canon Greenwell in Westmorland last century, one at Wiseber Hill, Kirkby Stephen, the other at Bent's Hill, Crosby Garrett. They occurred as isolated secondary burials in earlier barrows, a fragmentary bronze bowl and multicoloured glass bead were found with the first mentioned interment and shears, a single-edged knife, bridle-bit and buckle, all of iron, with the second. At Sandford in the parish of Warcop, a barrow was opened in 1766 and contained a secondary inhumation burial associated with part of an urn, a sword, spearhead and possibly a knife of iron, the burial rite suggesting an Anglian interment. Their position high up the Eden valley points to some movement over Stainmore on to the fertile, drift-covered limestone slopes on its western side. Other small finds, once in Crosthwaite's Museum at Keswick, include a horn sword hilt decorated with garnets and gold filigree work; a gilt bronze disc, fastened to an iron plate, embossed with interlace ornament; and an enamelled bronze escutcheon in Celtic trumpet pattern, probably found in Cumberland, and all of seventh century date.

The main conquest and settlement of the Lake Counties by the Northumbrians appears to date from the second half of the seventh century, for Symeon of Durham records that King Ecgfrith (670–85) gave St Cuthbert 'the land called Cartmel and all the Britons in it'. This gift is generally accepted as referring to Cartmel in north Lancashire and shows that the district was still in British occupation at that time. Carlisle must have been firmly held by the English some years earlier, for the Venerable Bede relates that St Cuthbert, Bishop of Lindisfarne, visited the town in 685 while the Queen was staying at her sister's nunnery there. St Cuthbert made a tour of the Roman walls of the town and marvelled at the fountain, which suggests that the Roman antiquities had not been allowed to fall into decay. Bede also wrote of a monastery at Dacre, founded by the English in the early eighth century.

The distribution of Anglian place-names mainly follows the better agricultural land in the lower Eden, Kent and Lune valleys, in Low Furness, the Cumberland coastal strip and the Solway plain. Most are on the deeper glacial drift and on soils which have some calcareous content, desirable for arable farming, which was the type of economy familiar to these newcomers. There is little evidence that the British were displaced

PLATE 25 *Above*, Ill Bell ridge: the route of the High Street Roman Road lies across the slopes in the middle distance. *Below*, aerial view of Hardknott Fort: the rectangular outlines of walls and barrack buildings, and the bath house outside the walls, show up clearly. From the fort the ground drops very steeply to the floor of Eskdale, here seen in sunlight.

PLATE 26 A charcoal-burners' hut. Charcoal-burning in these woods had come to an end by about 1930. Reproduced from *Two Lakeland Townships* by A. P. Brydson.

from lands more suited to a pastoral way of life, though Anglian names are found as high as 600 to 700 feet on the well drained drifts around the hills. Names ending in -*ing* and -*ingas* occur in these areas, usually combined with some topographical word and signifying a group of people dwelling in an area, as in the county name of Westmorland (*Westmoringa land*, the district of those living west of the moors). They are widely scattered and the majority are combined with an additional suffix – *hām* or *tūn* – for instance Hensingham, Rottington, Frizington, Witingham (now Whicham, but given in the old form in Domesday Book), all in west Cumberland; Aldingham in Low Furness and Helsington and Killington in south Westmorland. Other names contain the Old English elements *wīc* (dairy farm), *hām* (estate, homestead) and *tūn* (farmstead, village) and may also date back to the seventh or eighth century. All emphasise that these first Englishmen were farmers – Keswick (*cese*, cheese), Butterwick (*butere*, butter), Sedgwick (Sicga's dairy farm), Cunswick (the king's dairy-farm); Brigham (*brycg*, bridge), Sebergham (Sæburh's homestead), Heversham (Heahfrith's homestead); Dalton (farmstead in a valley), Coulderton (preserves a British word *culdir*, a narrow strip of land), Clifton (farmstead on the cliff) – to give but a few examples.

That there was some Anglian settlement in the main valleys of the Lake District is suggested by the retention of Old English *mere* for some of the chief lakes – Buttermere, Grasmere, Windermere – and also valley names such as Mickelden (*micel*, *denu*, great valley), while Great and Little Langdale are first recorded as Langedene (*lang*, *denu*, long valley) in the twelfth century, the second element being replaced by the more familiar dale, from Old Norse *dalr*, in the sixteenth century. Likewise Old English *cofa* (a hollow, cove, cave) survives in names such as Blind Cove, Snow-cove Gill and Lingcove Beck, though early records of these are lacking. Anglian settlement is also inferred by place-names such as Rydal (*ryge*, *dæl*, the valley where rye was grown) and Keswick already mentioned. The Old English word *ōra*, ore, occurs occasionally, as at Orgrave in Furness, recorded in Domesday Book, and indicates early haematite mining.

Farm buildings of the Anglian period have not yet been identified, for houses were largely built of wood and all trace of them often destroyed by later ploughing, while many villages first settled by the Anglians are likely still to be occupied. With improved techniques of excavation and of air-photography in recent years, a start has been made in recognising domestic buildings of this obscure time. Stone built churches of the period have not survived in the Lake District, but fragments of sculptured stone crosses in Northumbrian style and of eighth to tenth century date are known in the Lake Counties. After the Norse settlement, the blending of Anglian and Scandinavian styles seen on these monuments reflects the changing cultural influences of this district in the tenth to twelfth centuries. The finest, and earliest, cross in Cumberland, at Bewcastle, with its runic inscription and flowing vine-scroll ornament, lies outside the scope of this book, as do others at places north and east of the Lake District hills. None of this early sculpture has been found near the churches and chapels of the central hills; all comes from the fringe area in which Anglian place-names are most common. Crosses at Irton, Lowther, Dacre, Kendal and Heversham date from before the last quarter of the ninth century, while fragments from Workington, Waberthwaite, Kirkby Stephen and Urs-wick, also of Anglian inspiration, were wrought after that date. Round-shafted crosses at St Bridget's, Beckermet and the 'Giant's Grave', Penrith, reflect Mercian influence in the tenth and eleventh centuries. In addition the few finds of Northumbrian coinage (*stycas*) are again from places in the lower ground, as at Castlehead (Atterpile Castle) and from a cave in the limestone at Merlewood, both near Grange-over-Sands, while coins of Alfred (871–99) have been found at Dean north-west of the Loweswater Fells.

Towards the end of the ninth century Northumbrian power crumbled before the onslaughts of Danish, and later of Norwegian Vikings. Halfdan, the Danish king of York, harried Northumbria and Strathclyde, burning Carlisle in 875, but this is one of the few references to Danish power spreading west of the Pennines. An embossed silver and gilt-bronze cup in eighth century Anglian style was found buried in the churchyard at Ormside, near Appleby, before 1823 and in 1898 a late ninth century burial of a warrior, with his great iron sword, shield-boss and knife, was found at the same place. These finds may be connected with Halfdan's men returning homeward with loot from Dacre, or Carlisle. Professor Stenton argued that names in the upper Eden valley ending in *by* (farm-stead), such as Waitby, Crosby, Asby and Bomby, were given by Danish settlers from Yorkshire, but Professor A. H. Smith, in his introduction to *The Place-Names of Westmorland*, considered the Danish element negligible. Indeed, many of the place-names ending in *by* belong to the period after William Rufus built his castle at Carlisle in 1092 and moved English peasants from the south to till the better agricultural land.

The lack of documentary evidence stimulated an intensive study of place-names, which has thrown much light on the Scandinavian settle-ment of the district. It is clear from these that this last, large scale folk movement was by people of Norwegian origin, rather than by Danes. Furthermore, the presence of Gaelic personal names and inversion com-pounds, together with the word *erg* (shieling, hill-pasture), borrowed from the Irish *airghe* of the same meaning, shows that many of the Norse settlers of the Lake District came from Ireland. A clue to when this move-ment began was given by Symeon of Durham, writing in the eleventh century, when he spoke of a nobleman, Eardulf, and Tilred, Abbot of Heversham, fleeing eastward across the Pennines because of piratical raiders at a date which cannot be later than 915.

As yet archaeology has provided meagre evidence for the settlement and no farms or shielings of the period have been identified with certainty. This is largely due to the Norse preference for building in turf and wood. Scandinavian analogies have been cited for rectangular buildings at Ewe Close and Cow Green, Crosby Ravensworth, and at Little Langdale, Glencoyndale and Troutbeck Park, but none have been excavated with sufficient thoroughness to prove this identification. Excavations at Jarlshof in the Shetland Islands show clearly what Viking farms in the Lake District must have been like. Foundations at Old Whelter in Mardale, dug by W. G. Collingwood in 1922, were considered by him to be a Norse shieling, suggesting that the Old Norse name of the farm was derived from *hvilft* (hollow in a hillside), *ergh* (shieling). However, *The Place Names of Westmorland* says that the name Whelter comes from the plural, *hvilftar*, and makes no reference to a shieling. A terraced mound behind Fell Foot farm in Little Langdale was claimed by H. Swainson Cowper to be the site at which the Norse council, or Thing, met. W. G. Collingwood expressed doubts at this identification, showing that the field name for the site was The Orchard and that the artificial terraces might have been due to cultivation. Another possible assembly place for the Norse administration could have been in the vicinity of Shap, where the name *Thengeheved* in an early thirteenth century charter relates to a field in Swindale.

Few pagan Viking burials of the late ninth and tenth centuries have been recorded, their scarcity showing that many of the Norse who came as settlers rather than raiders, had already been in contact with, and possibly converted to Christianity in their previous homes in Ireland and the Isle of Man. All are men's graves with fighting equipment and are by inhumation, with the possible exception of a burial at Hesket-in-the-Forest east of the river Petteril. They have been found at West Seaton, near Workington, at Eaglesfield and Aspatria, while swords of Viking type from Rampside churchyard, near Barrow-in-Furness and Witherslack, and a bronze ring-headed pin from Brigham church, were also probably from graves. In addition a few fine silver brooches and torcs reflect the art styles and silversmith's skill of the Irish-Norse. Outstanding among these are a penannular brooch from Orton Scar, dating from the first half of the tenth century, and another of the same type from Brayton Hall, near Aspatria. Of similar inspiration are two spectacular silver 'thistle' brooches, one with a pin twenty inches and more in length, found near Penrith and at Fluskew Pike, north of Dacre.

Christian sculptured stone crosses and house-shaped hog-back tombstones of the tenth to twelfth centuries show the complex mixture of the people settled in the district in these disturbed times. Norse mythology is represented on some crosses, as at Gosforth and Dacre, alongside Christian symbols, while hog-backs from Lowther and Gosforth show battle scenes on sea and land, circular shields lining the gunwale of a Viking ship at Lowther are also carried by the opposed ranks of warriors depicted on the Gosforth stone (Fig. 18, p. 245). The chain pattern, common on Manx crosses of the period, is widely used in Cumberland, for instance on the well known wheel-head cross at Gosforth and at Muncaster, and is also seen in another medium decorating the silver-plated hilt of the Viking sword from Hesket-in-the-Forest. The wheel-head cross was probably inspired by the high crosses of Ireland, dating from the eighth and ninth century and brought to Cumberland by Norse settlers from across the Irish Sea. The distribution of these sculptured stones is comparable with that of earlier Anglian monuments and the occurrence of both styles, as at Dacre, Kirkby Stephen and Urswick, shows that Scandinavians worshipped at pre-existing Anglian churches. Stones worked in Norse style again occur in the fertile fringe around the Lake District hills, for instance at Haile, St Bees, Distington, Workington and Penrith in addition to the places already mentioned.

Anyone familiar with the district will be aware of the strong Scandinavian element in place-names. Fell (*fjall*, hill), dale (*dalr*, valley), beck (*bekkr*, stream), gill (*gil*, ravine), tarn (*tjörn*, small lake), are among the topographical names of frequent occurrence and all are of Norwegian origin. Names combining -thwaite, -garth and *sætr* point to clearings in woodland, enclosures and shielings, some of which will date back to the Norse settlement. Names with a Scandinavian flavour are not all early, because the Norse element has survived strongly in language and dialect to this very day. For instance, Old Norse *leikr* (play) and *hlaup* (leap) remain, with the same meaning, as laik and laup. Only those names for which an early record exists can be accepted with certainty as marking Viking settlement, while their interpretation is the specialist province of linguists and historians. However, the abundance of such place-names in the Lake District proper shows clearly the extent of Norse settlement there. Brathay (*breiðr*, *á* broad river), Greta (*griót*, *á*, the rocky or gravelly river); Loweswater (*laufsær vatn*, the leafy lake), Ullswater (*Ulfr's* lake); Birkrigg (Birch ridge), Hawkshead (*Hawkr's* shieling) and, Seathwaite (*sef*, *þveit*, sedge clearing) are but a few examples.

Irish–Scandinavian names are most common in south-west Cumberland and south Westmorland, but are not entirely confined to these districts. We have already mentioned that Irish *airghe* (shieling, hill pasture) appears as a lone word -*erg* in the dialect of the Norse settlers and occurs in such names as Birker (birch tree shieling), Mosser (shieling on the moss), Berrier (hill shieling), Sizergh (Sigrith's shieling) and Winder (windy shieling). Goedelic personal names also occur, for instance in the place-names Patterdale (Patraicc's valley), Fitbrandan (Brandan's meadow) and Melkinthorpe (Melkan's hamlet); while inversion compounds such as

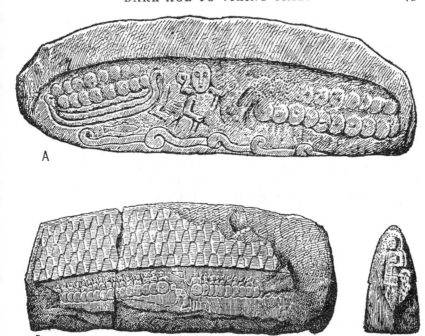

A

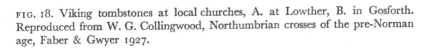

B

FIG. 18. Viking tombstones at local churches, A. at Lowther, B. in Gosforth. Reproduced from W. G. Collingwood, Northumbrian crosses of the pre-Norman age, Faber & Gwyer 1927.

Crosscrake (Kraki's cross), Seat Sandal (Sandulf's shieling) and Tarn Wadling (Gwyddelan's tarn), show the Celtic influence on word formation. Professor W. H. Pearsall, in a paper quoted below, argued that the westerly distribution of -*erg* names, often on rocky, damp or exposed sites, may mean that the Norse from Ireland arrived late, when earlier Scandinavian settlers, using the word *sĕtr* to express shieling, had already taken possession of the better land around the hills and had also penetrated into the heart of the Lake District. However, little satisfactory evidence exists to support this theory.

Comparisons with the Norse settlement of Iceland have been used by Professor E. Ekwall, W. G. Collingwood and others in an attempt to re-construct the sequence of their colonisation of the Lake District. Writing from an ecological point of view, Professor Pearsall drew comparisons with the modern methods of extending human occupation in the birch forests of northern Norway: 'The usual method there is to clear small areas of damp or alluvial ground in the woodland for hay crops and for firewood, both for winter maintenance. The economy is based on cattle which graze freely in the surrounding woodland, usually returning to the settlement in the evening. Grazing pressure around the original settlements is eased by sending younger men to outlying sites (shielings) and succeeding generations thus go farther and farther into the woods, the shielings of one generation being the homesteads of the next. The continued use of timber for fuel (and building) and the failure of natural tree regeneration owing to destruction of seedlings by grazing animals, leads to the disappearance of woodland in widening waves from the original settlements. From an ecological point of view an interesting feature is the considerable, or complete, replacement of herbs by grass in the original woodlands before their final destruction, which produces a condition familiar in the Lake District woods. The whole process is distinctly different from that envisaged in accepted descriptions of wholesale woodland clearance for arable purposes where removal of trees is more important. The process is a gradual one – the principal agent being the prevention of regeneration by grazing. In other parts of the world similar methods can be seen in use by pastoral peoples, though both in East Africa and in New Zealand fire is more frequently used by primitive men. There is, for example, the place-name *Swithenhate* in Cumberland that refers to clearance by burning. However, this additional element is less in evidence in wet climates such as those of north-western Europe. A rule which seems to apply more generally is that cattle are the chief element of pastoral use where large predators are present.' Further reference to clearance by burning is inferred in the names Brunstock, Brunthwaite and Brinns. The Norse reaching the Lake District in the tenth century did not find a virgin countryside, but one on which successive peoples, from prehistoric to Anglian times, had exerted considerable influence. Cultivation of arable plots as a supplement to animal husbandry had begun as early as Neolithic times, while planting cereal crops on suitable soils had been encouraged by both Romans and Anglians. Norse preference for a pastoral way of life, rather than an economy based on arable farming, made available many sites attractive for this use in little occupied localities, both in less well drained areas in the lower ground and in extensive areas in the uplands.

In the same paper quoted above, Professor Pearsall made interesting analyses of the place-names in Cumberland west of the river Eden which refer to trees, plants and animals. Now that the place-names for Westmorland are also published it would be interesting to extend this study to cover that county too. He divided the district into an outer region of deep drift and alluvial soils overlying Carboniferous limestone and Permian sandstone, and an inner region of shallower, or acid soils derived largely from Silurian and Ordovician rocks in the central Lake District; place-name records before 1400 were shown as 'early' and additional names before 1600 as 'late':

Names	O. 'Outer' deep soils		I. 'Inner' shallow soils		Proportions*	
	Early (E)	Total (T)	Early (E)	Total (T)	OT	IT
Alder	6	12	1	5	24	12
Ash	3	5	5	7	10	17
Birch	2	4	4	11	8	26
Oak	10	20	4	8	40	19
Willow	4	6	2	5	12	12
Aspen	—	—	2	2	—	5
Holly	—	1	—	1	2	2
Rowan	—	2	—	—	4	—
Yew	—	—	1	2	—	5
Hazel	4	6	1	2	12	5
Thorn	7	13	1	4	26	10
Apple	5	9	1	3	19	7

*As percentages of total, excluding hazel, thorn and apple.

'On the deeper "outer" soils oak names predominate, alder being frequent and ash, birch and willow are clearly of secondary frequency. In the shallow-soiled "inner" part of the district, birch is rather more frequent than oak and ash. Alder and willow attain considerable prominence, though alder falls to one half the percentage value of the outer zone. Of the usually less frequent plants, aspen and yew appear and largely replace hazel in the deeper-soiled areas. While it would not be wise to draw large inferences from these results, it is interesting to note that the names indicating plants of the base-rich soils, ash, aspen and yew, are collectively more abundant on the shallower soils rather than (as one might have expected) on the deeper ones, which include considerable areas overlying limestone. Presumably this is due to the presence of "new" soils, actually weathering fragments from rock exposures. There are, however, other differences in distribution of individual tree-names which indicate the probability that the woodland types were not uniform over the whole of the deep-soiled area. Thus in the "outer" region alder was evidently most frequent on the damp alluvia near the Solway.' Examples of the names of trees in the order given in the above table are included in the place-names Ellerbeck, Eskholme, Birkhill, Ackenthwaite, Salkeld, Espbarrow, Hollinghow, Rowantree Bank, Yew Bank (Yuebanc in the thirteenth century), Hazlegill, Thornbarrow and Applethwaite.

When applying this method of comparison to plants of cultivation and other non-woody plants, there is a striking difference between the recorded names in the outer and the inner regions. Twenty-four names in the outer region show that barley, oats, wheat, flax, hay and beans were grown, nineteen of these records dating before 1400; while in the inner area the only three records, all after 1400, refer to barley and flax. Examples of place-names referring to these crops include Bigrigg (Bygrigg in the thirteenth century, O.N. *bygg*, barley), Haverigg (Hauerig in the twelfth century, O.N. *hafri*, oats), Whitecroft (Waytecroft in the thirteenth century, O.E. *hwǣte*, O.N. *hveiti*, wheat), Linewath (O.E. *līn*, O.N. *lín*, flax), Hayborough (Hayberhe in the thirteenth century, O.E. *hēg*, O.N. *hey*, hay) and Benwray (Benewra in the thirteenth century, O.E. *bēan*). Other plants mentioned in place-names in Cumberland, chiefly later than 1400 in both outer and inner regions, are whin, bracken and gale, while ling is recorded once in the outer region. All are plants which occupy clearings and the increase in the inner region after 1400 may well reflect an increase in population and additional clearance of woodland at this time.

Analysis of animal names mentioned with sufficient frequency led Professor Pearsall to the conclusion that: 'The interesting features of the data are no doubt the preponderance of the cattle and swine names as compared with those of sheep and goats – especially in the central district. Almost two thirds of the domestic animal names belong to the former category. Further, the references to cattle will refer to enclosures and will not include free roaming stock (A. H. Smith, *Place-names of the West Riding of Yorkshire*, 1961). The best and earliest examples of the sheep names occur in the lowland districts which appear to have been settled at an early date (i.e. with early Anglian names).

Names	Outer (O) sites		Inner (I) sites		Total as Percentages*	
	Early	Total	Early	Total	O	I
Oxen, calf	9	12	4	6	28	27
Swine	8	14	4	9	33	41
Sheep	6	8	1	3	17	13
Goat	2	2	1	1	5	5
Horse	6	8	3	3	17	13
Buck, hart	2	6	—	2	14	9
Badger (brock)	—	1	—	—	2	—
Wolf	4	7	2	2	16	9
Fox	2	7	—	—	16	—
Coney	1	6	—	2	14	9
Cat	1	1	—	1	6	4

*Percentages of total domestic animals.

'The second pronounced feature is the increase in *coney* names from 1 to 8 in the later part of the two periods of assessment. Possibly this accounts for the parallel increase in the number of fox names. It is no doubt a result of the spread of rabbits after the Norman influence made itself felt.

Smaller changes in numbers are of doubtful significance as they must be considered against the fact that the total number of animal names doubled in the second of the two periods considered. It is evident that in the earlier pre-1400 period, wolves were the wild animals exciting attention as judged by place-names, for half the total references are to them, and this may perhaps be due to the existence of wolf-pits in specific localities. This proportion diminishes to one-quarter in the second period assessed, and the change is probably indicative of the more settled condition of the district.

'The general conclusions, necessarily of a tentative nature, which can be based on evidence of this type appear to be that the woodlands may have been of more varied character in the more irregular relief of the central Lake District. The noticeable feature of their composition is the greater proportion of birch and of lime-loving species like ash, aspen and yew, to some extent apparently at the expense of hazel. On the evidence of the place-names the outer region was mainly a damp type of mixed oak wood including much alder.

'The second difference is that there is no evidence from plant-names that there was any arable cultivation in the central Lake District in the earlier period and very little in the later. This suggests that the population, if engaged in agriculture, must have been entirely pastoral. The character of the early animal names recorded suggests that the early pastoral economy was almost wholly based on cattle and swine. It was presumably later and after the elimination of wolves that the present preponderance of sheep farming developed. This district is, of course, still pastoral but the animal population is now largely composed of sheep. There is, without going into detail, much evidence that this change from cattle and swine to sheep was due to the influence of the monasteries, as was widely the case in northern England.' Examples of place-names which include the names of animals in the order given in the above table are Oxen Park, Calva Hill, Grisedale, Ewelockhill, Gatesgarth, Rosewain, Buckholme, Hartrigg, Brockbarrow, Ulpha, Todd Crag, Coneygarth and Cat Bells.

The exact course of events taken by the Anglian and Norse settlements can never be known, but it was these people, together with the British inhabitants of the area, who laid the chief foundations on which the human history of the Lake District rests. All this took place in the six hundred years after the Romans left and before William of Normandy conquered England. The troubled state of the Border, the habit of self-defence developed since Roman times, the safety and splendour of the hills – all these have helped to build the independence of mind and spirit so evident in the men and women born and bred here down the centuries.

CHAPTER 15

THE CHANGING LANDSCAPE THROUGH POST-ROMAN CENTURIES

Willie had ridden and Willie had reived,
Willie had burned and Willie had thieved;
Lord Scroope he marched wi' rank and file
Poor Kinmont Willie to auld Carlisle.
Kinmont Willie, Border Ballad

IN the last four chapters we have seen something of the evidence on which is based our knowledge of the more distant past of the Lake District. Though the interpretation may change at any time, as further work in the earth sciences produces new knowledge, the enduring factual records of archaeological material, vegetation history, and linguistic interpretation of the place-names in their earliest written form provide the raw material from which the story of the earliest local interaction between man and his environment must be reconstructed. With the emergence of the Lake District into written history in the twelfth century, its story enters the province of the historian. The natural historian can now read, in the wealth of documentary evidence which has been sifted and described by local historians, accounts of the events and processes by which the Lake District landscape of today, and the habitats which it provides for its flora and fauna, have developed from that wilder Lake District which was so incompletely documented in Domesday Book.

Many books have been written on Lake District history, from Thomas West's account, in 1774, of the Antiquities of Furness, to the recent scholarly works of Canon Bouch and Professor Jones. In this chapter only those parts of history which directly concern the naturalist will be considered. It is a history which to naturalists is most tantalisingly sprinkled with gaps.

We should like to know, for instance, both how and when the swampy alderwoods of the valley floors were cleared and drained, of the stages by which the great dale-head farms such as Gillerthwaite (Ennerdale), Burnthwaite (Wasdale) and Gatesgarth (Buttermere) were first carved out of the wilderness and provided with drained and cleared fields for their crops and walled intakes for their stock. The Scandinavian names of these and many other farms need not necessarily mean that they date from the time of the Viking settlements, for as we have seen in the last chapter a strong Scandinavian element has persisted even until the present in local dialect. There are certain features of the local farmstead architecture which have parallels in Norway today – the covered spinning or storage galleries and the barns on a floor above the shippons, entered by a ramp. These are found locally in buildings of which the date cannot be earlier than the sixteenth century, so the architectural fashions of the Norse settlers would seem to have survived for many centuries, as did their language. In a document of 1334 what must be the land of Gillerthwaite appears as 'the head of Eynerdale'; it was then a 'vaccary' or large un-enclosed cattle farm. 'Gillerthwait' first appears in the sixteenth century when its tenants were repeatedly fined for breaches of customs of the manor including permitting their cattle and sheep to stray on to the forest – i.e. the land which was still the hunting chase of the lord of the manor. The enclosure of the Gillerthwaite land probably took place during Elizabeth's reign, for in 1568 the estate steward was given leave to make new arrangements for the government of the tenants and the letting of the land, which had been enclosed from the waste. There were four tenements at Gillerthwaite then, the rent of each being 13/4d (Littledale, R.P., Trans. C.W.A.A.S., 1931).

Professor Hoskins has described the landscape of Wasdale Head as 'showing the frontier of cultivation and the characteristic field pattern of medieval colonisation – winding lanes and tiny irregular fields: a hand-made landscape'. Bouch and Jones point out, however, that even at the beginning of the sixteenth century, every tenant at Wasdale Head still had a holding of arable and meadow in the unenclosed town field, though enclosure had by then proceeded further at Nether Wasdale and in Eskdale and 'the landscape was already beginning to assume a patchwork quilt appearance' as small fields were enclosed by stone walls. This process did not reach its maximum extent, however, until about 1600. During the early period of valley settlement, from the Viking invasions until the end of the sixteenth century, some high-level boundaries between the rough mountain pastures of adjoining dales would be delimited by boundary stones or walls, but of course most of the drystone walls which now run for so many miles over the fells are much more recent, dating from the enclosure of the common grazings during the last two centuries.

Between the visit of William Rufus to Cumberland and the building of his castle at Carlisle in 1092 and the end of the twelfth century, most of the Lake Counties had been divided out between Norman barons and Norman abbeys. Much of what is known of local history through the medieval centuries comes from the documentary records of the abbeys – particularly Furness, Holm Cultram and St Bees. Furness, by far the greatest, was founded in 1127, and received from Stephen on its foundation much of Low Furness; thereafter it steadily added more and more of the Lake District to its possessions. About 1163, Henry II confirmed the abbey in the possession of the whole of the eastern part of Furness Fells – i.e. the land between Windermere and the Brathay on one hand and

Coniston Water and Yewdale Beck on the other, which included Hawkshead, Satterthwaite and Colton. In 1209, the Furness monks bought Borrowdale for £156. 13s. 4d., and in 1242 David de Mulcaster of Butterilket in Eskdale granted them a great part of Upper Eskdale. About 1290 the monks were allowed to enclose the pastures of Butterilket and Lincove, which adjoined the forest of the Lord of Egremont. In the documents which record these transactions, some of the names of rivers and hills already appear in recognisable form but others cannot be found on the modern map.

With the enclosure of these rough fell pastures, the Cistercian monks of Furness began the conversion of what remained of natural vegetation on their land to sheepwalk and enclosed coppice woodlands. The Cistercians were farmers and wool merchants on a very large scale. Their conversion of large tracts of fell country, much of it at that time probably still wooded to some extent, into sheep pasture, must have greatly changed not only the vegetation but also the animal communities. We can suppose that sheep-farming had been introduced by the Norse settlers, but the nature of the Norse husbandry can only be deduced from that prevailing in their homeland, and from certain characters of the Herdwick breed of sheep which suggest a Norse origin (see Chapter 16). There is plenty of documentary evidence, however, that the Furness monks both cleared great areas of waste for their sheep farms and took part on a large scale in the medieval wool trade. This would be the time of origin of much of the semi-natural *Festuca–Agrostis* grasslands, including areas which have in subsequent centuries degenerated into wet *Nardus–Juncus squarrosus* heaths, by the processes of soil degradation discussed in Chapter 7. In the course of the century following their foundation, the Cistercian monasteries of northern England acquired a wealth and an influence which seems remarkable when one considers that they were on the borders of the wild and that often, as one ancient writer remarked, there was neither soil to grow crops nor sun to ripen them. Their prosperity was founded on their sheep, and on the wool trade resulting from them, and this influence spread through the whole rural economy. Instead of a mode of life in which a man maintained flocks and herds sufficient only for his own needs, a new system arose in which for the first time large-scale economic exploitation of the highland zone was possible.

So began the movement that in the next 500 years was to convert most of the Lake District to sheep walk. Little by little the nibbling ewes destroyed the oakwoods, the hazels and the birch scrub which remained, except where these were of commercial value as enclosed coppice. By the sixteenth century most of the unenclosed woodlands must have been almost completely derelict and no longer regenerating. During this period the red deer, originally a forest animal, must have been ousted by the sheep until, except for its foothold in the enclosed woods of High Furness, it lingered only in the wilder fastnesses of the Ennerdale and Martindale Fells. The wild boar, also a forest animal, is said to have been exterminated by the thirteenth century. This rapid spread of sheep, which are among the most defenceless of creatures, meant that the larger predators, particularly the wolf, must have been exterminated at about the same time. Eagles and other larger birds of prey would also be persecuted and greatly reduced in numbers by the sheep farmers. Though the golden eagle had only been extinct as a breeding bird since the end of the eighteenth century, and it is only a hundred years since the last authentic record of the shooting of an eagle by an enraged local farmer who was losing his lambs to it, the persecution of eagles, kites and peregrines must have begun with the Norse or medieval shepherds.

The extent of the wool trade of the abbeys of Furness, Shap and Calder is apparent from the fact that they were all known to Italian wool merchants in the fourteenth century, but the only clue as to the breed of sheep which supplied the wool comes from the fact that the northern wool was considered to be of poor quality and commanded only a comparatively low price, so that a hairy type of fleece seems probable. So it is not possible to know whether the flocks which increased over the Lake District 'as the wolf and the eagle were slowly exterminated' were of white-faced or black-faced hill sheep.

Father West in 1774 gave this account of the part played by the Furness monks in changing the landscape during these medieval centuries: 'Furness, through all those [early] periods, was favourable to the chase; nor was it till the latter part of the thirteenth century that the woods in High Furness were much destroyed, and the commons contracted: at that time the abbot of Furness, to increase the number of customary tenants, obtained licence of the king, Edward I, to inclose large tracts in Furness Fells which are still known by the name of parks, as Abbot Park, Stott Park, Oxen Park, etc.'

The enclosure of land from Furness Fells to provide more sheep farms for the Abbey continued through the centuries of monastic rule until the Reformation. A survey of the revenues of Furness Abbey taken two years before its dissolution gives the rents of 'Several (33) Granges in Furness Fells' as totalling £102. 14s. 2½d., and the list includes, in addition to the farms mentioned above by West, many still existing farms such as Marsh Grange on the Duddon estuary, as well as Lawson Park and Parkamoor, which remained sheep-farms until the recent acquisition of their land by the Forestry Commission and the National Trust respectively (Chapter 17). In Furness, including those parts which were owned by the Abbey, are many farms with names such as Sawrey Ground, Dixon Ground, Bolton Ground, etc. From surviving agreements between the Abbey and its tenants it appears that many of these were first enclosed from common pasture about the beginning of the sixteenth century. West comments thus: 'The abbots of Furness permitted the inhabitants to enclose quillets to their houses, for which they paid encroachment rent. The inclosures were called the grounds of the persons that first inclosed them, and some retain the same name at present, as Walker Ground, etc.' An agreement in 1509 between the Abbey and its tenants at Colton allowed the enclosure of $1\frac{1}{2}$ acres of 'such ground as hath been of the common pasture within the time of man's mind.' Documents quoted by West record that after the Dissolution, parts of the Abbey lands passed to Henry VIII, and so to his successors until, in 1614, James I disposed of much of the land in Colton, Satterthwaite, Haverthwaite and Claife, where he 'sold the freehold and inheritance to every one of the said tenants of his own tenement, with a rateable part and portion of the commons and wastes: after which sale the tenants did enclose and improve the said commons and wastes.' This formed part of the wave of enclosure during the early seventeenth century which seems to have been characteristic of the Lake Counties as a whole, and during which the pattern of small walled fields in the dale-heads, as at Wasdale Head, must have been almost completed.

Many villages did, however, retain open town fields until much later. Records of the manor court of Broughton-in-Furness show evidence of an open arable town field in the now moorland district of Subberthwaite in 1659. The town fields of Coniston, between Church Beck and the enclosed land of Coniston Hall, survived into the mid-nineteenth century, divided into 'dales' or shares, from which the occupiers took what they could with scythe or sickle. Most of the enclosure of remaining open town fields was completed during the general enclosure of the commons at the beginning of the nineteenth century.

The Furness monks, and doubtless also those of the other abbeys, exploited the woodland resources of their land as well as the pasture. The enclosure and preservation of large areas as commercially managed coppice woodlands, particularly in Furness Fells, resulted (see Chapter 8) in the preservation of many elements of the woodland fauna and flora. By the time of the Reformation, most of the original woodland must either have been converted into sheepwalk, or have been enclosed as coppice, or have become scrubby downgraded woodland on the common grazing lands where browsing of the trees and bushes provided additional winter feed for stock.

Medieval landscape history in those parts of the Lake District which were not under monastic ownership involves the question of the many 'Forests' and their nature. Both royal forests, such as Inglewood on the borders of the Vale of Eden and the Lake Country, and the private forests such as Copeland between the Esk and the Ehen, were forests only in the legal sense, and were not necessarily covered with trees. They were regions where the Forest Law prevailed, protecting the interests of the royal or private owner who desired to hunt game, against the interests of local men who wished to enclose and improve land for pasture or agriculture. No man might assart, that is take new land into cultivation, or cut down trees, or hedge, ditch or drain in either royal or private forests, and though it is unlikely that these areas were continuous high forest, much of them must have been scrubby woodland in which the larger forest animals – deer, wolves and wild boars – found refuge from the ever-increasing destruction of their habitats by medieval colonisation of the wastes. In all these areas 'These forest regulations acted as a damper on agricultural improvement and in the twelfth and thirteenth centuries, a period of expanding population, were felt to be particularly repressive. ... As the population of the area increased and the demand for land became greater the area of the forest decreased. Land which had once been forest land reserved for the lord's hunting was first opened to cultivation, then deserted by the deer. The forest area became more and more the mountain fastnesses. Cultivation of land led to disafforestation as the deer retreated before men breaking up the waste.' (Liddell, W. H., *T.C.W.A.A.S.*, 1966.) It is important to remember that 'disafforestation' is here used as a legal term, meaning the freeing of the land from forest laws as it was taken over as farmland, rather than necessarily as the felling of a high forest. By 1578 the 'forests' of south-west Cumberland had been reduced by progressive 'disafforestation' to comparatively small areas in the mountains and the upper parts of the valleys of Buttermere, Ennerdale and Eskdale. One of the latest refuges of the red deer in this part of Cumberland was 'The Park', the fell-side south-east of Ennerdale Water now called 'The Side', where in 1675 it was said that there were 'Hartts and Staggs as great as in any part of England'. This fell-side still carries an attractive wood of well-grown ash, oak and birch trees, with a particularly rich carpet of mosses on its bouldery floor, and has probably never been completely treeless.

'The destruction of these great deer "forests" was continuous and inevitable. An increasing population promoted an increasing demand for arable land and pasture for cattle and this in turn would lead to a decreasing amount of land left waste for the deer. The rights accorded to Calder Abbey illustrate how far the destruction of the forest had gone by the middle of the 13th century. Others enjoyed the right to use all the forest, but only Calder could "cut down and prostrate the branches of trees throughout all the woods of (Copeland) Forest, for the feeding of animals in winter to the first of May." ' (Liddell, op. cit, quoting from the Register of the Priory of St Bees.) This is the earliest documentary record which has been found of the use of leafy branches for feeding animals – a practice now thought on botanical evidence to have been begun about 3000 B.C. by the earliest Neolithic farmers (see Chapter 13).

As the forests became more and more reduced by the expanding settlements of an increasing population, there was for a time, from the end of the thirteenth century onwards, a stage when the deer were confined by fences to areas which were called 'Parks'. The Dale Park valley in Furness Fells, tributary to Grizedale, owes its name to one of the latest of these deer parks, which was enclosed by Abbot Banks of Furness as a hunting chase in 1516. 'The Fence' (The Side) in Ennerdale, and other parks at Wasdale Head, Troutbeck and Cockermouth, as well as the heights of Claife which were imparked by an earlier abbot in 1338, were all examples of such deer parks; within them the deer were hunted by the owners of the land, while outside the parks the tenants and lesser men could hunt the fox, hare and rabbit over what had become extensive common grazings. The surviving native red deer are now found where continuity of land ownership and management has preserved their habitat from the encroachment of sheep-walk ever since these medieval centuries.

The landscape which was taking shape in the sixteenth century, then, at the time of the dissolution of the monasteries, though still a wilder countryside than today, inhabited mainly by people living in small scattered communities, would nevertheless include certain familiar elements. Settlement had penetrated into some of the inmost mountain valleys, and walled green enclosures of cleared and drained land would surround each settlement. Some of the villages still had town fields in which individuals held strips (dales) for hay or cultivation. On the open fells, the grasslands which had been developed from former woodlands provided safe common grazing for sheep and cattle, since all the large predatory animals had gone. Red deer, already much reduced in numbers from earlier times, were still to be found in Ennerdale and Wasdale fells as well as in those parts where they survive today. Though there was probably little high forest with valuable timber, we have seen that biological evidence suggests that many woods, in Borrowdale and other valleys, have never altogether ceased to be woods. On the one hand there would be the enclosed and well-managed coppice woods, providing an asset of at least equal value with grassland or arable, like those in Grizedale Forest which passed from the Furness monks to William Sandys at the Dissolution and, worked on a fourteen-year rotation, provided charcoal for three bloom-smithies (see p. 147). On the other hand there would be many unenclosed woods, in which a more casual management would combine modest utilisation of timber and exploitation for firewood with provision of grazing and browsing for stock. The unenclosed commons and wastes would include scrubby woodland and isolated trees and bushes – indeed, certain commons on lower land survive in this state today. On these commons, use would be made, in the very ancient manner, of leaves and twigs of trees for feeding stock.

There would therefore be some economic competition between the interests of livestock and the woodland industries. In 1565, 'at the request

PLATE 27 Herdwick sheep in Langdale: ewes, lambs and sheepdogs in the meadows of Stool End beneath Bowfell.

PLATE 28 *Above*, Herdwick sheep crossing Wasdale Bridge: white-faced sheep with horned rams and hornless ewes, on a packhorse bridge. *Below*, Birks Bridge: a gorge in the upper Duddon where the water runs clear and green.

of the tenants of Hawkshead and Colton, the bloomeries in Furness were suppressed, that the tops and croppings of their woods might be preserved for the nourishment of their cattle in winter.' (Garnett, 1912). On the other hand, Bouch and Jones (1961) interpret the suppression of the Furness bloomeries in 1564 as in the interests of the Mines Royal (formed in that year).

Much of the surviving commons of the Lake District, open scrubby woodland with conspicuous evergreen bushes of holly and juniper (savin) must represent down-graded forest which has been exploited for centuries as common grazing, with winter feed for browsing animals in the tender shoots and evergreen leaves. West writes, in 1774, 'The woodlanders of High Furness were charged with the care of the flocks and herds, which pastured the verdant sides of the fells: . . . and in winter to browse them with the tender sprouts and sprigs of the hollies and ash. This custom has never been discontinued in High Furness; and the holly trees are carefully preserved for that purpose, where all other wood is cleared off, and large tracts of common pasture are so covered with these trees, as to have the appearance of a forest of hollies. At the shepherd's call the flock surround the holly-bush, and receive the croppings at his hands, which they greedily nibble up and bleat for more. . . . The mutton so fed has a remarkable fine flavour.' This practice was noted by Wordsworth in his *Guide to the Lakes*, and Garnett (1912) also comments on its survival into the early nineteenth century. According to Thompson (1946) holly and thorn leaves and branches were used even more recently as winter feed for Herdwick sheep (Chapter 16).

As for the cultivated land, Bouch and Jones point out that the rather primitive system of cultivation of the common fields which was practised through the medieval centuries in the Lake Counties 'can at best have yielded little more than sustenance.' This cultivation system appears to have been closer to the 'infield' and 'outfield' arrangement found in the Celtic north and west than to the three-year rotational cropping and fallow of open fields characteristic of the English settlements farther south and east. Because of poor returns from arable cultivation 'the economy of these [the Lake] counties depended a good deal on the rearing and sale of cattle, sheep and wool, the beasts being maintained partly by means of not very abundant meadows and partly by rough pastures and the extensive fell commons.'

This dependence of the economy on pastoral farming, having most of its resources in cattle and sheep, must have rendered the local population particularly vulnerable to the Scottish raids which continued up to the Union of the Crowns in 1603, and, in parts of the northern Lake District at least, must have been the dominant factor in the economy. On the northern fringe of the Lake District where it meets the Cumberland lowland, and in the south round the Morecambe Bay estuaries, peel towers of fire-resisting stone were built in great numbers in the fourteenth and fifteenth centuries. These, of red sandstone in the north and grey limestone in the south, survive either in ruin as at Arnside, incorporated into later buildings as parts of farms (Wraysholme and Blencow) or larger houses (the Halls at Levens, Sizergh, Dalemain and Johnby). Throughout the sixteenth century this building of semi-fortified dwellings continued. There is little purely domestic architecture in the Lake District which dates from before the Union of the Crowns, but there are exceptions. Collingwood's opinion was that the remote dales of the central Lake District would be comparatively untouched by the Scottish raids; he pointed out that though many of the castles round the perimeter date from the turbulent times of the long series of Scottish raids in the fourteenth century – Greystoke, Penrith, Lowther, Millom, Muncaster, etc. – unfortified domestic building had begun before the end of Elizabeth's reign, as at Coniston Hall, the Old Hall at Hawkshead, and Graythwaite Hall; all are in High Furness where there is little record of Scots raids.

The liability to border service in this frontier region was one important condition attached to the usual way of holding land, as customary tenants, in which succession was normally hereditary and carried some of the advantages of freehold. This was the basis of the class of 'statesmen' – small yeomen or peasant-proprietors whose smallholdings carried grazing rights on the extensive fell commons and certain obligations including border service. Rising population in Tudor times tended to bring about further subdivision of these already small farms, and the weaving and knitting of woollen fabrics which became such a widespread home industry in the Lake Counties was one way in which inadequate subsistence from minute holdings was supplemented.

By the end of the seventeenth century enclosure of the arable fields and meadows had proceeded further, and substantial building in stone was going on. From about 1650 building in stone had been begun for smaller farms and cottages, and it is supposed that these would be sited in the same hamlets and villages as the medieval dwellings of wood and clay which have not survived. Local materials were used for the stone houses of this period (c. 1650–1750), so that even now it is usually possible to detect a geological boundary very quickly by the change in building. The angular grey flaggy stones of the central Lake District, usually externally roughcast or whitewashed, with wooden lintels and transoms in older houses and barns of this period (such as Dalehead in Martindale), change rapidly at the boundary with the Trias to neat square red sandstone, with freestone lintels and window-borders – a very characteristic Cumberland house. On the Carboniferous Limestone the stone houses are of the grey lichened silvery stone which is so typical still of Ulverston and Kendal, but is found also in the northern Lake District fringe at Caldbeck and Hesket Newmarket. The characteristic farmhouse in the central

Lake District has a long roof-line and no windows in the gable-end; many of the earlier stone farms had stone-flagged roofs with very massive roof-timbers, but by the middle of the eighteenth century slate roofs had become general. Flags were, of course, widely used for floors until the nineteenth century.

In some parts of the northern fells of the Lake District there is little evidence for an early, medieval period of enclosure and farming systems such as those of Ennerdale, Wasdale and Eskdale. A landscape such as that of Dash Beck, foaming down as 'Whitewater' from the great high wastes of Skiddaw Forest, shows traces only of the enclosure of Dash Farm, which, according to documents in the County Records Office, took place in 1660. On the south-west facing fell slopes, large regular fields surround the farmhouse, with its rectangular stone front so characteristic of seventeenth and eighteenth century building in the Lake Counties. All around and above is the open fell, and its common grazing. Here the soil is the tenacious boulder clay derived from the Skiddaw Slates, and great stretches of rushes in the enclosed meadows show the difficulties of maintaining adequate drainage, even on sloping ground, at this altitude – about 1,000 feet. It has been supposed by some authorities that permanent settlement, and hence fell enclosures, on this northern fringe of the Lake District, would be delayed for longer than in the southern parts because of the Scots raids, and that little improvement of the land may have gone on until the Union of the Crowns ended the activities of 'Kinmont Willie' and his like. Kinmont Willie Armstrong was rescued in 1596, and Carlisle was then a frontier fortress.

Arable farming was not important until after the end of the sixteenth century in either the northern fells of the Lake District or in the hilly country of the border, though during the sixteenth century there were arable open fields in many of the townships of lowland Cumberland (Elliott, G., T.C.W.A.A.S., 1959). These provided autumn grazing for stock on the stubbles. General use of the term 'riving' for areas of land in these open fields (common now in the field names in Aspatria, Blencogo and Holm Cultram) reflects the reclamation of new land from the waste. Each of these open fields consisted of infield and outfield, the infield being cropped nearly every year and receiving nearly all the manure. Some coastal places, for example Drigg and St Bees, are known to have used sea-weed (tangle) as manure on the infield. The outfield was usually partly under plough and partly fallow at any one time, and oats was the chief crop.

As for agriculture in general, there seems no doubt, from the reports of many different observers, that in the eighteenth century the agriculture of the Lake Counties was backward, and that, according to Bouch and Jones, 'Great stretches of potentially useful land lay waste.' Many town fields remained open, and both the agricultural techniques and the arrangement of holdings were wasteful and unproductive, with frequently no attempt to maintain soil fertility except to allow a reversion to grass-land when the land became exhausted by a series of cereal crops without proper rotation. At this time the cereals eaten were largely those produced locally, the common ones being oats and the variety of barley called 'bigge', though some wheat was grown. Pastoral farming was more productive, though with so much common pasture there was little selective breeding of stock. By about 1800 Cumberland was producing about £30,000 worth of butter for other parts as well as its own require-ments in milk, butter and cheese. Sheep were much more numerous than cattle, and the high fell grazings were becoming so much sought after that farmers were willing to move their flocks to some distance from the farm. By about 1800 the spread of the cultivation of turnips for winter feed had reached the Lake Counties, and ended the necessity to slaughter most of the beef cattle in autumn.

The improvement of land which followed the further enclosures of the later eighteenth and nineteenth centuries has been described by Garnett in *Westmorland Agriculture 1800–1900*. The enclosure had 'been going on sporadically for centuries, both by means of intakes from the commons and waste and by combining dales or strips into crofts and closes. From about the middle of the eighteenth century, however, to the middle of the nineteenth, enclosure became more systematic. It could be achieved either by agreement among the tenants and landlord concerned or by private Act of Parliament.' (Bouch and Jones.) During this period there was in many places a decline in the number of 'statesmen', but though the enclosures probably hastened the decline in the numbers of smaller holdings, by consolidation into larger ones, the disappearance of the smaller yeomen had begun earlier. Wordsworth estimated that between 1770 and 1820 the number of statesmen with freehold land was halved while the size of the holdings doubled. As an example of the decline in numbers of the statesmen, Garnett quotes the figures for Ravenstonedale, where in 1541 the numbers of landholders in the dale was 187, in 1734 it was 181, and by 1877 the number was reduced to 70, but over the same period the value of the land had increased from £1,988 in 1734 to £8,784 in 1877.

The farmers had their grazing on the commons and unenclosed fells, most of it without 'stint' – i.e. with no restriction upon the number of animals they could put on it. An estimate in 1793 was that three-quarters of the total area of Westmorland was uncultivated waste. Much of this, of course, would be high mountains, but the lower fell country and the lowland commons were also extensive. Garnett's view of the vegetation of these was 'Benty grass, brackens and heath, with savin bushes and holly trees and patches of sweet green pasture here and there between, constituted the growth of the commons and moors.' These commons appear to have been densely crowded with the local animals – not only the sheep and cattle on which their owners' prosperity was mainly based, but horses and flocks of geese had to be supported. Not surprisingly, the quality of the sheep and cattle seems to have been uniformly low, for not only was any sort of selective breeding made impossible by the unfenced commons, but also most of the animals were quite inadequately fed.

Garnett gives a vivid account of the farming difficulties in this humid climate, before the importance of an adequate system of field drains and liming was understood (see Chapter 7). In the enclosed land of the valley bottom meadows, naturally established grassland for hay meadows became so thick with mosses (the species of moss are not given) within seven to ten years that it must then be ploughed and sown with corn – oats, barley and then again oats – until the moss was destroyed; during the ploughing farmyard manure was applied if it was available. After a few crops of corn, with decreasing yields, the natural grassland was allowed to re-establish itself, and then in seven to ten years the process had to be repeated. It was only as knowledge advanced, and where capital was available for deep draining and liming, that the terrible handicap of this humid climate and wet and often sour acid soil was overcome. Partly by the dissemination of new knowledge as communications improved, and partly under the stimulus to agriculture provided by the enclosures and the opportunity to improve the enclosed land, there was a great improvement in farming techniques and hence in the productivity of the land during the first sixty years of the nineteenth century.

Most of the Parliamentary Enclosure Acts under which the common wastes were enclosed were passed between 1800 and 1854. Typically, they provided for the wastes and commons to be walled around with stone walls, for a part of the enclosed land (varying between a quarter and a sixteenth) to go to the Lord of the Manor, part to the vicar or rector, while the remainder was shared out between the various landowners of the parish. On the 2½-inch, Sheet SD29, Ordnance Survey map will be found reference to, for instance, 'The Lord's High Allotment' on Broughton Moor among the names given to the enclosures of this period (see also pp. 262-3). Mineral rights over the land remained with the Lord of the Manor.

After these enclosures 'Commons that had only been capable of half starving the animals pastured upon them, with paring and burning, fencing and draining, liming, ploughing and sowing, changed in the course of a few years from an annual rental value of between 6d. and 1s. per acre to one of from 20s. to 30s. per acre.' (Garnett.) Often the improvement doubled the number of animals which the land could support. One of the main objects of the improvements was to destroy the heather and heath vegetation which had replaced the original primeval woodland on these commons, and to remove the acid surface (mor) humus from the soil surface. Up to an altitude of *c.* 1,000 feet, this was extensively brought about in the early nineteenth century by paring, burning and liming, after fencing and draining. The drains were made either with stones found on the land or with tiles. 'Paring' with a special type of spade removed the tough stems of heather and heath and the undecomposed acid humus litter, all being then burned. On suitable land this process could be replaced by ploughing with a one-horse plough. Between 150 and 250 bushels of lime to the acre was then applied on top of the spread ashes, and ploughed in. The cost of reclaiming the commons by this process, after which oats could be grown except on the rockiest land, was about £8 an acre, over the period 1825 to 1845. Even land too poor and acid for cultivation was turned into good hay meadow by this treatment. After 1850, paring and burning 'was superseded by ploughing after draining with a much lighter application of lime.' In 1877 the cost of reclaiming land by this method was about £16. 18s. 9d. per acre. In this improved farming, superphosphate and Peruvian Guano were used as well as lime, and a cropping rotation of oats, or potatoes, followed by turnips, and then seeding to permanent pasture with rye grass, Timothy and fescue, etc., was established.

In the central Lake District, the enclosures of this period of land improvement in the early nineteenth century werē, in general, the origin of the drystone walls which, 'running like live things about the fells' (Hugh Walpole) enclose the 'allotments' up to the limits of the intakes, usually at about 1,000 feet. Above the highest walls there is a very large proportion of the Lake District which is still legally common land, unenclosed, and freely open to public access by tradition or legal provision. A few high walls run as boundaries, sometimes in surprising places. Some of these unenclosed fell commons are stinted, with limits to the number of animals which a farmer may graze, but most are unstinted, when the limits to the number of sheep are set only by the number of ewes which his enclosed pastures will feed at lambing time. Sometimes there is a strong contrast between the degraded pasture, now mainly *Nardus* and bracken, of unstinted and hence overgrazed fell commons, and neighbouring areas where the common grazing is stinted and so restricted. On the north-west slopes of Skiddaw this contrast can be seen between Bassenthwaite Common, which has been stinted since the enclosure of the open fields in 1796 and has much good *Agrostis–Festuca* grassland, and adjoining commons on the Skiddaw fells where the grazing is unstinted and *Nardus* and bracken predominate.

The walls which were built between 1750 and 1850 were the work of wallers who often camped on the high fells for days at a time while at work. Pierced at intervals by the hogg-holes which can be opened to let the sheep pass, and provided here and there with stiles for human passers-by, many of these walls survive in good order and still provide sheep-proof enclosures (when the hogg-holes are blocked) and boundaries between neighbouring flocks. Other walls have fallen in; frost and snow may begin the work and scrambling sheep and careless walkers carry it on. It is not now an economic proposition to rebuild these walls at modern wages, and where it is really necessary to provide a sheep-proof boundary, wire fencing is replacing the old walls. The walls of this period of the late enclosures can be recognised by the usual standard height of 4 feet 6 inches, with two sets of 'throughs' and a cam top, which can be found illustrated in many books on the district. In 1845 such walls cost, to make, 8 shillings per rood of 7 yards, including the cost of carting and gathering. The cost of construction of such walls in 1969 was c. 1600 shillings for 7 yards.

So by about 1850 the settlement pattern and the walls of the rural Lake District had taken very much the pattern which they still show. The development of the urban Lake District began about the same time. The railway came in 1847 to a terminus at the hamlet which became Windermere Town, main drains were laid in Ambleside and Bowness at about the same time, and the population of Keswick grew from 1,350 in 1801 to about 4,730 today. The Lakes Urban District Council was formed in 1935.

Changing farming practices after this will be discussed in the next chapter, and the development of the tourist Lake District in Chapter 17. The rural situation in the fells and dales can be summed up in a verse of local speech quoted by Professor G. P. Jones. He says: 'There was little or no social difference between the Lakeland farmer, whether statesman or leaseholder, and such workers as he employed':

> And o'fare't alike – beath maister and man
> In eatin' and drinkin' or wark;
> They turn'd out at morn and togidder began
> And left off togidder at dark.
> Guide to the National Park, p. 45, 1969

CHAPTER 16

TRADITIONAL OCCUPATIONS IN RELATION TO LANDSCAPE AND HABITATS

12 September, 1800 '*The fern of the mountains now spreads yellow veins among the trees; the coppice wood turns brown.*'
11 November, 1800 '*William had been working at the sheepfold. They were salving sheep.*'

Dorothy Wordsworth: *The Grasmere Journal*

WOODLAND INDUSTRIES

IN earlier chapters we have seen how the preservation of great tracts of enclosed coppice to supply oak, birch and hazel for a variety of woodland industries has been one of the main determinants of the Lakeland landscape, and the history of the Furness coppices has been outlined (Chapter 8). Through the seven centuries of commercial exploitation of these coppices to supply charcoal for smelting iron, from their management by the Furness Abbots until the end of charcoal smelting at Backbarrow in 1921, the collier (charcoal-burner) was a familiar sight in the woods. Other uses of the woodland resources of Furness Abbey are given in the Commissioners' report at the Dissolution, dated 1537.

'There ys moche wood growing in Furneysfells in the mounteynes there as Byrk Holey Ashe Ellers Lying lytell shorte okes and other Undrewood but no tymber of any valewe wherein the Abbots of the same late Monastery have been accustomed to have a Smythey and sometyme two or thre kepte for making of Yron to thuse of their Monastery. And so nowe the said Com'yssyoners have letten unto William Sandes & John Sawrey as moche of the said woodes that is to say of Byrkes Ellers Hasells old rotten trees and other underwoodes as wyll maynteyne iij Smytheys for the whiche they ar content & agreed to pay yerely to the Kinges Highnes as longe as hit shall please his grace they shall occupye the same . . .

'Also there ys another yerely p'fytte com'yng and growing of the same woodes called Grenehewe Bastyng Bleckyng byndyng makyng of Sadeltrees Cartwheles Cuppes Disshes & many other thynges wrought by Cowpers & Turners wt makyng of Coles and pannage of Hogges according as hath alwayes ben accustumed to be made in the said woodes to the yerely valewe by estymacyon of xiijli. vjs. vijd.'

Quoted by Alfred Fell: *The Early Iron Industry of Furness*

Greenhew was a payment due from tenants for taking wood; basting included the manufacture of coarse matting and swills, the swills being of split oak with hazel rims. The coarse matting, according to the Grizedale foresters, was made at least partly of the phloem (bast) of the lime (*Tilia cordata*), the wood of which was also used by the Furness monks for a turning industry. Blecking was the bleaching or drying of bark used for tanning, and binding was another name for coopering. The cowpers made barrels, which were also of oak. Saddletrees (for the saddles of pack ponies), cartwheels and agricultural implements were made of ash wood, and since turners surviving into this century in various parts of the country used elm wood for cups and bowls, the elms of High Furness were probably being used in monastic times by the turners. The 'makyng of Coles' was, of course, charcoal-burning, and the 'pannage of Hogges' refers to the custom of wintering the yearling sheep (hogges) in the shelter of the woods, so that they could browse on the young shoots as well as eat what grass there was. By the beginning of the eighteenth century, with iron smelting well established on a larger scale in the neighbourhood, the coppices were coming to be protected and preserved as valuable assets, and 'Protection given to enable the coppice shoots to re-establish themselves after each cutting, has not only preserved the crop, but also the fertile forest soil and much of its indigenous flora and fauna' (Chard, 1967). So this local management of a natural resource, the timber crop, has actually led to the preservation of a natural habitat, and saved the woods of High Furness from the complete devastation of, for instance, the woods and the woodland habitat round Devoke Water – though, of course, the existing coppice and the grown-up coppice woodlands are in no sense a natural landscape.

In spite of modern population mobility, there is still a remarkable concentration in High Furness of surnames which reflect the former importance of charcoal-burning and the other woodland industries; Woodburn and Ashburner are frequent, there is still more than one woodmonger of the old trade name of Barker among the remaining woods, and Cowpers and Turners recur through local history. Some past history may be read on large-scale maps in the names of the coppices – Ashburners Side for a whole wooded fell-side, Furnace Wood and Great Ore Gate Coppice, while Wintering Park and Hogg Close Wood record the wintering of stock in the woods.

The charcoal-burners lived in the woods in huts like wigwams made of poles, and were still familiar sights in the early part of this century, though all are gone now. Their old pitsteads on flat terraces are still thickly scattered through the steep woods of these valleys, but most traces of their huts have disappeared. All children brought up on the works of Arthur Ransome, who lived for much of his life among the High Furness woods, have read about the wigwams and smoking piles of the charcoal-burners, seen through the eyes of W. G. Collingwood's young grandchildren who were 'the Swallows'. (Plate 26b, p. 241.)

Charcoal was made by controlled combustion with a strictly limited air supply of a pile of coppice poles and branches, of oak, birch, hazel or alder. The pile of concentrically placed pieces was covered with coarse grass or rushes and earth, and fired – then carefully watched for about twenty-four hours until combustion was complete. The location of the early bloomeries and the charcoal forges of the seventeenth and eighteenth centuries, round Coniston Water and in the remote dales of High Furness at places like Force Forge and Cunsey, shows that it was more economical to transport the ore to a source of local charcoal than *vice versa*. During the eighteenth century there was, however, much transport of charcoal by water down the lakes of Windermere and Coniston, from woods near the upper ends of these lakes.

The only kinds of wood which seem to have been regularly kept separate when making charcoal were savin (juniper) and alder, which had certain specialised uses. Savin charcoal was particularly valuable in the manufacture of gunpowder, and commanded a high price at the gunpowder works. These were established from 1764 onwards in the southern Lake District; the last to close, Elterwater, was worked until 1930. Juniper is a slow-growing shrub or small tree, which does not respond to coppicing as do oaks and hazels, and there seems to be no adequate record of whether junipers were felled or only lopped, to provide the raw material for savin charcoal. Certainly the high value of the charcoal would be a good reason for conservation of juniper by refraining from burning the moorlands where it grew.

Descendants of the Turners and Cowpers of monastic times founded the characteristic local industry, the bobbin-mills. These were powered by water-wheels which were usually, as with the corn-mills, overshot wheels in these steeply falling becks, and turned bobbins from birch and hazel wood for the cotton-mills. Cheaper sources of bobbins brought the local industry almost to an end. General coppicing for bobbins came to an end about 1925, but some of the mills survived for a time after that, making other products in turned wood, and there are three bobbin-mills still at work in the Lake District.

The manufacture of the very characteristic local basket of woven split oak, the swill, has not entirely ceased, though the days are gone when nearly every village in High Furness had its 'swilling-shop' with young apprentices learning the trade. There is a working swilling-shop at Haverthwaite, and swills can still be found on sale in Kendal shops. The typical swill is a shallow, coracle-shaped and handleless basket which was made in quantity for gathering the potato crop and other agricultural purposes, and for local sale as a gardening basket or firewood container. Variants with handles were also made, and one of these was designed for the Morecambe Bay cocklers. A swilling-shop had a long iron boiler in which the coppice poles of oak were gently simmered until softened;

while the week's supply was boiling on Mondays, over its fire of billets, the swiller used to bend the hazel rods which formed the rims of the swills into the characteristic oval shape. For the rest of the week he spent his time riving the boiled oak into flat strips, from which the basket was fashioned by weaving them in and out and round the hazel rim. An experienced swiller had a trained eye for good coppice woodland, and would make his offers to local coppice owners after careful consideration.

Now the coppices are fast disappearing as the stools are singled and stored into high forest (p. 147), but in those which remain, oak is cut regularly for wood for packing-crates, coppice poles of hazel and ash (rods and setters) are tied in bundles for ships' fenders, birch coppice is cut for fire-fighting besoms, and ash poles are used for barrel hoops.

FARMING

Old Tyson was a farmer
A statesman of the fell;
Norman Nicholson: *The Bow in the Cloud*

The characteristic animal husbandry of the central Lake District keeps sheep on the fells and dairy cattle in the dales, with beef cattle on the intermediate land in numbers which have fluctuated with economic conditions. At present beef cattle are increasing, partly because high labour costs make milking herds expensive, partly because there is now a subsidy on hill cattle kept above 600 feet, and in some remote valleys because no farmer's wife will now tolerate the isolation of farms such as Swindale Head, so the dale-head pastures have been turned over to beef cattle, and the farm stands empty. The prehistoric settlers who cleared the high woodlands would keep cattle as well as sheep, so there is a long history of cattle on at least the lower fells. At times of population pressure and most intensive farming, with settlement going high into the fells, cattle would be kept at higher altitudes than today. The decline in upland subsistence farming since about 1870, seen in many abandoned high-level farms, has meant a decrease in the number of cattle kept on many parts of the hills, replacement by more sheep, and a decline in available labour following amalgamation of holdings. There is strong evidence to correlate this change with a great increase in the spread of bracken (see Chapter 10).

A typical Lake District fell farm has a small milking herd, often Friesians, which in summer grazes the dale pastures and in winter stays indoors in the shippons, fed on hay grown on the best of the valley meadows and on imported concentrates. The beef cattle, of varied cross breeding, may be wintered inside or outside. The sheep in summer graze the highest intakes and the unenclosed fell commons to the mountain summits. The flocks are brought down for mating in late autumn, after which some of the breeding ewes remain on lower ground but some, and the non-breeding sheep, return to the lower fells for the winter, except for the lambs of the previous spring, the hoggs, which usually spend their first winter on lower ground, often on the coastal salt marshes of the Solway and Morecambe Bay. The native breed of sheep is the Herdwick, a small coarse-woolled animal of great hardiness and remarkable agility ('terrible lish' is the local expression). On the eastern fells which pass over the Pennines the black-faced hill sheep have always been kept, and of these the Swaledale has recently increased in numbers in the central Lake District and is often crossed with the Herdwick, while Rough Fell, Dalesbred and Scottish Blackfaces are also kept. The Herdwick has a strong homing instinct which usually keeps it on its own heaf on these unenclosed fells, but local farming practice has from time immemorial been adapted to the need to manage flocks on unenclosed common grazings; each farm has its own mark, a combination of a particular daub on the fleece with a particular nick on the ear – the smit mark and the lug mark respectively – which is recorded in the local 'Shepherd's Guide' and serves to identify strays. The gathering of these wide-ranging flocks which graze the fells up to the highest summits can only be achieved with the help of the sheepdogs, which in the Lake District are typically the local sort of Border collie. They may be seen in action under special conditions at the summer Sheepdog Trials at Rydal and Troutbeck and at many local agricultural shows.

The management of a Herdwick or cross-bred mountain flock is closely related to the ecology of the fell grazings, which as we have seen are essentially biotic communities developed from the upper woodlands. Mating with the tup (ram) is arranged for late November or early December, so that the twenty weeks of the gestation period do not end before mid-April, when the grass in the dales and on the lower fells has normally begun to grow again. Until recently the Herdwicks were not fed extra rations in winter, but depended on what they could find on the hill grazings through the winter, with results described by Garnett (1912), who said that in hard winters they 'will eat anything green, holly and savin and ivy and moss from the rocks and walls.' In recent years there has been a notable increase in the practice of feeding hill ewes during the winter, and racks of hay can be seen in dale pastures where they have never been used before. The result of this is that the size of the farm's flock can be increased, for in former times this was limited by the number of ewes which could be wintered on the farm. Winter feeding has proved to be of great value in lambing time, for in poor seasons when cold springs or drought delayed the first growth of grass on the bleached winter pastures, ewes dependent on natural grazing tended to have little milk and to reject their offspring. Weakly lambs run the hazards of the predators of the hill grazings – foxes and carrion crows attack living lambs, and buzzards and ravens are quickly on the spot to share the carrion that may remain. The hunts work closely with the farmers in lambing time to try to trace and destroy those foxes which are confirmed lamb-worriers (see page 188).

The lambing ewes may now be fed, but the non-breeding sheep on the lower fells, dependent on what they can find, will in these hungry spring days before the coming of the new grass eat anything green; any tree seedling on their grazings is nibbled down and destroyed, and on steep and broken craggy fell-sides these agile sheep clamber from ledge to ledge, destroying the herbaceous vegetation on all but the sheerest cliffs and sometimes getting themselves cragfast in the process. They are, indeed, so terribly lish that a very high and intact stone wall or a first-class fence is necessary to exclude them from woods and gardens; the spring glory of daffodils in Lake District gardens and orchards as well as in the woods and lakeside meadows is due to the unpalatability of the daffodil. It is one of the few plants which survives the depredations of the Herdwicks, which at this time of year will take a standing high jump at a five-foot stone wall. (Plate 23, p. 208.)

It is immediately clear to any ecologist that the Lake District is in general heavily over-grazed (p. 180). In many places both grazing down of the plant cover and the scufflings of the sheep in the sheltered places where they lie are tending to initiate soil erosion by destruction of the protective cover of vegetation. This, if it develops, carries away the topsoil and leaves a sterile subsoil which will not be recolonised by a soil-forming succession (see Chapter 9) so long as the sheep continue to trample it. There is thus, under present conditions, a general down-grade tendency over much of the sheep-walk.

The indications are that this down-grading has been accelerated during the last few decades, and that it has gone hand-in-hand with an increase in stocking with sheep, itself the result not of any ill intentions on the part of the hill farmer but of the inexorable pressure of modern economy and changing farming techniques on men who need to make a living from their farms. The Lake District is not a countryside where absentee land-lords encourage exploitation of the land, but one where estates have continued for many centuries in occupation by holders of ancient names, and the land is in general farmed by their tenants or by small independent proprietors, descendants of the customary tenants and yeomen whose names, like Tyson and Dixon and Atkinson and Postlethwaite, recur through local history from the time of the enclosure of the 'grounds' in the sixteenth century. These men have a responsible attitude to the land in which their roots go deep, and it would be wrong to think of the Lake District in the same terms as, for instance, parts of the Scottish Highlands where the sheep are comparative newcomers, shepherded by salaried shepherds who are the employees of some distant landlord. Nevertheless, the Lake District is over-grazed, and it is of interest to trace the interaction of ecology and economics by which this has come about in at least one part of it.

The name 'Herdwyck' was originally applied, in monastic times, not to the breed of sheep but to the type of sheep farm, such as Lawson Park, in which the farm and the sheep were let together to a tenant. Most Lake District sheep farms are still let on the same terms: a stated stocking of sheep goes with each farm, it is taken over by an incoming tenant and when he leaves he must leave an equivalent number of sheep on the land. So long as the farming economy was tied to the natural capacity of the land, sheep stocks could not be much increased, for the limiting factor was the number of sheep which could be wintered on the farm. A hundred years ago, in one parish of the southern Lake District not far from Lawson Park, the 'establishment' of sheep on each farm, which is known, was probably not very much greater than in monastic times. There was then no additional feeding for any of the sheep except the hoggs, which spent their first winter in the hogghouses, simple barns of drystone walling which are now, in ruin, scattered all over the farms of this and many other parishes, among the hay meadows. Hay was stored in the hogghouses at haytime, and fed to the housed hoggs through the winter. B. L. Thompson, in his book *The Lake District and the National Trust*, says that leaves of holly and branches of thorn were also given to the hoggs for browsing, and suggests that to this practice is due the number of old hollies and thorns still found among these upper hay meadows in many places, and in the woods and scrub above them. The farmers still depended on winter browsing in certain woods and larch plantations to supplement the hill grasslands as winter grazing for the older sheep and lambing ewes.

At some time, about sixty years ago in this particular area, but much earlier in, for instance, parts such as Skiddaw Forest where there are no hogghouses, the sheep farmers began to send their hoggs to winter on lowland farms, especially on the rich grazing of the coastal flats round the Solway and Morecambe Bay. This practice enabled them to increase the size of the flock far beyond that which could be wintered on the farm, and must have increased the pressure on the hill grazings when the hoggs returned in April from their winter by the sea. For a long time a further limit would be set to the flock by the number of lambing ewes which the valley intakes could support in spring, but winter feeding of the ewes with hay removes this restriction. Recently, it has become more profitable on some farms to house and feed ewe (gimmer) hoggs under cover, rather than pay for agistment on lowland grazing – a return to the earlier practice but using bought-in feeding-stuffs rather than the natural products of the farm as in the hogghouse days. All these changes must tend to increase the summer stock of sheep on the fell grazings, and it is difficult to avoid the conclusion that to this is due the recent acceleration of the signs of over-grazing.

The main income from the flock comes from the sale of store sheep to be fattened in the lowlands, and draft ewes which, after three to five seasons on the fell, are drafted to lower and better land where they are crossed with a ram of larger breed to produce cross-bred fat lamb. Pure Herdwick male lambs fattened for the butcher fetched c. £2 at 1969 prices, whereas the progeny of Herdwick ewes drafted to the lower pastures and crossed with a Leicester ram fetched up to £8. The National Trust, landlord to many Lakeland sheep-farmers, is well aware of the economic problems involved, and is prepared to add extra valley land, wherever possible, to its fell farms. Its *Report* says: 'The heads of the valleys tend to have the harshest climate, and as a result the hoggs – that is the lambs of the previous spring – are sent away to milder conditions for their first winter, and the cost of hogg wintering is a major expense to the farmer. Moreover, in the valley heads, the grass begins to grow late in the spring, just when the ewes are lambing and just when the young cattle, housed through the winter, should be turned out. It follows that some extra land a little farther down the valley, especially if it is sheltered or has a bit of building on it, is a really valuable addition. Another use for it is for the draft ewes – those which have finished their useful life with the flock and are to be disposed of. They are normally sold in the autumn to some other farmer with better land, who puts them to a Wensleydale or Down tup and sells them with their lambs at a good profit in the spring. Extra land at the valley foot enables the fell farmer to keep his draft ewes through till the spring and reap this profit for himself.' (1963–4.)

The coarse fleece of the Herdwick is of comparatively little value and now used mainly for carpets, though some is mixed with finer wool for tweeds. The profit from the sale of the products of the June clip is therefore less than that which comes from the sale of draft animals and fat lamb.

As well as the gatherings for tupping and clipping, the sheep-farming year includes other gatherings of the fell sheep for dipping as a protection against the worst of the parasites to which the flesh of sheep is heir. Formerly these precautions took the form of salving with a mixture of butter and tar; then arsenical insecticides, and now organic compounds are used. Salving, in the eighteenth and early nineteenth century, was a messy operation, the mixture of butter and tar being applied to the skin through the parted wool; it was done between mid-October and mid-November. The insects and other parasites are members of a natural community and many hairy or woolly-coated animals in the wild are subject to their attacks, but the close crowding of a domestic animal in its habitat increases both the numbers of its parasites and the intensity of their attack. The blowfly (*Lucilia sericata*) is one of the chief enemies of these mountain flocks, for a heavily attacked – a 'wick' sheep – with the maggots eating away its living flesh, can so easily creep into the bracken and die a horrible death before its plight is discovered; the corpse then provides both a medium from which countless more blowflies hatch out in turn and food for ravens, crows and buzzards. Dipping now helps to prevent the blowfly attacks, and also protects the sheep against scab, which is caused by mites (*Acarina*) which eat into the skin. The sheep-tick (*Ixodes ricinus*) is also technically a mite; this burrows into the skin and sucks blood, and in heavy infestations weakens the sheep. Liver-fluke, the malady caused by the parasitic flat-worm (*Fasciola hepatica*), is in some parts not very common, probably because the water is not sufficiently calcareous for the alternative host, the freshwater snail (*Limnea truncatula*). Nevertheless, some of the ancient sheep-walk of the Lake District is 'sheep-sick' owing to heavy infestation with flukes and ticks; this was one important economic reason for the change to forestry on the centuries-old sheep-farm of Lawson Park.

The origin of the Herdwick sheep has given rise to much speculation. Among much legend and theory, several facts emerge from recent genetical work on sheep, and seem to confirm one of these theories. 'The Herdwick is therefore possibly the sole survivor of a hairy Norse sheep that came from the north, and it is said that a similar sheep existed in south-west Scotland two hundred years ago.' (Ryder, 1964.) The name Herdwick was not used for the sheep breed until quite recent times, but in the records of Furness Abbey was first used for the sort of sheep-farm which has been described, where the sheep go with the farm. From this usage as the description of a sort of farm, the name has been transferred to the sheep, but there is little evidence for the exact characteristics of the breed before selective sheep-breeding during the eighteenth and early nineteenth centuries. The distinctive features of the Herdwick now are the small size, stocky build, grey faces (usually darker in the lambs), horns only in the males, great hardiness and tremendous agility, a characteristically mild and intelligent expression, and a coarse strong hairy fleece. The earliest account of the breed is given by Clarke in his Survey of the Lakes in 1787, but this includes unsubstantiated legends.

Ryder, in his recent account of the history of sheep breeds in Britain, points out that the combination of white (=grey) face with a high frequency of the gene controlling the presence of haemoglobin A (gene frequency in the Herdwick is 0.80) is not found in any other breed of mountain sheep in Britain, but does occur in some Scandinavian breeds. The wool of the Herdwick resembles that found at some Norse settlement sites in Scotland in having both hairs and finer wool; this differs from the wool of the Brown Soay sheep of St Kilda, etc., which is thought to be the most primitive of British sheep, because in the Soay (as in the Shetland sheep) the fleece is of soft fine wool with kemps (outer long strong fibres) but is not hairy. The coarse hairy fleece of the Herdwick, which often has black fibres, resembles that of the black-faced mountain breeds, rather than the primitive sheep of prehistory which the Soay is thought to

PLATE 29   Yew Tree Farm, Coniston; the bracken harvest.   Traditional building including a covered gallery ("spinning-gallery") on the barn.   Bracken was cut for bedding stock until recently.

PLATE 30   Birk How farm, Little Langdale.   *Above*, in a state of disrepair when first acquired by the National Trust.   *Right*, after restoration.

approach most closely. A fairly recent introduction of black-faced blood into the Herdwick seems possible, on this evidence.

The black-faced hairy sheep with horns on both rams and ewes, now represented by the Pennine breeds – the Swaledales and Rough Fell – and the Scottish Blackfaces, are thought to be descended from sheep introduced into north-east Britain, but the date of introduction is uncertain. These breeds also have a high gene frequency for haemoglobin A. The scraps of leather excavated from a store at Hardknott (see page 233) thought to be possibly a Roman cobblers' workshop were from a hairy sheep and not from one like the Soay. In about A.D. 1400 Cumberland and Westmorland were noted for the coarseness of their local wool, but there is no record of the characters of the sheep which produced it.

Histories of agriculture show that in the east of the Lake District, in areas such as Longsleddale, replacement of Herdwicks by black-faced breeds has taken place within the last 150 years, and this process is gradually extending as the Swaledale ousts the pure Herdwick. It is not certain, on the available evidence, whether the distinctive characters of the Herdwick had been combined in a type of sheep which was introduced by the Norse settlers into the Lake District (and possibly into south-west Scotland also) but the evidence from genetics is in favour of this. There is no evidence, however, for the persistence in pure form of *all* the characters of the Herdwick through the time since the supposed introduction by the Norse settlers of this small white-faced hairy sheep with a high haemo-globin A gene frequency. The presence or absence of horns is a feature which seems to have varied through the years, according to agricultural histories. Similarities which have been pointed out (for example, Ellwood, 1897) between Norwegian and local sheep marks, and between Old Norse and local dialect terms relevant to sheep and sheep-farming, have no bearing on the breed of sheep, but only on the language spoken by the farmers. The origin and derivation of the local scale of numbers for counting sheep is still controversial. The fact that the Romans were using skins of hairy rather than woolly sheep at one Lakeland site does not provide certain evidence about the sheep in north-west England, and the hairy wool of the northern monasteries could have come from either black-faced or white-faced hill sheep.

Garnett, in his *History of Westmorland Agriculture 1800–1900* (1912) points out realistically that until the commons were enclosed and particularly until an Act was passed in 1907 to regulate the pasturing of entire (un-castrated) males on the common lands, it was not possible to develop or maintain pure breeds of sheep. His account shows that a native black-faced breed – 'the Black-faced Heath breed' – was very common in Westmorland in the eighteenth and early nineteenth centuries, and from it was developed the Rough Fell and the Swaledale sheep, as well as the Scottish Blackface. These black-faced breeds remained common in east

Westmorland, though in 1840 the Herdwicks still extended over the eastern fells through Longsleddale and Ravenstonedale.

The National Trust owns and lets to tenants at a normal agricultural rent many of the famous sheep-farms of the Lake District, such as Troutbeck Park, Butterilket in Eskdale and Black Hall in the upper Duddon, as well as a host of smaller ones including Birk How in Little Langdale. Its policy is admirably set out in the Lake District Report of the Trust for 1963 and 1964, page 28: 'The Trust has given much thought as to what should be the size and shape of its farms in the Lakes, especially the sheep-farms at the heads of the valleys. Much of the character of the district depends upon its farming, both as regards the detail round about the farmstead and in general on the fells and in the fields. Unless both the tenant-farmer and his landlord are prosperous there is no hope of keeping the house and buildings in trim repair let alone carrying out necessary improvements in the traditional local style, nor will the right type of tenant be attracted when the farms come to be re-let. Upon the right type of tenant and his prosperity depends the continuation of the characteristic way of farming based mainly on fell-sheep and stock rearing. It is said that fell farming is not so much an industry but more of a way of life; certainly the man who can put up stone walls and knows how to manage sheep among the fells needs to have been born and bred amongst them. Unless he can make a reasonable living and provide himself – and his wife – with decent living conditions, the necessities and some of the luxuries of life, he is unlikely to survive for many more generations in this modern competitive age. Unless he has the prosperity to finance his farming – livestock, machinery, manures, – it is bound to go downhill, to fail to provide him with a living and to take on a down-at-heel appearance, which defeats the Trust's prime object.'

The Lake District reports of the Trust contain abundant evidence and illustrations of the enlightened management of the Trust as a landlord, and the part which it is playing in maintaining the traditional fell sheep-farming as the dominant form of land use in the Lake District. The old farmhouse of Birk How was falling into disrepair when the Trust embarked on renovation; by using traditional materials they were able to convert it into a dwelling acceptable by modern standards without any loss of its old beauty – not even of the houseleek. (Plates 30, p. 273.)

SLATE QUARRYING

Lake District slate has been used for roofing for a very long time, for it would appear that some of the Roman buildings, including the fort at Ambleside and the barrack blocks at Hardknott, were roofed with local slate. After this, however, there was a long period when buildings were usually roofed with more perishable materials including turf and thatch, though slate appears to have been used locally from the latter part of the twelfth century. It would not, however, be until the general wave of rebuilding in stone which began in the seventeenth century that both building stone and roofing slate would come into demand locally. By the late seventeenth century, Wren was using Lake District slate for roofing buildings in London, including Kensington Palace. The small and long-abandoned quarries which are scattered all over the Lake District are places where stone and slate, and flags for flooring, were locally quarried on a small scale for local needs. This small-scale working must have gone on here and there for nearly three centuries. Most of these little old quarries on the fells are now overgrown with vegetation and are rapidly becoming part of the landscape; their greening tip-heaps, scattered with parsley fern and saplings of rowan, ash and birch, provide new habitats for plants, and the rock faces of the quarries make sites for nesting birds.

Some of the Lake District slate is, however, of such excellent quality that certain of the quarries have remained in operation and produce large quantities of slate and stone for export, both from the district and to other countries. The seventeenth-century farmers on Gawthwaite Moor above Kirkby-in-Furness found that their local slate was of particularly good quality, and began to quarry it out from surface workings as a more profitable way of life than farming; they, like all the customary tenants, paid a royalty on the slate to the Lord of the Manor. In 1803 the land became through inheritance the property of Lord George Cavendish, later the Earl of Burlington, and he 'organised the activities of the various small quarries as a joint undertaking, which allowed systematic development and increasingly efficient working.' (from an article in *The Quarry Managers' Journal*, 1964). Today the main quarry of the Burlington Slate Quarries Ltd. at Kirkby is the largest slate quarry in England, and the export trade of the company produced nearly a quarter of a million pounds of foreign currency in the year 1967–8. Burlington slate has been worked for so long now that it is well known locally that roofs slated with it have given good service for over two hundred years.

At the other end of the Lake District, the Honister quarries have been producing equally durable slate for a long time; it is known that they were in full operation in 1753. The main workings of the Honister, or 'Buttermere' green slate, are in the crags which tower above the western side of Honister Pass, and provide some of the most spectacular quarries of the district. The other green slate quarries lie in a belt which stretches from Kentmere, by Kirkstone, Langdale and Elterwater, to the great group of quarries round Coniston. Many of the quarries of this belt had fallen into disuse before the war, but have been re-developed in the last thirty years to provide both green roofing slate and large quantities of green stone for building and a variety of architectural purposes. Old quarries like Moss Rigg, Spout Crag and Broughton Moor have been

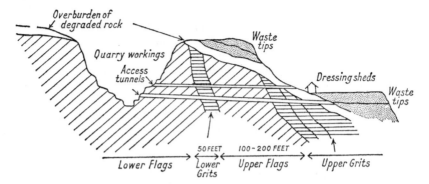

FIG. 19. Section through the Burlington Slate Quarry (Coniston Flags). From Quarry Managers' Journal.

re-opened or extended, their names can be seen on lorries on all the motorways of Britain, and their green slate and stone is exported in quantity, as far afield as Canada and Australia.

Modern quarries make full use of mechanisation to win the slate from the rock face and to transport the blocks of slate to the finishing sheds, but the riving of roofing slate is still done by hand by craftsmen, just as it was done in the eighteenth century by the old quarrymen who manhandled their sleds of slate across the precipice of Honister Crag. It is a truly local craft in which the son is still willing to follow his father's trade, for the Burlington Quarries state proudly that several of their 120 workers 'represent the fourth generation of their families to work in the Kirkby quarries'. While all roofing slates, both blue and green, are riven by hand, the thin slabs which are now used so extensively for facing and cladding can be either naturally riven or sawn, and the quarries of this belt include large sawing sheds equipped with elaborate modern machinery.

From the seventeenth- and eighteenth-century methods of working surface deposits, whether from shallow pits on Gawthwaite Moor or from the face of Honister Crag, the industry advanced to deeper workings by horizontal tunnels called levels, and open quarry holes. In many of the large holes, access and drainage were provided by 'levels' opening farther down the hillside. Modern development of the industry has improved access to workable slate. Honister Crag has been honeycombed with galleries and tramways which ended the difficult and dangerous delivery of the slate in sleds down the face of the crag. Broughton Moor and Spout Crag have been opened up as wide open quarries from an earlier stage of tunnels and levels from which the old quarrymen had won their slate.

The good slate of the Lake District is of two kinds. The green slate of

Coniston and the quarries from Kirkstone and Elterwater to Broughton Moor is, like the Honister slate, part of the Borrowdale Volcanic Series; while the blue or blue-grey slate of Kirkby-in-Furness and the old quarries at Brathay, Coldwell and Bannisdale, in the southern Lake District, is derived from sedimentary rocks of the Silurian series. In both rocks the parent material of the slate is a fine-grained deposit which accumulated by deposition in rather shallow water, but in the green slates the accumulating material was of volcanic ash which had been shot out from volcanic vents of Ordovician age, and come to rest in neighbouring shallow seas, whereas in the blue slates the accumulating sediment was a finer marine mud or sludge, derived from erosion of the contemporary land surface. It is this difference in basic composition and mineral content which determines the difference between the green and the blue slates, for in both of them the slaty cleavage was imparted later, when lateral pressure from crustal movements brought about a reorientation of the constituent particles, so that all came to lie parallel in a direction which determines the cleavage of the slate. When the 'river' applies pressure to a block of slate it splits or cleaves or rives along the plane in which its particles lie. This direction is, in good slate, quite independent of the original bedding-planes of the rock – the successive layers in which the accumulating sediment was built up. The banding or striping which can be seen across the face of many naturally riven slates represents the bedding-planes, and the best workable slates are found where the banding and striping dips at a low or moderate angle to the cleavage-planes, along which the slate can be riven. Many 'flags', which are somewhat slaty sediments splitting into very thick slabs compared with a roofing slate, are rocks in which the cleavage is either very poorly developed or coincides with the bedding planes, as in the 'sheerbate flags' of the Coniston Grits. In both volcanic and sedimentary slate, there are kinds in which the bedding-planes are not horizontal and parallel, but show ripple-marks and 'current-bedding' which perpetuate the conditions of sedimentation in the shallow seas in which they were formed. The green slate from Spout Crag Quarry, high on its Langdale fellside, is famous for the beautiful markings which result from ripple-marks and current-bedding.

It is the basic difference in composition between the green slates of the volcanic rocks and the blue slates of the Silurian sediments which is responsible not only for their different colour but for their different properties. The green colour of the volcanic slate is due to the presence of the mineral chlorite, and much of the present demand for this rock for facing and cladding modern buildings results from this most lovely colour, which ranges from the pale green of the Elterwater quarry, through the silver grey and green of Spout Crag, to the light sea green and olive green of the lower and upper levels respectively in the great

Broughton Moor quarry. The volcanic ash from which the green slate was formed is a more coarsely grained sediment than the marine sludge from which the blue slate originated, and this is reflected in the types of roofing slate. The fine-grained blue Burlington slate is riven into thin slates of standard sizes from blocks of about twelve inches in thickness, delivered to the riving sheds. Burlington quote eight different grades, some of standard size and some which can be delivered in any size. The strength and durability of the Burlington slate is at least equal to that of the purple Welsh slates, and to most people its colour is much pleasanter. The beautiful roofing slates produced at Broughton Moor and Honister, also guaranteed to a life of centuries, are, since they are derived from a coarser-textured volcanic ash, thicker than Burlington slates when hand riven, and come in random and not standard sizes. To the builder they are more like rough-hewn tiles, and are normally laid in diminishing courses from eaves to ridge. From this basic difference it is apparent why the more standardised and therefore cheaper Burlington slates, which at the time of maximum output from the quarry in the mid-nineteenth century must have roofed hundreds of miles of the grim urban terraces of northern England, are still the local material of choice when cost is the first consideration.

The use which has been made in local building of the slaty rocks of the Lake District provides a good example of the relationship between vernacular architecture and local materials which is stressed by W. G. Hoskins in his books on the making of the English landscape. For traditional walling and building no rock inside the limestone fringe can claim much beauty except that of colour; Lake District stone is angular and ungracious until long softened by time or protected and camouflaged with external rendering and colourwash. Until Victorian times local builders accepted the limitations of the stone and kept their building plain. The traditional long roof-line, low-pitched roofs with end chimneys, and plain gable-ends are found in most of the old farms. Plain stone and slate porches, and chimney-tops of tilted slates, were usual.

Very occasionally, as at Fell Foot in Little Langdale, slates were hung to protect a stone wall from the weather, but such slated walls were never common. It is the plain good proportions of the older houses which makes them so satisfying to the eye, and among the churches, too, it is the plainest and smallest which are most memorable; Cartmel Fell, Wasdale Head, Martindale and Mungrisdale remain in the mind's eye longer than Wordsworth's church at Hawkshead, sitting 'like a throned lady' with spreading aisles, and restored from the snow-white limewash which covered it in the eighteenth century. There is plenty of comely building in local stone in the older parts of the villages and smaller towns, and Hawkshead's picturesque centre is extended on one side into some of the best of all twentieth-century council houses. But the architectural horrors of Keswick, Ambleside and Windermere arose when the Victorian builders forgot the limitations of their material and tried to be decorative. Scattered through the district are examples of unfortunate ephemeral architectural fashions of the twentieth century. It is one of the difficult tasks of the Lake District Planning Board to try to ensure that new building in the National Park is of a kind which will not offend the eye of the majority of this and following generations. The guiding principle that local materials used in the traditional manner is the safest line to follow (as in the Hawkshead council houses) comes up against the hard economic facts bewailed by Professor Hoskins – that substitute materials imported from outside the district are cheaper.

In the last decade, modern urban architects have found that the essential hardness of this local stone and its long resistance to weathering, combined with the splendid colour of so much of the green and blue slates, makes it an attractive material for facing and cladding the matchbox blocks of contemporary buildings. Inch-thick slabs from the green heart of Wetherlam, Honister or Broughton Moor, wrought by frame saws, must be to the modern architect something of what Barnack and Ketton stone were to his medieval counterpart. Men won Jurassic stone from Barnack and Ketton to build cathedrals at Peterborough and Ely, and Gothic and classical courts in Cambridge, and must have left a considerable mess in the quarries at the time. To those who deplore the debris of the quarrying industry in the southern Lake District, there is at least the comfort that it is not possible for the exile to travel far in London now without being able to lift his eyes to a piece of Lakeland stone; the new St Thomas's Hospital is clad with Moss Rigg, the new Times building and new additions to Imperial College with Broughton Moor, and the Strand Underpass is lined with facing blocks of natural riven Burlington blue-grey.

CHAPTER 17

THE LAKE DISTRICT TODAY

'We have not quite determined how far it shall carry us' said Mrs
Gardner, *'but perhaps to the Lakes.'*
No scheme could have been more agreeable to Elizabeth . . .
'My dear, dear aunt' she rapturously cried. *'What delight, what felicity!*
. . . What are men to rocks and mountains?'

Jane Austen: *Pride and Prejudice*

AT the time when Elizabeth Bennet made her abortive attempt to visit
the Lakes during the Napoleonic Wars, enclosure among other factors
was bringing about a marked improvement in native agricultural methods.
The Wordsworths at Dove Cottage, Grasmere, at the turn of the century,
regularly walked four miles into Ambleside and back to collect their post,
and since Dorothy was accustomed to note in her journal the passage of
tourists in carriages (for example, 9th June, 1800) it can be supposed that
they were not numerous. But the intentions of Mr and Mrs Gardner in
Pride and Prejudice show that a carriage trip to the Lakes was an accepted
form of holiday for a London business-man at that time, for one can
always trust Jane Austen's sociological observation. The early turnpike
roads must have encouraged travel for pleasure, and the existence in the
late eighteenth century of such events as the Keswick Regatta has suggested that by then there must have been a considerable influx of settlers and
visitors, since such events did not form part of the chosen relaxations of
farmers, woodmen and miners (Bouch, 1948). The beginning of the
tourist traffic, heralded by these signs, was the start of the problem which
is still very much with us – the problem of reconciling the way of life of
the native population with the desires and requirements of the multitudes
who wish to come, like Elizabeth Bennet, to gaze on rocks and mountains.

The problem of a rapidly changing situation is no new thing in the Lake
District. In the early nineteenth century William Wordsworth in his
Guide deplored the passing of the 'estatesmen', the customary tenants and
small yeomen, and blamed the Industrial Revolution for depriving these
men of their subsidiary source of income, the spinning of their own wool
at home by the women and children. Wordsworth understood that many
of these small holdings of land did not of themselves provide even a
modest subsistence, and that when the statesmen were deprived of their
subsidiary income from spinning, amalgamation of bankrupt holdings and
purchase of many properties by 'offcome' gentry was the inevitable result.
After exhorting these latter to show good taste in the design and layout

of their properties by following the simple local traditions (much in the manner of the present-day Planning Board) Wordsworth maintained that: 'In this wish the author will be joined by persons of pure taste throughout the whole island, who, by their visits (often repeated) to the Lakes in the north of England, testify that they deem the district a sort of national property, in which every man has a right and interest who has an eye to perceive and a heart to enjoy.'

William Wordsworth in his time was aware of many of the problems of this situation; what he could not foresee was the invention of the internal combustion engine. His misgivings, it is now curious to reflect, were confined to the railways. While now the valley roads roar ceaselessly every fine weekend from Easter to October, it is surprising to remember how the steam locomotives, which to us appear such harmless and friendly monsters from a nostalgic past, constituted such a frightful threat to Wordsworth. His paradox is still with us. He wanted the Lakes to become 'a sort of national property' but he did not want the railways to disgorge hordes of holiday-makers to enjoy the national property at Windermere, Keswick and Coniston.

W. G. Collingwood's 'Old Lake District that we have loved', to which he said good-bye in a book published in 1928, came to an end at about the time when the charcoal-burners were disappearing from the woods and the R.S.P.C.A.'s notices at the foot of the passes were disappearing – notices exhorting coach passengers to walk up Kirkstone, Newlands Hause and Honister to spare the horses. That was the time when, under the threat of a national timber shortage, the newly formed Forestry Commission was planting hundreds of acres on Whinlatter with larch and the much-disliked Sitka spruce, and changing the face of that part of the Lake District. Manchester, finding Thirlmere not enough to supply water for its growing needs, was beginning the works which were to alter the face of Haweswater and submerge the farms of Mardale and Riggindale. But it was a sad time, when the price of wool was dropping to rock bottom (2½d. a pound) and many fell farmers were hard pressed to make a living from mutton, butter and visitors, and when unemployed men in their thousands in the Lancashire cotton towns and in Barrow and Workington would never have believed that their children would grow up to an affluence in which their motor cars would clog the roads of the Lake District every fine weekend. In nostalgia for the more peaceful past it is perhaps as well to remember this.

The problem which has come to the Lake District since 1950 is that embarrassing numbers of people now take advantage of their mobility and visit the district in their motor cars. The sheer increase in numbers touring the district by motor vehicle instead of on foot, on horseback or by pedal-cycle, has brought in its wake the problem of developing local amenities to fit the requirements of visitors who are mostly towndwellers

The basic problem of the Lake District Planning Board, which administers the National Park, is to set a course of development acceptable both to the visitors and to the needs of the resident native population. The declared aim of the amenity societies, supported by many people who appreciate and love the Lake District, is to preserve it more or less in its present state. As Dr Lund has already argued in Chapter 4, there is no course of action which will please everybody, and we can all recognise that in many ways the Planning Board has a thankless task. The fears of the preservationists were roused in the 1920s and 1930s by the acquisition of Upper Ennerdale, Mardale and Riggindale by the Forestry Commission and Manchester Corporation; today such fears are largely replaced by the anxiety that too many concessions to recreational requirements will change the character of the Lake District. Like Shakespeare's Othello, we may kill that which we love.

A great deal has been written about the problems of the Lake District, today and in the future. In 1967 the Ambleside Rotary Club organised a symposium called 'Whither the Lake District?' and the published lectures make stimulating and entertaining reading. The Lake District Planning Board, the National Trust, the Friends of the Lake District and the Lake District Naturalists' Trust, as well as other local bodies, are all making great efforts to disseminate information to visitors, both about the district as it is and the problems which face those who administer it. The Planning Board, aided by the Countryside Commission, opened in 1969 the first National Park Centre in Britain, at Brockhole, south of Ambleside. Here visitors may walk and picnic in the grounds beside Windermere, and in the house study demonstrations of the geology, natural history and recent past of the Lake District. They can also collect many leaflets setting out further information which they can use to plan their time in the district to best advantage. Brockhole had 30,000 visitors in its first two months as a National Park Centre. Its main aim is to foster understanding of the physical and human development of the Lake District, and to bridge the gulf between most urban visitors and those who maintain the Lakeland countryside.

THE AMENITY SOCIETIES

'For centuries, the Lakes have been a peaceful country', wrote Professor Haverfield in 1913 (Chapter 12). This is implicit in the landscape, which is so mercifully free from traces of man's inhumanity to man, once the Roman occupiers had gone. One of the main attractions of this mountain country, whether consciously realised by its admirers or not, is that it is the only part of Highland Britain where men have, in general, lived at peace with each other since the end of Roman Britain. The centuries of Border raids appear as no more than cheerful brigandry when compared with the long tragic history of Scotland and Ireland and the fierce defeat of the Welsh. This is pre-eminently the part of Britain where the Celt came to terms with the Anglian and the Northman with fewer traces of bitterness and strife than appear in most of the Highland zone. Even the harrying of William the Norman left few traces on the central fells and dales. The Lake mountains may lack the distant grandeur of west Sutherland, but instead of ruined crofts and depopulated glens we have the settled peace of Chapel Stile and Rosthwaite, Hartsop and Mungrisdale and Boot. Instead of evidence in the great houses of an alien settlement, by plantation or late purchase, there are the broad acres and halls of Muncaster, Sizergh, Lowther, Graythwaite, Greystoke and Dalemain, still occupied by the descendants of the men who built them. As we have seen in Chapters 14 and 15, economic and social history in these northern counties led to the evolution of an independent breed of men, and an agricultural system where master and hinds sat down in amity to meals at the same table. All this essential domestic peace of the Lake Counties finds expression in the feeling of satisfying continuity which is implicit in the farm lands and settlements of the dales.

The enormous urge to preserve the Lake District which has found expression in the creation of the amenity societies, and in organised opposition to the demands of the great City of Manchester for water storage and of the Forestry Commission for plantable land, springs very largely from the conviction, often inarticulate, of so many people that here is a treasure, not only by nature very beautiful, but matured by centuries of peaceful cultivation and industry, which is not only irreplaceable but unique in Britain. The opposition generated in the 1920s to the take-over of the Haweswater valley by Manchester, and later to the planting of the western dale-heads by the Forestry Commission, sometimes appeared fanatical and unbalanced to the outsider. But much of this tremendous feeling arose from deeper springs of human behaviour than aesthetic values. Those who knew and appreciated the satisfying results of centuries of peaceful evolution of the Lakeland landscape felt that the threatened destruction of the ancient settlements in Mardale, and at Gillerthwaite and Butterilket, was an act of violation akin to unprovoked war in a peaceful countryside. The friendly human history of the Lake District can be read in the conjunction of signatures appended to the petition presented to the Forestry Commission in 1935, where the ancient names of Lowther, Le Fleming, Howard and Strickland are followed by multitudes of other local names, including many sons of the district educated at local grammar schools founded by local benefactors, who had gone on to distinction in the outside world. It was fitting that it should be one of the greatest of these, in Norman Birkett, who was able as his final act to halt, temporarily, the advance of Manchester's demands on Ullswater in 1962.

The amenity groups which have been concerned with safeguarding the landscape of the Lake District include, of course, the National Trust, formed in 1895, the Council for the Preservation of Rural England, formed in 1926, and the Friends of the Lake District, formed in 1934, together with the Lake District Farm Estates, a company formed to buy farms of high landscape value and lease them to farmers under certain conditions. The Nature Conservancy and the Lake District Naturalists' Trust have in recent years acquired certain areas as Nature Reserves, where of course nature conservation is the main object. Fig. 20, p. 285, shows the present-day ownership of land in the Lake District – that part which is owned or controlled by these amenity groups, by the Forestry Commission, by the City of Manchester, and that in private ownership. In 1951 the Lake District National Park came into being. British National Parks, unlike those of some other countries, are not nationally owned. In this country a National Park is specifically an area to be enjoyed by the nation, but does not become, as in Wordsworth's vision of the Lakes, 'a sort of national property'.

FORESTRY

In the late eighteenth century the first commercial planting of European larch (*Larix decidua*) began in the Lake District. A little later (from 1820 onwards) the main plantations were established by the Marshall family of Monk Coniston, in Patterdale, Buttermere, near Derwentwater, and at Monk Coniston. The strain of larch they used was that introduced by the Duke of Atholl on his Scottish estates, and it has proved to be a good stock. Larch has become naturalised in the Lake District both on hitherto bare fell-sides and as a component of mixed woodland, and the planting of commercial plantations has continued. Many of these were, of course, felled to provide pit-props etc. during two world wars. During the nineteenth century commercial forestry was practised by many private landowners, including the Curwens of Belle Isle, Windermere, who planted extensively in the woods on the western side of the North Basin of Windermere. Plantations of larch, Norway spruce and pine were established. There is some evidence that attempts to plant oak as a commercial crop (as distinct from planting oaks in 'amenity woodlands') were unsuccessful. Early in the twentieth century Manchester began to plant trees on the Thirlmere drainage basin, which was in a comparatively treeless condition when acquired as a water catchment area. This planting, primarily to control the rate of run-off and minimise erosion of soils (see Chapter 7), was the first large-scale afforestation programme in the Lake District, and the extensive planting of alien conifers in the regimented ranks associated with commercial forestry aroused great opposition from amenity interests. The early stages of the spruce plantations round

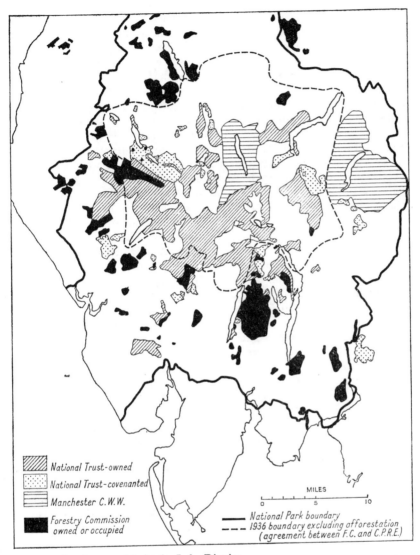

National Trust-owned
National Trust-covenanted
Manchester C.W.W.
Forestry Commission owned or occupied

MILES
0   5   10

National Park boundary
1936 boundary excluding afforestation
(agreement between F.C. and C.P.R.E.)

FIG. 20. Land ownership in the Lake District.

Thirlmere made a striking impact on the eye with their straight boundaries and uniform rows of dark trees, but Thirlmere is different now, for some very progressive forestry is going on there. (Plate 32b.)

The present position of forestry in the Lake District was discussed by Mr J. S. R. Chard, Conservator, North-west' Forestry Commission, in a public lecture in Ambleside in 1967. He said, 'Wordsworth said many rude things about larch and many others have tried to copy him since. I think the most interesting comment is that all or most of the Marshalls' principal plantations are now cared for by the National Trust. It is always a comfort and encouragement to foresters to remember that the National Trust was set up originally to prevent the felling of a commercial plantation on the shores of Derwentwater. This was probably no more beautiful than many others of the same era, but it had the right setting and romantic and emotional associations with the Lakeland poets. What we do know is that it is quite certainly in every way more beautiful now than it was then, and this has been achieved not by some special technique labelled "amenity", but by the practice of sound and enlightened forestry by the National Trust. And larch in its correct silvicultural mixture is the most outstanding and valuable species in the crop.

'The management of this and adjoining areas owned by the Trust provide leading examples of successful multiple use which many of you will know. Larch is now generally accepted as part of the traditional Lakeland scene, and this is I think partly because it seeds and regenerates itself freely. You get old trees and young trees growing side by side in a natural association. It is deciduous and the ground under the older trees is suitable for grazing. You can graze the plantations in the winter and its leaf-fall helps to restore the fertility to the bracken-covered soils on which it is usually planted.

'Now in looking back I think we should pay tribute to the fact that the great larch plantations of the nineteenth century foresters – Gummershow, Chapel House, Claife, Grizedale, Combe, Hospital, and many others, not only provided this form of integration and multiple use between forestry and sheep farming, but they made an outstanding contribution to the safety and economy of the country in time of war. When industry was still based on coal each ton of coal required one hundredweight of pitwood to get it to the surface, and we could no more do without pitprops than we could do without food. The difference was that if all the pitwood had had to be imported, it would have needed six times as much shipping space as it did to import food, and even so the U-boats nearly starved us out.

'Thirlmere was the first large scheme of afforestation in the Lake District to use a preponderance of evergreen conifers in preference to larch, and this massive intrusion upon the traditional landscape was widely resented, as I know that to some extent it still is. But I think that those who talk that way have not really looked at it with their blinkers off for quite a long time. I have known it all my working life, and I am quite certain that it gets more and more beautiful as every year goes by. A very interesting point to ecologists and foresters is the way the native hardwoods are coming back amongst conifers now that the sheep have been kept out.' (Chard, 1967.)

The Forestry Commission's first Lake District planting began at Hospital Plantation on Whinlatter Pass in 1919, and now their land in this region constitutes Thornthwaite Forest. On the slopes of Hobcarton End and Grisedale Pike the Sitka spruce plantations reach up to nearly 1,700 feet. The first plantings were carried out with no thought of amenity interests, but to supply a national need for timber in the years after 1918. Sitka spruce, which grows well on the poor hill lands of Britain and regenerates freely in the Lake District, is now in demand for paper pulp and particle boards, and much of the output from Thornthwaite Forest goes to the new Thames Board Mill at Workington, part of the hopeful new industry arising among the decay of the old in West Cumberland. Larch, both European and Japanese, Douglas fir, hemlock and red cedar have been planted on the lower land, and deciduous trees border the roads through the forest. Many parts of Thornthwaite are now approaching maturity; the plan is to harvest the forest gradually and to produce finally a well-grown mature conifer forest, mainly of Sitka spruce on the higher land which is too wet for larch. (Plate 32, p. 289.)

In 1925 and 1926 the Forestry Commission acquired most of the land of Ennerdale above the lake – the slopes of the dale on both sides of the Liza Beck, including the old dale-head farm of Gillerthwaite (p. 251). Planting of both sides of this valley with larch and spruces (Norway and Sitka) began in 1927. Farming has ceased in this upper dale, and apart from some new houses for foresters, the dwellings are now used for tourism, with Youth Hostels at Black Sail and Gillerthwaite and a climbing club in the former Gillerthwaite farmhouse. It is probable that more feeling against afforestation was aroused both locally and among the amenity societies by this acquisition and planting of Ennerdale than by any other single act of the Forestry Commission. The straight-edged plantations which have blanketed the lower slopes of Pillar and Steeple and Red Pike, up to a height of 1,200 feet on the old sheep lands of Gillerthwaite, aroused the passions of so many people who had walked and climbed in this most lovely and remote valley, that it is easy to see why opposition solidified into a test case between the amenity societies and the Forestry Commission when further afforestation in the Lake District was planned. In 1935 the Forestry Commission acquired 7,000 acres in Eskdale and Dunnerdale which they proposed to transform into the 'Hardknott Forest Park'; those who opposed this most strenuously included the Friends of the Lake District, led by H. H. Symonds, and

13,000 people in 1935 signed a petition against any future commercial planting by the State in the heart of the Lake District.

An agreement reached in 1936 between the Forestry Commission and the Council for the Preservation of Rural England ended any plans for state afforestation of the 300 square miles which includes the central mountains and the uppermost parts of the dale heads (see Fig. 20). Only the high wild part of Eskdale above the farthest farms was included, and two great ancient sheep-farms were destined to be planted as part of the Hardknott Forest Park – Butterilket at the head of Eskdale and Black Hall at the head of the Duddon. In 1943, under pressure from the amenity groups, particularly from Symonds for the Friends of the Lake District, the Forestry Commission entered into a covenant with the National Trust, agreeing not to plant on the Butterilket land in Eskdale. Planting in the Duddon began at Birks farm, round the skirts of Harter Fell, but at each successive phase of planting there was consultation between the foresters and representatives of the National Trust and the Friends of the Lake District. The happy results of this consultation can be seen in the contrast between the attractive young growth on Harter Fell and the regimented appearance of the earliest plantations of Thornthwaite.

When the foresters came to the boundary of the lands of Black Hall at the beginning of the great mountain bowl of the uppermost reach of the Duddon, representatives of the amenity groups took a firm stand against any further planting. In 1958 agreement was finally reached whereby the Forestry Commission gave up all plans to afforest any part of the lands of Butterilket and Black Hall, and the Government agreed on a price at which to sell these farms to the National Trust, under whose ownership traditional fell-farming continues (p. 274).

Though the story of the battle to save the western dale-heads from afforestation must present the National Trust and the Forestry Commission as adversaries, the current reports of both bodies on their Lake District properties show how much they have in common now, in care and concern for both the Lakeland landscape and their tenant farmers. The two ancient sheep-farms ('herdwycks') of Furness Abbey which face the west on their high ridge above Coniston Water, Lawson Park (p. 290) and Parkamoor (p. 294), have come to be an example of the two different ways, both good, in which these ancient settlements can be integrated into the Lake District of today: Lawson Park belongs to the Forestry Commission and Parkamoor was given to the National Trust in 1968.

In all the controversies over afforestation there is a subjective element which is not amenable to rational argument. Some people like trees in one place but not in another; some do not like any conifers; some like the pine because it is native and dislike larches and spruces because they are not, and many who admire the coniferous forests of the European mainland feel obliged to dislike the Thirlmere conifers because they are told that

PLATE 31 Grizedale Forest with the Coniston fells in the background: preservation of remaining deciduous woodland and afforestation of the higher ground with conifers has restored the forest cover to one Lake District dale.

PLATE 32 Afforestation good and bad. *Above*, the Hobcarton valley – plantation of a kind deplored by all. *Below*, Thirlmere: in the foreground, on land fenced from sheep 70 years ago, young oaks are growing up among the pioneer birches – the only natural forest regeneration in the whole Lake District.   In the background, planted conifers in natural groups are stabilising screes and beginning the formation of new forest soils.

these are intolerable interlopers. Many people who look forward to the rosy cones and the new vivid green of the larches in spring, and admire their gold in the back-end, have to recognise that this is a taste very different from Wordsworth's.

Leaving aside aesthetic controversy, there is the very serious question of the down-grade tendency of Lake District soils which has been emphasised throughout this book. We have seen that these soils are becoming poorer and more acid through leaching by the mountain rainfall (Chapter 7), and that under present land use there is in many places a strong tendency towards soil erosion which leads to permanent bodily removal of soil from slopes, leaving bare and unstable screes, with deposition of silt in the lakes and gravel in upper valleys (Chapters 13 and 16). At the same time, the useless bracken is spreading continuously, and many once-good grasslands are bleached and acid *Nardus*. To quote Mr Chard again, 'Any trained forester or ecologist will recognise these as symptoms of an exploited and degraded landscape in which, for want of enough trees in the right places, erosion and soil impoverishment are going unchecked.' It has been explained in earlier chapters how, in the present state of human knowledge, the only way by which the original stability and fertility of the old forest soils can be restored is by afforestation. The effect of planting such trees as will flourish on any soil is to bring about once more the re-cycling of nutrients from the deeper layers of the soils, and so to up-grade the soil. The bracken-infested intakes, once the site of oak forest on good brown-earth soils, can be planted with larch and, in places, deciduous trees. Over great areas of barren *Nardus* grassland on acid and comparatively ill-drained soils, in Thornthwaite, Ennerdale and Lower Dunnerdale (including the Lickle valley) plantations of spruce and lodgepole pine are beginning to restore fertility to high-lying soils impoverished by several millennia of leaching since the upper forests were first cleared by pre-historic men. This is a satisfying ecological fact which should help to reconcile the objectors who would prefer on aesthetic grounds to see all the fellsides flame with the useless bracken in October and November. The autumn gold of the larches can replace it with the promise of usefulness to man, winter feed for the sheep under the new integration management of the Forestry Commission, and recompense to the soil, so that the land is getting better instead of worse.

The objectors who are genuinely distressed by the alien quality of the conifers could perhaps remember that the pine is not an alien, but seven thousand years ago it grew on these fells as freely as it does today by Loch Maree, in Glen Affric, and in Rothiemurchus Forest. These are all considered to be beautiful places and are not so very far away. To those who deplore the replacement of the traditional farming by forestry, Mr Chard has the answer: 'The better land has nearly always remained in other ownerships, and by a consistent policy of always buying at the bottom of the market the Forestry Commission has acquired only those areas which have become an economic burden to agriculture. This is the only land we normally acquire. We get land which is sheep-sick, gone back, run down or unimprovable.' (1967.)

In its most recent forest at Grizedale (see page 146) the Commission is pursuing a very successful policy of multiple use of a forest which should commend it to all visitors to the National Park. The well preserved native oakwoods are being managed as hardwood forest (see Chapter 8). The large areas on the ridges of degraded sheep-walks and the remains of old larch plantations have been replanted or planted in a way which provides for the preservation of these fells as a habitat for deer. 'The basic choice of species has been Japanese larch in heavy bracken, Norway spruce in the better flushes, Scots pine, or more recently lodgepole pine, where there is heather, and Sitka spruce predominating elsewhere.' (Chard, 1966.) Of the seven original farms on the estate in the late 1930s, there has been consolidation and reduction to four efficient farms and two small holdings. The ancient sheep-farm of Lawson Park had carried sheep for so long that the ground was so thickly infested with flukes and ticks that it was 'sheep-sick', and the isolation of the farmhouse was no longer acceptable as it had been to our more self-sufficient forebears. The high sheep pastures on the moorland ridge between Coniston and Grizedale have been converted into conifer plantations, among which it is possible for visitors to walk the forest roads and observe the wild life of the forest against its mountain background. Farming has been concentrated on the best land of the valley bottom, a change from extensive to intensive husbandry (mainly dairy cattle) which has not diminished the total agricultural production. 'Now when we came to plant the fells behind, the landscaping at Grizedale was completed mainly by the judicious use of larch, and especially by matching this naturally with the main areas of bracken-covered ground. The perpetuation of the native woodlands is obviously of critical importance to the survival of much of the indigenous fauna and flora, and the provision of deciduous areas of larch within the new plantings helps to extend this habitat for many species. In particular the new larch woods are of great importance in providing grazing areas for deer. Both the oak woods and the larch woods are playing a key role in successful developments for multiple use.' (Chard, 1967.) (see Fig. 21, p. 291.)

The next stage at Grizedale was to develop wild life conservation and provide opportunities for observation of wild life. 'I think we should all remember', says Mr Chard, 'that the British fauna is predominantly a forest fauna and it is the increasing interest in wild life stimulated by films and television which attracts visitors to our forests. They do not come to see the trees: they come to see the birds and animals and flowers. Most come from the towns and they have to be given a better understanding of the forest before they can be let loose in it.' Several cheerful films have

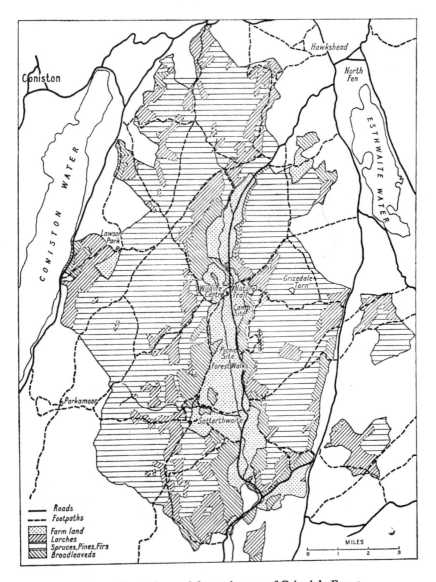

Roads
Footpaths
Farm land
Larches
Spruces, Pines, Firs
Broadleaveds

MILES

0   1   2   3

FIG. 21. Vegetation and footpaths, etc. of Grizedale Forest.

been made showing parties of visitors 'let loose' in the Grizedale Forest and the things they found to interest them there. The Forestry Commission is contributing very substantially to the provision of recreational facilities in the Lake District, by opening up their forests (as the young plantations mature) to those visitors who want to look at birds and beasts and learn to understand the forest environment. This understanding is being given at Grizedale by the provision of a museum and wild-life centre (a sensible place to take children on wet days), arrangement of nature trails with adjacent parking facilities, and the provision of an observation tower and hides from which it is possible to watch and photograph deer and other wild life.

Car-parks in the forest adjacent to main roads, such as the one at Bogle Crag, provide opportunities for quiet picnics and the starting points for a variety of unobtrusively marked routes through the forest, each marked with helpful notes about the kind of footwear required and the average time needed for the walk. On each route is a pleasant picnic site. A forest like Grizedale can absorb a much greater number of holiday-makers without seeming crowded than can the well-known open spaces such as White Moss Common near Rydal. On the site of Grizedale Hall, now demolished, the Forestry Commission has provided a well-organised camp-site for tents with an information room and a shop, just across the road from the wild-life centre and museum. The forestry research nursery in the former gardens of the hall provides demonstrations of normal forestry methods and research into tree breeding.

The animals which can be seen by the quiet watcher in Grizedale Forest include both red and roe deer, foxes, badgers, stoats and weasels, red squirrels, short-tailed voles, woodmice, bank voles, rabbits and hares. The rare pine marten is seen occasionally by foresters. Among the birds are buzzards, sparrowhawks, kestrels and owls, together with most of the woodland birds of the district – titmice, woodpeckers, treecreepers, red-starts, pied flycatchers, chaffinches, bullfinches, pheasants, grouse and black game. The predators in the forest community are not ruthlessly hunted as they used to be in most woodlands by gamekeepers, but are left to take their natural place. Without the predators there can be population explosions of such species as the short-tailed vole which can destroy young plantations, and the oak leaf roller moth which can completely defoliate oaks.

THE NATIONAL TRUST

Formed in 1895, by three founders including Canon Rawnsley of Keswick, to preserve places of historic interest or natural beauty, the National Trust is now one of the largest landowners in the Lake District. According to its 1969 list of properties, the Trust owns 72,884 acres of the Lake

District and is in a position to protect a further 14,188 acres. On this land it owns 14,710 sheep. A former Chairman of the Lake District Park Planning Board pointed out that 'Our aim is that the National Park shall afford to those who live in it the chance to make a living in a competitive world; and to those who visit it the solace of natural beauty with the challenge of wild mountains. Already those considerable portions of the Lake District which are owned by the National Trust are managed with these ends in view.' (Kenneth Dobell, in *Lake District: National Park Guide No. 6.*)

One of the greatest benefactors of all time to the National Trust in the Lake District was Mrs William Heelis, née Beatrix Potter. As well as her own farms in Sawrey and Troutbeck she left to the Trust thousands of acres of the Lake District which she had bought to save them from 'development'. Hill-top, her first farm, in the village of Near Sawrey, she bought in 1905, partly from the royalties from the first of her books. It was Mrs Tiggywinkle, the hedgehog who lived 'in a hole in the side of the hill called Catbells', and Squirrel Nutkin, who sailed on a raft across Derwentwater using his tail as a sail, who made possible the preservation of Hill-top Farm. And Pigling Bland, who complicated his life by crossing inadvertently the county boundary from Lancashire to Westmorland at Colwith, Tom Kitten whose home was at Hill-top, and Jemima Puddleduck whose background is so recognisably the knobbly little wooded hills round the Sawreys, all contributed by their successful sales to the preservation of more than 4,000 acres of the great Monk Coniston estate, parts of Hawkeshead, and of farms in Langdale, Eskdale, Wray and Sawrey, as well as nearly 2,000 acres of Troutbeck Park, one of the most famous sheep farms in the Lake District, which includes the summits of Ill Bell, Froswick and Thornthwaite Crag, with part of the High Street Roman road. (Plate 25, p. 240.)

The summits of the central Lakeland mountains belong to the National Trust and, like all its properties, can never be bought or sold, nor be acquired without Special Procedure in Parliament. The tops of Scafell Pike, Lingmell, Broad Crag, Great End, Kirkfell and Great Gable all form part of this central property of the Trust which is the real heart of the Lake Country. Great End and Great Gable were given to the Trust by the Fell and Rock Climbing Club in 1923 as a War Memorial to its members killed in the 1914–18 War. The summits of Bowfell and the Langdale Pikes and adjacent fells, forming the 16,842 acres of Lord Lonsdale's Commons, are leased to the Trust at a peppercorn rent by the 7th Earl of Lonsdale. We have already seen how the Trust finally acquired the lands of Butterilket and Black Hall in 1961, completing their possession of most of Upper Eskdale and the head of Dunnerdale; at the head of Great Langdale the three farms Stool End, Wall End and Middlefell Place all belong to the Trust, and at the head of Borrowdale the land of

Seathwaite farm, including Taylor Gill and Grains Gill as far as Stockley Bridge, were bought by the Trust in 1944. Most of the Buttermere valley is either owned by the Trust or protected by its covenants. The total property of the National Trust in the Lake District, shown in the map in Fig. 20. p. 285, represents an impressive proportion of the whole. This land has all been bought by the Trust with its own funds, or presented to it by benefactors, or in certain cases has been transferred to the Trust from the Treasury which has accepted land in lieu of death duties. Members of the Trust who pay their annual subscription to it have certain privileges of access to properties for which an entry fee is charged. Though the Trust holds the land in trust for the nation, the ordinary citizen has no rights with respect to Trust lands and properties by virtue of his position as a taxpayer. The farms and many of the historic houses which belong to the Trust are rented to private individuals who have as much right to privacy on the property they lease as has anyone to the privacy of his own garden. All the fell commons are, of course, freely open to public access under the ownership of the Trust, as are the vast majority of those unenclosed fell commons which do not belong to the Trust.

In the previous chapter an account has been given of the work of the Trust as landlord in encouraging and supporting native fell farming on the viable farms which it has acquired. Its policy in dealing with marginal land is exemplified by its plans for the small farm Parkamoor which it has possessed since 1968. This property, with 415 acres of woodland and fell, an isolated farmhouse at an altitude of nearly 800 feet without access by metalled road, and no valley land at all, is no longer a viable unit as a sheep farm (page 271). The Trust has fenced the woodlands – mainly native deciduous woods with some larch – and let them to neighbouring farmers as valuable winter grazing for sheep, the house has been let to a tenant as a remote residence, and the open grassland and moorland on top of the ridge will probably also be let as additional grazing to another farmer. This form of land use will preserve Parkamoor in its present comely state while at the same time making a contribution to efficient sheep-farming on neighbouring units.

THE NATIONAL PARK

The Lake District National Park was formed in 1951, it is administered through the Planning Board, which is a joint committee of the three County Councils of the Lake District – Cumberland, Westmorland and Lancashire. When an area becomes a National Park, the change is mainly in administration and there is no change in ownership of the land. This cannot be stressed too often. The aims of the Planning Board have been ably set out by its former Chairman, Kenneth Dobell, in the first chapter of the official *Guide* to the Lake District National Park, which is quoted on page 293, illustrating the agreement between the aims of the National Trust and the Board. The Development Plan of the Planning Board was published in 1956, a first review of this in 1961, and a Basic Map of land use in 1965.

The Lake District is so small that it would be easy to spoil it, and for its future we must trust in the wisdom of the planners and all the forces of conservation. Though the area of the dales is small and vulnerable, the mountains are real mountains and have room for all who seek their recreation there. Even in the crowded days of August there is space on the fells. Six hundred people every summer day may ascend Helvellyn, by the popular routes, but the non-gregarious walker who knows the fells can still find solitude with the ravens not very far from the beaten tracks. The fells are beginning to look well-trodden by comparison with the remoter bens of northern Scotland, and probably it will soon become necessary to do something about the erosion of the popular tracks, for the broad scars on Gable and Helvellyn and Bowfell and Coniston Old Man grow more conspicuous every year. But the management of the Thirlmere and Haweswater catchment areas could find a way to repair the vegetation cover over these gouges, just as they repaired the ravages of the tractors which laid a new water-pipe from Blea Water in 1964.

Many of the mountain soils are in jeopardy, and much of the grazing becomes poorer every year. In the present state of human knowledge, the larch and the spruce seem to be the only long-term answer to this major ecological problem. An alternative, but unthinkable, economic future for the Lake District is that it should eventually become a playground, the bare fells carrying only bog vegetation, bracken and *Nardus*, and the dales between the amenity woodlands a continuous series of camp-sites, weekend cottages and commuter communities. Those who love the Lakeland landscape in its present form must hope that the wise views on the management of the National Park which were expressed by Kenneth Dobell (p. 293) will prevail, and that all the forces of conservation and planning, with perhaps new advances in agricultural techniques in marginal hill farming, will combine to preserve the fells and dales in their present beauty. The loveliness of the sheep lands of Eskdale, Dunnerdale, Langdale and Borrowdale, and the green leafiness of Grizedale where the deer graze freely, suggest that great future hope for the land of the Lake District lies in the hands of those former adversaries of the 1930s, the National Trust and the Forestry Commission. We who have written this book have tried to portray the land of the Lake District as a community to which men have belonged for five thousand years, and to show how it is one of the treasured parts of Britain which has so far been fortunate enough to have been used with love and respect.

GLOSSARY

Aerobic – describing either organisms which require oxygen to live, or conditions where oxygen is present.

Anaerobic – describing either organisms which flourish in the absence of oxygen, or conditions where oxygen is absent.

Andesite – a sub-basic volcanic igneous rock consisting of plagioclase felspar with hornblende or augite or mica, sometimes with quartz.

Base – in the chemical sense, a substance which neutralises an acid.

Base-rich – of a soil, one containing much lime or potash.

Beaker people – late Neolithic invaders of southern and eastern Britain who practised single, as opposed to collective, burial, and used pottery of a characteristic pattern.

Blanket-bog – an area of peat which is not confined to a basin but covers ground of moderate slope.

Breccia – a rock which is made up of angular fragments of either igneous or sedimentary rocks, cemented together. A *flow-breccia* originates from a lava-flow which cooled and fragmented before movement ceased.

Brown-earth – the characteristic soil type under deciduous forest in north-west Europe.

Collared Urns, and Encrusted Urns – large, hand-made pottery vessels named after their salient features and decoration.

Conglomerate – a breccia in which the fragments are well rounded, not angular.

Creep-soil – a soil formed from downward-moving rock or soil particles.

Diorite – a sub-basic plutonic igneous rock.

Dolerite – a basic hypabyssal igneous rock (intermediate between volcanic and plutonic).

Drift – superficial deposits of mineral material which were carried and dropped by an ice-sheet.

Dyke – an intrusion of igneous rock of sheet-like form, vertical or nearly so. (If horizontal, it is a *Sill*.) If the intrusion is harder than the rock into which it is intruded, weathering leaves it as a wall-like structure. If the intruded rock is softer and more easily weathered, a trough results.

Erratic – a stone or boulder of a rock foreign to the site on which it is found, indicating transport by ice from an area where that rock crops out.

Eutrophic – with high nutritional requirements.

Fen – a swampy area where the ground-water-level reaches the surface, and a peat which is not acid has accumulated.

Flush – an area of soil enriched by transported materials, either soil or dissolved mineral salts.

Gabbro – a basic plutonic igneous rock.

Gley – a permanently waterlogged mineral soil with a characteristic blue-grey or mottled colour.

Grimston ware, Peterborough ware and Rinyo-Clacton ware – Neolithic pottery of varying form and decoration, named after the type sites. Roughly speaking these represent Early, Middle and Late Neolithic wares, but overlap with each other both in space and time.

Granite – an acid plutonic igneous rock.

Granophyre (=*Syenite*) – a sub-acid plutonic igneous rock.

Grits – coarse sandstones, especially if the grains are rough.

Halstatt – first Continental iron-using economy, called after the type site, which developed in West Central Europe in the tenth and ninth centuries B.C. and expanded west and north by the sixth century.

Henge monuments – late Neolithic and Early Bronze Age ceremonial centres with a ditch inside the encircling bank, and with one or two entrances leading into the central area. Called after Stonehenge and Woodhenge in Wiltshire.

Igneous – used to describe rocks erupted from the heated lower layers of the earth's crust, either as ash, lava or as an intrusion.

Interglacial – an interval between two glaciations during which the temperature rose at least as high as during the post-glacial period.

Interstadial – a climatic fluctuation within a glacial period, of smaller amplitude than an interglacial.

Kettlehole – a hollow in glacial debris formed by the melting of a block of dead ice.

La Tène – the later, Celtic, iron-using economy which evolved in the middle Rhine in the fifth century, developing a characteristic art style under the stimulus of Greek, Etruscan and, later, of Roman, trade. The culture expanded into much of western, central and northern Europe during the later centuries B.C.

Laccolith – a form of intrusion of igneous rock which causes arching of the over-lying country rock, seen in the intrusions of certain granites into rocks of the Borrowdale Volcanic Series.

Leaching – solution and removal of minerals from a soil by rainwater.

Metasomatic replacement – replacement of a rock, usually a limestone, by an ore deposit: haematite in Carboniferous Limestone is the Lake District example.

Mor – an acid soil humus which accumulates at the soil surface and is too acid for the presence of earthworms.

Moss or peat-moss – a northern name for peaty land, the peat formed mainly by bog-moss.

Moraine – in English, a mound or ridge of glacial drift. An irregular type of hummocky moraines, formed by groups of mounds with intervening hollows, is sometimes called 'kettle-moraine', and is interpreted as the deposit of ice which melted *in situ*. (By some Continental authors 'moraine' is used where in English we use 'drift'.)

Mull – a fertile soil humus, not acid, which is well-mixed with the superficial layer of the mineral soil and inhabited by earthworms.

Nunatak – land or hill projecting through a continental ice-sheet.

Oligotrophic – with low nutritional requirements.

Ombrogenous – peat which lies above the ground-water-level, so that plants growing on its surface depend on rainwater for their supply of minerals.

Palstave – a form of axe with cast stop-ridge and flanges designed to take a forked haft. Convex- and angle-flanged axes were hafted in the same way.

Petit-tranchet derivative arrowheads – wide-edged, transverse or cutting arrowheads, usually of Neolithic date, developed from the narrower Mesolithic form.

Plutonic – describes igneous rocks which have solidified and consolidated at some distance below the earth's surface.

Podsol – a soil type in which the layers below the surface are much leached and there is a surface layer of acid humus.

Quern – a hand-mill for grinding grain. Saucer and saddle forms with stone rubbers precede the rotary type, in which the top stone with hopper is revolved on a stationary lower stone.

Raised bog – a peat bog developed on a level substratum and having the form of a dome, the peat being thickest at the centre of the bog, so that the surface is convex.

Rhyolite – an acid volcanic igneous rock showing flow structure.

Run-off – that part of the rainfall that runs off as surface water without penetrating the soil or rock cover.

Sauveterrean – an assemblage of post-glacial flint tools, including many microliths (i.e. very small), first recognised at two rock-shelters at Sauveterre-la-Lémance, Lot-et-Garonne, France.

Scree – rock detritus below a rock outcrop.

Sedimentary rocks – all rocks which originate other than by igneous action; usually by deposition in water.

Shales – soft rocks formed from consolidation of clays.

Slates – rocks in which the constituent particles have been rearranged by pressure to lie parallel, in a direction along which the slate cleaves (=rives) easily.

Solifluction – the flowing or creeping of soil down a slope which occurs in cold climates as a result of alternate freezing and thawing of the soil water, often associated with a frozen sub-soil.

Stone-polygon – an arctic soil formation in which a central area of soil or mud is surrounded by polygonally arranged rows of stones.

Stone-stripes – parallel rows of stones running down a slope and separating areas of soil or fine gravel.

Stock – a form of intrusion of igneous rock like a stout column.

Shatter-belt – a line of weakness in rock resulting from a fault along which movement has occurred, causing shattering of the rock; later erosion often excavates this shattered rock to form a trough.

Tuff – a volcanic rock formed from fine-grained detritus. Some tuffs may have a slaty cleavage imparted later, by pressure; others may have cleavage properties resembling those of flint.

BIBLIOGRAPHY

General

PEARSALL, W. H. (Ed.) (1969). *The Lake District*. National Park Guide No. 6. London. This small handbook includes chapters introductory to many topics dealt with at greater length in the present book.

PEARSALL, W. H. (1950). *Mountains and Moorlands*. London.

WORDSWORTH, WILLIAM (various editions from 1835 to 1853). *Guide through the District of the Lakes*.

COLLINGWOOD, W. G. (1932). *The Lake Counties*. London.

COLLINGWOOD, W. G. (1928). *Lake District History*. Kendal.

WORDSWORTH DOROTHY (various editions). *The Grasmere Journals: 1800–03*.

WAINWRIGHT, A. (1955–66). *A Pictorial Guide to the Lakeland Fells*. Books I–VII. Kentmere.

NICHOLSON, N. (1963). *Portrait of the Lakes*. London.

NICHOLSON, N. (1944). *Selected Poems*. London.

GRIFFIN, A. H. (1968). *The Roof of England*. London.

THOMPSON, B. L. (1946). *The Lake District and the National Trust*. Kendal.

Whither the Lake District? (1967). Rotary Club of Ambleside. A series of informed public discussions on the future of the Lake District, its tourist and industrial development, its communications and preservation as an area of very great natural beauty.

WILSON, ALBERT (1938). *The Flora of Westmorland*. Arbroath.

Chapter 2

EASTWOOD, DIXON, HOLLINGWORTH and SMITH (1931). *Memoirs of the Geological Survey of England and Wales: Whitehaven and Workington District*. London.

EASTWOOD, T. (1967). *British Regional Geology: Northern England*. 3rd edition. London.

HOLLINGWORTH, S. E. (1954). The Geology of the Lake District. *Proc. Geol. Assoc.* 65.

MARR, J. E. (1916). *The Geology of the Lake District*. Cambridge.

MITCHELL, G. H. (1956). The Geological History of the Lake District. *Proc. Yorks. Geol. Soc.* 30.

MONKHOUSE, F. J. (1960). *The English Lake District*. The British Landscape through Maps, No. 1. Sheffield. A description of the Ordnance Survey One-inch Tourist Map of the Lake District.

Chapter 3

COOPER, W. H. (1960). *The Tarns of Lakeland*.

HOLLINGWORTH, S. E. (1949). A chapter on 'Geology' in *National Forest Park Guides* No. 5 *Hardknott*. London.

HOLLINGWORTH, S. E. (1951). The Influence of Glaciation on the Topography of the Lake District. *Journ. Inst. Water Engs.* 5.

MARR, J. E. (1895). The Tarns of Lakeland. *Quart. Journ. Geol. Soc.* 51.

Chapter 4

BRAITHWAITE, G. F. (1884). *Salmonidae of Westmorland*. Kendal.

MACAN, T. T. (1969). *Biological Studies of the English Lakes*. London.

MACAN, T. T. and WORTHINGTON, E. B. (1951). *Life in Lakes and Rivers*. London.

GURNEY, R. (1923). The Crustacean Plankton of the English Lake District. *J. Linn. Soc.* 35.

GARNETT, M. (1946). The Birds of Windermere. In *Lakeland Natural History*. Carlisle.

OLDFIELD, F. (1970). The Ecological History of Blelham Bog National Nature Reserve. In *Studies in the Vegetational History of the British Isles*. Cambridge.

PEARSALL, W. H. (1921). The Development of Vegetation in the English Lakes. *Proc. Roy. Soc.* B 92.

PEARSALL W. H. (1949). *The English Lakes*. In Penguin *New Biology*, London.

Chapter 6

MANLEY, G. (1936, 1942, 1943, 1945). *Q. J. Roy. Met. Soc.* Papers on various aspects of the climate of the Northern Pennines.

MANLEY, G. (1946). Temperature trend in Lancashire 1753–1945. *Q. J. Roy. Met. Soc.* 72; 1–31.

MANLEY, G. (1952). *Climate and the British Scene*. London.

MANLEY, G. (1965). *The North-western Environment*. Inaugural lecture, University of Lancaster.

METEOROLOGICAL OFFICE. Averages of Temperature for 1931–60; Averages of Rainfall, 1916–50; British Rainfall (annual volumes); Monthly Weather Report, *passim*. London.

Chapter 7

HALL, B. R. (1967). The Soil Associations of Furness. *Proc. North of England Soils Discussion Group*.

Chapter 8

CHARD, J. S. R. (1966). The Red Deer of Furness Fells. *Forestry* 39

MACPHERSON, H. A. (1892). *A Vertebrate Fauna of Lakeland*. Edinburgh.

MATTHEWS, L. HARRISON (1952). *British Mammals*. London.

PHILIPSON, W. R. (1948). *Birds of a Valley*. London.

RATCLIFFE, D. A. (1960). The Mountain Flora of Lakeland. *Proc. Bot. Soc. Brit. Isles* 4.

SHEPHERD, S. (1964). *Brocky, the story of a badger*. London.

SHORTEN, M. (1954). *Squirrels*. London

TANSLEY, A. G. (1939). *The British Islands and their Vegetation*. Cambridge.

YAPP, W. B. (1953). The High-level Woodlands of the English Lake District. *The Naturalist*. (NS) 1.

Chapter 9

Those references listed for Chapter 8.

BLEZARD, E. (Ed.) (1943). The Birds of Lakeland. *Trans. Carlisle Nat. Hist. Soc.* VI.

BLEZARD, E. and STOKOE, R. (1962). The Birds of the Lake Counties. *Trans. Carlisle Nat. Hist. Soc.* X.

Chapter 10

Those references listed for Chapters 8 and 9.

BENSON, C. E. (1902). *Crag and Hound in Lakeland*. London.

Lake District Naturalists' Trust, Reports of.

Chapters 11, 12 and 14

Transactions of the Cumberland and Westmorland Antiquarian and Archaeological Society. Old Series 1–16 (includes articles from 1866 to 1900) and New Series (1901 to present day). Important articles from these Transactions are catalogued analytically in *A Bibliography of the History and Topography of Cumberland and Westmorland* (1968) by Henry W. Hodgson.

BARNES, F. (1968). *Barrow and District*. Contains a useful short bibliography for the Furness district.

An Inventory of the Historical Monuments in Westmorland (1936). Royal Commission on Historical Monuments.

COLLINGWOOD, W. G. An Inventory of the Ancient Monuments of Cumberland. *Trans. C.W.A.A. Soc.* (NS) XXIII.

COLLINGWOOD, W. G. An Inventory of the Ancient Monuments of Westmorland and Lancashire North of the Sands. *Trans. C.W.A.A. Soc.* (NS) XXVI.

COLLINGWOOD, W. G. (1927). *Northumbrian Crosses of the Pre-Norman Age.*

COLLINGWOOD, W. G. (1896). *The Vikings in Lakeland.*

COLLINGWOOD, W. G. The Angles in Furness and Cartmel. *Trans. C.W.A.A. Soc.* (NS) XXIV.

COLLINGWOOD, R. G. An Introduction to the Prehistory of Cumberland, Westmorland and Lancashire North of the Sands. *Trans. C.W.A.A. Soc.* (NS) XXXIII.

BIRLEY, E. The Archaeology of Cumberland and Westmorland. *Trans. C.W.A.A. Soc.* (NS) LVIII.

BIRLEY, E. (1961). *Research on Hadrian's Wall.*

CHERRY, J., with appendix by W. Pennington. Flint Chipping Sites at Drigg. *Trans. C.W.A.A. Soc.* (NS) LXV.

PLINT, R. G. Stone Axe Factory Sites in the Cumbrian Fells. *Trans. C.W.A.A. Soc.* (NS) LXII.

CLOUGH, T. H. McK. Bronze Age Metalwork from Cumbria. *Trans. C.W.A.A. Soc.* (NS) LXIX.

CLOUGH, T. H. McK. The Beaker Period in Cumbria. *Trans. C.W.A.A. Soc.* (NS) LXVIII.

FELL, C. I. Two Enlarged Food-vessels from How Hill, Thursby and notes on the distribution of Food-vessels in Cumberland, Westmorland and Lancashire north of the Sands. *Trans. C.W.A.A. Soc.* (NS) LXVII.

POWELL, T. G. E. *et al.* Excavations at Skelmore Heads, near Ulverston. *Trans. C.W.A.A. Soc.* (NS) LXIII.

BLAKE, B. Excavations of Native (Iron Age) Sites in Cumberland 1956–8. *Trans. C.W.A.A. Soc.* (NS) LIX.

RIVET, A. L. F. (Ed.) (1966). *The Iron Age in Northern Britain.* Edinburgh.

STEAD, I. M. (1965). *The La Tène Cultures of Eastern Yorkshire.*

SALWAY, P. (1965). *The Frontier People of Roman Britain.* Cambridge.

ARMSTRONG, A. M. (1950–2). *The Place-names of Cumberland.* English Place-name Society, 3 vols. Cambridge.

SMITH, A. H. (1967). *The Place-names of Westmorland.* English Place-name Society, 2 vols. Cambridge.

EKWALL, E. (1922). *The Place-names of Lancashire.* Manchester.

CALVERLEY, REV. W. S. (Ed. W. G. COLLINGWOOD) (1899). *Early Sculptured Crosses, Shrines and Monuments in the present Diocese of Carlisle.*

COWEN, J. D. Viking Burials in Cumbria. *Trans. C.W.A.A. Soc.* (NS) XLVIII and LXVII.

CRAMP, R. The Viking type Penannular Brooch and Torc from Orton Scar. *Trans. C.W.A.A. Soc.* (NS) LXIV.

PEARSALL, W. H. (1961). Place-names as Clues in the pursuit of Ecological History. In *Namn och Bygd.* Uppsala.

Chapter 13

HELBAEK, H. (1952). Early Crops in Southern England. *Proc. Prehist. Soc.* 18.

OLDFIELD, F. (1963). Pollen-analysis and Man's Role in the Ecological History of the South-east Lake District. *Geografisker Annal.* 45.

PENNINGTON, W. (1964). Pollen analysis from the deposits of six upland tarns in the Lake District. *Phil. Trans. Roy. Soc.* B 248.

PENNINGTON, W. (1965). The interpretation of some postglacial vegetation diversities at different Lake District sites. *Proc. Roy. Soc.* B 161.

PENNINGTON, W. (1970). Vegetation history in the north-west of England: a regional synthesis. In *Studies in the Vegetational History of the British Isles.* Cambridge.

WALKER, D. (1966). The late-Quaternary history of the Cumberland lowland. *Phil. Trans. Roy. Soc.* B 251.

Chapter 15

BOUGH, C. M. L. (1948). *Prelates and People in the Lake Counties.* Kendal.
BOUGH, C. M. L. and JONES, G. P. (1961). *The Lake Counties 1500–1800.* Manchester.
ELLIOTT, G. (1959). The System of Cultivation and evidence of Enclosure in the Cumberland Open Fields of the Sixteenth Century. *Trans. C.W.A.A. Soc.* (NS) LIX.
GARNETT, F. (1912). *Westmorland Agriculture 1800–1900.* Kendal.
LIDDELL, W. H. (1966). The Private Forests of South-west Cumberland. *Trans. C.W.A.A. Soc.* (NS) LXVI.
LITTLEDALE, R. P. (1931). Ennerdale. *Trans. C.W.A.A. Soc.* (NS) XXXI.
WEST, T. (1774). *The Antiquities of Furness.* London.

Chapter 16

ELLWOOD, T. (1897). The Mountain Sheep: their origin and marking. *Trans. C.W.A.A. Soc.* (OS) XV.
FELL, A. (1908). *The Early Iron Industry of Furness.* Ulverston.
HARRIS, A. and DAVIS, R. B. (1968). The Hodbarrow Iron Mines. *Trans. C.W.A.A. Soc.* (NS) LXVIII.
MARSHALL, J. D. (1958). *Furness and the Industrial Revolution.* Barrow-in-Furness.
MITCHELL, W. R. (1966). *Men of Lakeland.* London.
NATIONAL TRUST. *Lake District Local Report for 1963–4.*
NATIONAL TRUST. Information leaflet 1967. *Hill Farming in the Lake District.*
POSTLETHWAITE, J. (1913). *Mines and Mining in the Lake District.* Whitehaven.
Quarry Managers' Journal, 1964. The Burlington Quarries.
RANSOME, A. (1931). *Swallowdale.* London.
RANSOME, A. (1936). *Pigeon Post.* London.
RYDER, M. L. (1964). The History of Sheep Breeds in Britain. *Agricultural History Review* 12.

Chapter 17

CHARD, J. S. R. (1967). Integration and Multiple Use of Forest and Associated Land. In *Whither the Lake District* (Rotary Club of Ambleside).
SYMONDS, H. H. (1936). *Afforestation in the Lake District.* London.
NATIONAL TRUST, Properties of (1969).
NATIONAL TRUST, Local Reports. *The Lake District,* 1945 to 1967.
The Hardknott Forest Park. Forestry Commission Guide (1949).
The Thornthwaite Forest. Forestry Commission.
Wild Life Centre, Grizedale Forest. Forestry Commission. Penrith.

INDEX